1$16⁵⁰

SPECIFICATIONS:

for Architecture, Engineering, and Construction

Architectural Record Series

SPECIFICATIONS:

for Architecture, Engineering, and Construction

CHESLEY AYERS, P.E.
College of Engineering,
Detroit Institute of Technology

McGRAW-HILL BOOK COMPANY
New York   St. Louis   San Francisco   Auckland   Bogotá
Düsseldorf   Johannesburg   London   Madrid   Mexico
Montreal   New Delhi   Panama   Paris   São Paulo
Singapore   Sydney   Tokyo   Toronto

Library of Congress Cataloging in Publication Data

Ayers, Chesley.
  Specifications : for architecture, engineering, and
construction.

  1. Civil engineering—Contracts and specifications.
2. Building—Contracts and specifications. I. Title.
TA180.A9   624'.021'2   75-2250
ISBN 0-07-002638-6

  34567890 KPKP 7843210987

*The editors for this book were Jeremy Robinson and Patricia A. Allen,
the designer was Naomi Auerbach, and the production supervisor was
George E. Oechsner. It was set in Optima by Typographic Sales, Inc.*

It was printed and bound by The Kingsport Press.

Contents

Preface

This volume is intended as a reference book and a reader for architectural and engineering students studying the writing of specifications. It is written assuming the reader has had no experience working in professional offices and no previous contact with specifications. For this reason, a chapter has been included giving a brief description of the engineering process from the conception of an idea to the completion of the final product and its maintenance.

No attempt has been made to include master specifications intended to be copied in part and serve as a guide for the experienced writer. With the rapid technological developments, any detailed description of an existing product or method is apt to become obsolete before it can be put to use by the reader. Rather, the text emphasizes the methods and reasons for writing specifications in the proper manner. References are made to the leading court decisions which affect specification writing.

An attempt has been made to cover all phases of a specification writer's work and to give him the background necessary to understand the basic problems in producing a satisfactory document. Contract management is covered in chapters on contracts, changes, bonds, invoicing, and liens; field problems are discussed; and government contracts and industrial specifications are covered in separate sections along with chapters on preparing, writing, and checking specifications.

The publisher has set the five samples in the Appendix in typewriter type to acquaint readers with the appearance of a specification; the text of the book is set in justified type for easy reading. The chapters are divided similarly to a specification, and the various categories of headings, limited to underlining on a typewriter, are designated by a variation of type styles. The purpose is to familiarize the reader with the arrangement of a specification and to assist him in preparing his own work.

This is the author's second book on the subject. The first book was developed from lectures delivered during a course in contracts and specifications at the Detroit Institute of Technology. While texts covering the contracts were easy to obtain, a book covering all phases of specifications could not be found. As a result, the lectures were taken in shorthand by a stenographer and typed. Copies were given to the students. During the following ten years, the notes were corrected, brought up to date, and expanded to cover the questions asked in class. The result was a text, published in 1968. This book was accepted and a second edition was published in 1970. That book is now out of print. After consultation with the publisher, it was agreed that a new text was required to present the latest developments in specifications. The result is this book.

The studying of the text will not make the reader a finished specification writer. Skill in this field depends upon technical knowledge, experience, and engineering judgment, for which there is no substitute. The instructions given herein are intended to provide a basis for a systematic method of writing and developing a proper presentation. This is the first step. Until it is mastered, one can go no further. However, when the information contained herein is supplemented by assignments for the actual preparation and writing of specifications under the supervision of a professional, or by classroom discussion, the student should be able to prepare an acceptable document.

Chesley Ayers

Acknowledgments

It is difficult to acknowledge the origin of all the material used in this book. In part, the book was written from notes accumulated years ago while preparing lectures for students at the Detroit Institute of Technology. This was long before the writing of a book was considered, and, therefore, the source is obscure. The principles set forth in this text are a combination of the author's experience as a specification writer, along with principles he has learned from others. For the latter, the author acknowledges having leaned heavily on what he learned from the meetings and publications of the Construction Specifications Institute. Their monthly magazine, *The Construction Specifier,* has been published since 1949, and throughout the years has covered almost every aspect of specification writing. Direct quotes are noted by the date, when known, and are published with the permission of the Construction Specifications Institute.

The author wishes to thank the American Institute of Architects for permission to reprint the Documents A201 and A310, "General Conditions of the Contract for Construction" and "Bid Bond"; the National Society of Professional Engineers for permission to reprint "Standard General Conditions of the Contract"; and the Construction Specifications Institute for permission to reprint the Specification Format.

The author also wishes to thank Dr. Richard Fellrath, Attorney and Counselor at Law for his legal advice; Diana Lamb, Doreen Saari, and Barbara Zielinski for the typing; Janice Legge for proofreading; and his wife for her patience while this was being written.

Table of Cases

ONE

A Description

1.01 WHAT IS A SPECIFICATION?

A. A specification is a description of a particular product. For example, when buyers enter an automobile salesroom and state the model, type, color, and extras they want, they have specified their needs.

B. If it is that simple, why do we study specifications? In business transactions, written specifications are preferred to oral specifications. Buyers write a description of what they want, and the seller replies with a written price. To obtain the lowest price, the specifications are sent to several bidders, each of whom replies in writing with a specific price. The buyers select one bidder and enter into a contract with him.

C. This procedure introduces complications. In oral specifications, the salesman can state that the color specified comes at an extra cost and that the extras desired cannot be placed on the model desired. In a written specification, the details should be determined in advance and written in such a manner that each bidder can quote a price on the specific product desired. If the specification is vague or incomplete, each bidder must call upon the buyer for clarification. Such calls often result in different information being given to the various bidders. The resulting confusion costs time and money to both the buyer and the seller.

D. In large corporations, specifications are usually written for all purchased items. A purchasing agent may, for example, write a specification for lead pencils on a purchase order. This requires no engineering. However, other purchases are made to very exacting requirements. For example, some sheet steels must be able to be formed in dies without tearing; others must harden to resist impact. Writing specifications for such items requires a person with a technical background who understands engineering terms. Specification writers are not easy to find and are usually in demand.

1.02 DEFINITION

A. Webster defines a specification as "A statement containing a minute description or enumeration of particulars, as of the terms of a contract, details of construction not shown in the architectural drawings, etc.; also, any item of such a statement." I think a more practical definition for our use is: A specification is a description of an article or a method so complete that it can be bought or built by others to the complete satisfaction of all concerned.

B. When we interpret these definitions, we can reasonably conclude that specifications have two (2) purposes: one, to convey the thoughts of the designers, their vision of a complete project, to the hundreds of people who will assist in constructing it; and second, to provide a definite document on which a legal contract can be based and executed.

1.03 METHODS

A. A specification can be a drawing, a model, or a written description. For example, a single circle on a piece of paper with a dimension showing the diameter and the words "Title: Ball Bearing —Material: ASTM A 295-46T —No. Req'd: 10,000" in the title block would be a specification. Specifications are often prepared in this manner. The same result can be obtained by furnishing a sample ball bearing of the type desired or by writing a description of the product with no drawing.

B. While writing a specification for a ball bearing is simple, describing an x-ray machine or computer in words alone would be difficult; to describe it in sufficient detail to be completely manufactured by one unfamiliar with the design would be almost impossible. Likewise, lettering a complete specification on a drawing would also be costly and time-consuming. A combination of the two is the solution.

C. Throughout the ages, precise methods have been devised to produce satisfactory specifications. Until the invention and use of the typewriter, specifications were chiefly drawings and models. When typewriting became common, the volume of written matter increased, and with the computer coming into use, the amount of written matter will be increased still more.

1.04 HISTORY

A. ANCIENT

1. Genesis

a. Specifications are not new. They have been essential to construction since people first learned to build and use tools. The first specifications were composed before people learned to write and were, by necessity, given orally. One of the oldest recorded is in the book of Genesis in the Bible. The following is from Chapter 6, verses 14 through 16, where God said to Noah,

b. "Make an ark of resin wood; make it tight with fibre and cover it with pitch inside and out. This is how you shall make it: the length of the ark three hundred cubits, its width fifty cubits, and its height thirty cubits. Make an opening for the ark and finish it a cubit from the top. Set a door in the side of the ark; make it with bottom, second and third level."

c. While the foregoing was probably clear to Noah, like many current specifications, it is not entirely clear to many readers. Resin wood (called gopher wood in some editions of the Bible) may refer to the resinous trees such as the cypress; the meaning of the Hebrew word is not clear. The cubit was about a foot and a half. The meaning of the word "opening" is not clear. It probably means an open latticework around the whole ark to bring in light and air and in some way serve as support for the roof. The words "and finish it" possibly mean placing a roof a cubit above the top of the window.

2. The Ark of the Covenant

In Exodus, Chapters 25, 26, 27, and 28, the specifications of the ark of the covenant, the tent cloth, the wooden walls, the veils, the altar, the court of the dwelling, the oil for the lamps, and the priestly vestments are all described in minute detail. It should be read.

3. Drawings

As time passed, people learned the value of a drawing for showing what they had in mind so that others could look at it and create what the drawing showed. It is probable that drawings or models were made before the construction of the beautiful buildings in the Valley of the Nile, the pyramids, the tombs, temples of the Pharaohs, and other ancient structures of early eras. The early history of the Mediterranean area discloses that building plans were in use at that time.

4. Solomon's Temple

At the time when Solomon's temple was built, specifications had reached a high degree of development. Solomon's specifications for the building of the House of the Lord and his own temple make fascinating reading. The student is advised to read III Kings, Chapters 6 and 7, in the Douay Bible or I Kings, Chapters 6 and 7, in the King James Bible. After reading how stone, cedar, and cypress were used and how the inside was overlaid with pure gold, one might think that by comparison we are pikers today.

B. MEDIEVAL

1. Architecture was at its peak during the Gothic period. The churches of this period were built over several generations and under the direction of several master builders. The master builder was an artist as well as a builder. Drawings were prepared for the worker and for future master builders, although the original plans were not always carried out. As a new generation took control, changes were made that often required removing work previously placed. Strassburg Cathedral is an excellent example. It was started as a Romanesque church, a Gothic nave was added to the existing Romanesque choir in 1176 A.D.; one tower was erected in 1439 and the other originally designed tower is yet to be erected. So today, like many Gothic churches in France and England, it remains incomplete. When one looks at the facade, the left tower is seen as a beautiful openwork spire four hundred and sixty-six feet (466'-0") high; there is no spire on the right. Drawings of this church are still in existence, and they are beautifully done.

2. The Gothic church is a beautiful skeleton structure consisting of piers, buttresses, arches, and ribbed vaulting all held together in equilibrium by a combination of forces neutralizing each other and depending upon the proper adjustment of thrust and counterthrust. The structures are so intricate that even today a complete analysis of the stresses would be difficult. The master builder was an engineer as well as an architect. It seems reasonable that the master builder understood the arch and its thrust. However, it would appear that the relationship between weight, size, and span was learned through trial and error. Beauvais Cathedral in France was started in 1225 A.D. and had the roof fall in while still under construction in 1284 A.D. Additional piers were added in 1337 through 1347. The openwork spire five hundred feet (500'-0") high over the crossing caused the building to collapse in 1573 partly because there was no buttress to take the thrust in the west. The church is less than half complete today.

3. By the seventeenth century, contracts were made between the kings and contractors for the construction of buildings and bridges. Vauban, in France, during the reign of Louis XIV, was one of the first to establish rules for writing contracts and specifications. The specifications contained precise stipulations regarding the execution of the work, including the origin and quality of materials, duties and responsibilities of contractors, and acceptable methods of accounting. The rules established for contracts are typical of prerevolutionary France. For example,

on the day bids were due, the entire specification was read aloud by the Superintendent of Construction, after which the bidders gave him their bids. Then three candles were lit, and while they continued to burn, new bidders could submit bids, or previous bidders could withdraw their offers. When the last candle burned out, a contract was made with one of the bidders.

C. ENGINEERING

1. Engineering as a profession was much slower to develop than architecture, although engineering as well as architecture can be traced back to ancient Egypt. The reason for this is that most engineering projects were state-financed, designed by military engineers, and constructed by captive labor. It was not until the middle of the eighteenth century that John Smeaton (1724-1792) began to designate himself as a civil, or civilian, engineer, to differentiate his practice from that of the military engineer. Under his leadership the Smeatonian Society fostered professional thinking about the character of civil engineering. Others took charge at his death, and in 1818 the British Institution of Civil Engineers was established. The founders formulated and adopted the classical definition of civil engineering as ". . . the art of transforming materials and directing the great sources of power in nature for the use and convenience of man. . . ."

2. In America, the Boston Society of Civil Engineers was not established until 1852, followed by the American Mining, Metallurgical and Petroleum Engineers in 1871, the American Society of Mechanical Engineers in 1880, the American Institute of Electrical Engineers in 1884, and the American Institute of Chemical Engineers in 1908.

3. Specifications during the early part of the nineteenth century took the form of drawings with notes lettered on the sheets as required to describe what could not be shown. The long separate document giving a word description had to await the invention of a useful typewriter in 1829; its adoption for general use occurred some fifty (50) years later.

D. MODERN SPECIFICATIONS

1. The modern form of specifications came into being in America along with competitive bidding and the need for contract documents. While there was only a single builder in a community, specifications could be oral. Where trustworthy people limited their business to skilled people who valued their reputation, there was little need for ironbound contracts. There was one accepted way of constructing a project, and it was unnecessary to detail every item in the construction. A specification written in 1875 for a chapel appears in article 12.02 A. This, with a plan and elevations, could be considered typical for the time.

2. H. H. Richardson (1838-1886), one of the foremost architects of the

nineteenth century, was known to dislike competitive bidding. His specifications consisted of beautiful detailed drawings and simple documents stating the materials and methods that would meet his approval. This principle was followed by such noted offices as McKim, Mead & White and Cram, Goodhue and Ferguson. The best was none too good for these exacting firms.

3. It must be remembered that at the turn of the century in America there was a large influx of immigrants from Europe. Many of these were highly skilled workmen, trained during a long apprenticeship in the exacting methods required for fine craftsmanship. The higher pay and shorter hours offered in America caused many to leave their homes in Europe. In 1899, bricklayers were laying an average of twelve hundred (1,200) bricks a day and earning thirty-five cents per hour (35¢/hr). Their helpers earned fifteen cents per hour (15¢/hr). It was during this period that the written description of the work became an item of such importance that some of the larger offices hired full-time specification writers. These early specification writers established the precedent of dividing the specifications into trades. Although the number of trades was less than that required today, the work required by each trade was broadened. Masonry, for example, consisted of excavating, concrete, concrete finishing, brickwork, stonework, clay tile work, and ceramic tile work.

4. The Woolworth Building, designed by Cass Gilbert, was completed in New York City in 1913. This magnificent structure, seven hundred and ninety-two feet (792'-0") (60 stories) high, was the first of the true skyscrapers as we know the term today. The era following the First World War saw the skyscraper constructed throughout America. While the style of other buildings was borrowed, at least in part, from European buildings, the skyscraper is a basic American development in a true American style. Specifications during this era suited the times. While the supply of European-trained workmen was getting smaller, the quality of work produced and the pride in the workmanship of the individual were sufficiently high for it still to be unnecessary to detail every item in the specification.

5. The First World War caused labor rates to rise and caused a shift of population to the cities. This brought about a need for housing and other buildings. The mass-produced buildings, built by financial speculators without the direction of architects or engineers, were often poorly constructed. We can see the results in our slum districts. The speculator was not interested in good building. Speed, not quality, was his aim. Blocks of identical houses were the result.

6. The depression of the early thirties changed the economic picture. Many discharged employees started in business for themselves, making many more bidders for considerably less work. This resulted in price

cutting and a speeded-up production. Likewise, owners could no longer afford to require the best. They required their architects and engineers to design with a limited budget; this required the specification writer to revise his style of writing. He could no longer specify "the best of materials and workmanship" and let the clerk of the works reject everything that could be done better. He had to specify what he wanted. During this period, many manufacturers introduced new lines of products designed to fill the low-cost market. As time went on, conditions improved, but owners had been educated and would no longer accept the old loosely written specification.

7. Scientific developments have also brought changes to specifications. Air conditioning is a common requirement, plastics have been introduced, staples have replaced nails for many applications, electronic devices have been introduced, welding and bolting have replaced rivets, and former paint materials and methods have been revised. The old part-time specification writer can no longer keep abreast of the many rapid modern changes.

1.05 THE SPECIFICATION WRITER

A. As any specification writer will gladly explain, it is the designers who receive credit for the unusual features in a project. Likewise, it is the inspectors, who have the authority to accept or reject work and the power to dismiss those they consider incompetent, who receive homage from the contractors and their employees. And it is the construction engineers, in their hard hats at a construction site, directing the movement of workers and giant machinery, who enjoy the glamor and public recognition usually associated with such work. Yet, it is the specification writers who control the actions of their more glamorous coworkers. They work in an office without the glory, yet they know the success of the project depends upon their specifications. Their knowledge and their ability to think clearly and to express their ideas on paper can be, and usually are, the deciding factors in the success or failure of a construction project. Good work on their part will result in smooth-running construction, and, conversely, an inadequate specification can be a cause of hardship for all concerned. No profession in the entire construction industry has more responsibility than that of the specification writer.

B. Today specification writers are specialists in the construction field. They should have a basic education in architecture and in engineering. They should also have a basic legal education, particularly in the field of contracts. They should have studied both inorganic and organic chemistry, geology, and metallurgy. They must have a complete and current knowledge of construction materials and construction procedures. They must understand test procedures and techniques. They must be knowledgeable on the costs of both materials and labor in the part of the country where they are working. Should they be working on a federal project, they must be thoroughly familiar with government policies and practices. Most important and above all else, however, they must have the ability to translate their thoughts into clear, understandable English in a written form. Good specification writers must have a well-rounded vocabulary in order to express themselves in concise and simple words. Considering the extent of knowledge required, the efficiency needed, and the ability to work under the pressure of time that is requisite, it is a wonder that anyone could qualify for such work. Fortunately, there are a few engineers who have the ability, and they enjoy the responsibility and extra pay that go along with this exacting profession.

1.06 THE PURPOSE OF SPECIFICATIONS

A. A specification is a legal document and an integral part of a contract between the owner and the contractor. It is also an engineering document which is used by the architect or engineer, the owner, the material supplier, the workers, and the clerk of the works.

B. A specification is an engineering, as well as a legal, document. It serves to bring any misunderstanding between the architect or engineer and the owner to the surface so that it can be resolved before the project is sent to the bidders. Specifications also inform the owners as to what can be expected from the contractor. The estimators require them to establish their costs. Specifications define the work for subcontractors and in that way assist the contractor in soliciting bids from them and in making contracts. The specifications establish the quality of materials and instruct workers on how to install those materials at the job site. They also establish a standard which the inspector (called the "clerk of the works" on construction work) can use to accept or reject work.

1.07 MODERN SPECIFICATIONS

Today's specifications, when correctly prepared, reflect the most advanced knowledge of engineering materials and construction methods and acceptable procedures. These are all welded into a concise and understandable contract document which meets all of the legal and engineering requirements for the project.

TWO

The Building Business

2.01 AN IDEA PLUS MONEY

In construction, as in most other engineering fields, an entire series of events begins with an idea. Someone has an idea. A government wants a bridge, a sewage disposal unit, or a street lighting system; a corporation wants to improve its plant or an individual wants to place a new product on the market. However, an idea is only an illusion unless it is combined with another ingredient, money. Raising money can be a major project for a small organization, a smaller project for a wealthy individual or group, and a consideration for .a government.

2.02 THE ARCHITECT OR ENGINEER

A. SELECTION

1. When the project financing is solved, selecting an engineer or architect is the next step. It is the duty of the engineer or architect to convey the idea of the owner into substantial form so as to produce the desired result. The architect or engineer has responsibilities. He must design something the owner wants. To do this he should use his skilled engineering judgment and take the time necessary to produce the desired result. But he has a greater responsibility, and that is designing something that is safe to use and safe for the general public.

2. At times ethics are involved. If a client asks an architect or engineer to place his seal on plans prepared by another, or to perform some other illegal practice, the commission would have to be refused. There are penalties for such practices; the architect or engineer could lose his license to practice his profession.

3. Both architects and engineers write specifications in the same manner. In fact, these two professions have a great deal in common. An architect works mostly on plans for buildings, while an engineer is involved with bridges, dams, sewage systems, and the like; but the procedure is common in both. Architects hire engineers to design the structural, mechanical, and electrical features in their buildings. Likewise, engineers hire architects to create the aesthetic features of their work. It is not unusual to find that an architectural firm will employ more professional engineers than registered architects. Many firms have both architects and engineers as principals and refer to themselves as "architects and engineers." Throughout this text the term "architect or engineer" or simply "architect-engineer" will be used frequently and will apply equally to both professions.

B. STATEMENT OF WORK

When an owner employs an architect or an engineer, he usually prepares a statement of work. This statement of work can be oral or written. The statement tells the architect or engineer exactly what he is to do. The architect or engineer, after studying the requirements, quotes a price to the owner for his services. If the fee is satisfactory, a contract between the owner and the architect or engineer is entered into. This is called "The Agreement between the Owner and the Architect or Engineer."

C. THE AGREEMENT

1. If the statement of work is oral, the architect or engineer would be well advised to place it in writing when the agreement is made. The agreement between the owner and the architect or engineer should always be written.

2. While all phases of the work should be stated in the agreement, the author has found from experience that two requirements often lead to a misunderstanding unless they are covered in detail. The first is the accuracy required in the estimate of the cost of the project. The owner often expects the engineer's estimate to be within a few dollars of the actual cost, whereas the professional knows that a cost spread of ten percent (10%) between bidders is not unusual. The second is the degree of quality assurance provided by the architect or engineer. The agreement may provide that the architect or engineer must visit the job site to observe the progress of the work, and the owner may believe that this is assurance that every detail in the construction has been observed and approved as being in conformance with the specifications. This point will be examined in more detail later in the chapter.

D. FEES

1. General

Architects or engineers are usually paid in one of three ways. They

can be paid in a lump sum of money for performing all the work required in the statement of work, they can be paid a percentage of
the cost of the final product, or they can be paid their cost of producing
the plans and specifications plus a fixed fee or percentage of their
costs as profit.

2. Example

Here is an example. An owner in a statement of work states he wishes
to construct a bridge in a specific location for a cost not to exceed
a million dollars ($1,000,000).

3. Fixed Price

The architect or engineer may quote a fixed price of sixty thousand
dollars ($60,000). If he enters into a contract of this type, he will, upon
completion, collect only sixty thousand dollars regardless of what the
plans cost him to produce. The method of payment should be stated
in the contract. Usually he is paid twenty-five percent (25%) of his
fee when the sketches are complete and accepted, an additional fifty
or sixty percent (50% or 60%) when the working drawings are complete
and accepted, and the remainder when the structure is complete.

4. Percentage

a. The architect or engineer may enter into a contract with the owner
where he would receive a percentage of the final cost of the structure. If the percentage agreed upon was six percent (6%) and the
final construction cost was $987,654, the architect-engineer would
receive $59,259.24 as his fee.

b. As the exact cost of the project is not known when the sketches
and final drawings are submitted, payment may be made upon the
estimated cost. If the estimated cost was one million dollars
($1,000,000), the architect or engineer would have to submit a bill
of fifteen thousand dollars ($15,000) when the sketches were ac-
cepted ($1,000,000 $\times .06 \times {}^1/_4$).

5. Cost Plus

The architect or engineer may quote on cost plus a fee. The contract
could state that the architect or engineer will be paid the salaries of
his draftsmen and employees directly connected with the project and
the cost of all blueprinting plus a fee of one hundred and fifty percent
(150%). The architect or engineer would be required to keep time slips
on his employees. If his payroll for this project was seventeen thousand
five hundred dollars ($17,500) and his blueprint bill was for five
hundred dollars ($500), his total fee would be forty-five thousand dol-
lars ($45,000). In this type of arrangement the architect would probably
bill and receive payment on a monthly basis.

E. THE ARCHITECTURAL OR ENGINEERING OFFICES

1. Departments

A large architectural or engineering office is made up of various departments, each responsible for a specific phase of the work. The same work is performed in a small office, the difference being that one individual often performs more than one phase of the work.

2. Client Relations

The most essential person in an architectural or engineering firm is the client relations man. He is the salesman for the office. He brings in the clients, and as the student must realize, nothing much happens in any business until a sale is made. It takes individuals of a special type to be successful at selling architectural or engineering services. They must have a broad knowledge of construction and costs, and they must be able to associate with people who control money. In school, as well as in practice, engineers deal mainly with things, not people. They are trained to be introverts. As a result, engineers who can sell are in demand.

3. The Designers

After the contract is signed, the client deals with the designers, who must understand the problem and present a solution on paper. The designers must have artistic talent. They work with soft pencils and erasers. They must be able to sketch and make renderings of their ideas and present them to the client for approval. However, designers must be more than artists. Clients who wish to build a hotel are more interested in the number of rooms he can have on each floor than the color scheme in the lobby. He is basically interested in a layout of a building that will bring in the maximum income.

4. The Civil Engineers

Civil engineers are people who determine the location of the project on the site, and design the roadways, bridges, and parking lots. They are also responsible for storm water drainage and the sewage disposal plant.

5. Architectural Draftsmen

When the designers get their sketches approved, the work is turned over to the architectural draftsman, who takes the sketches and from them produces the working drawings. He must produce drawings that can be understood and used in the field.

6. Structural Engineers

When the draftsman's work is under way, the structural engineers start their work. They work out strengths and deflections, foundation sizes, the size of beams, thickness of floor slabs, etc. It is their job to make the building structurally sound against wind, gravity, and other forces.

7. The Mechanical Engineers

When the structural work is under way, the mechanical engineers start work. It is their job to design a heating system, a cooling system, a water supply system, and a sanitary system as required. They have to work with the architectural draftsman to ensure that the proper room is provided for fans and ducts. They must also give the weights of their equipment to the structural engineers and the power requirements to the electrical engineers.

8. The Electrical Engineers

The electrical engineers must supply drawings showing power lines, motors, transformers, and similar equipment. Electrical engineers transform electrical power into light energy or physical energy in an economical way.

9. The Landscape Architects

The landscape architects locate trees, shrubs, bushes, and flower beds on the property to present an artistic setting.

10. The Specification Writers

a. When the plans of the various departments are near completion, the specification writers start work. Their first job is to check and coordinate the plans from the various departments. Then they write their specifications and prepare the work for bidding. It is their primary duty to know materials. Specification writers are the people who, working with the designers, determine what material will be used.

b. Actually there are five things specification writers must do to fulfill their job.

(1) They must coordinate the civil, architectural, structural, mechanical, electrical, and landscape drawings.

(2) They must check the drawings to make sure there has been no omission or lack of information necessary to make a complete project.

(3) They must select the proper materials and methods of installation to assure that the owners will receive a quality product with the utmost economy.

(4) They must balance cost with the owners' budget so that the owners obtain full value for their money.

(5) They must write specifications clearly and concisely to describe the requirements in a manner to avoid delays, disputes, or

costly claims, and must provide a document that will give a basis upon which a legal contract can be executed.

c. Only a few engineers have the ability to make good specification writers. Some lack the knowledge of contractual relations. Many lack the ability to write intelligently, spell correctly, or even express themselves well. Others prefer to confine themselves to problems of stress and strain, heat gain and loss, or the division of space. By preference, they avoid problems involving negotiations and refuse to learn the diplomatic niceties that such work requires. Specification writing is a full-time job and should not be considered something of minor importance to be rushed out when the drawings are completed. Specification writing is a specialty that requires specialists. Of course, in a small engineering office, a specification writer may be required to combine the writing of specifications with other work. But specifications should be his primary work, as it is rare to find a draftsman or even his boss with the basic requirements for good specification writing.

d. Another duty of specification writers which requires considerable time is talking with salesmen. Salesmen usually realize that the key to selling their product is to have it specified. Therefore, when they visit architectural or engineering offices, usually they talk to the specification writers. To specification writers salesmen can be a nuisance. However, many salesmen are an excellent source of information. Specification writers must learn to distinguish between the time-waster and the educator. They should limit their time with the former. However, those who refuse to see or spend time with the latter soon become behind the times and lack information on new products. It is the new, untried product that most salesmen promote. Those selling cement, structural steel, or lumber seldom call on the architects or engineers.

e. The pay of specification writers is usually higher than that of other salaried personnel in an architectural office, since they must have knowledge of entire projects, which entails a broader education.

11. The Contract Administrator

a. When the plans and specifications are complete and are approved by the owners, the contract administrator's first duty is to have the proper professional seal or seals affixed to a complete set of plans and specifications. The seal of the principal architect or engineer in the organization usually appears. In some states, projects involving both architecture and engineering require the seals of persons in both professions. The plans and specifications are then filed with the proper government official along with an application for a building permit.

b. When the building permit is granted, the project administrator should obtain proposals from satisfactory contractors who are willing to bid on the project. When bids are received, the administrator sees that a contract is awarded.

c. Some architectural or engineering firms require the general contractor to obtain the building permit. This can lead to difficulties if the officials require changes before granting the permit.

12. The Engineers' Estimators

a. Some large architectural and engineering firms employ one or more full-time estimators to keep the cost of a project within a cost the owners can afford. Estimators keep abreast of the latest material and labor costs. They advise owners as to what can be expected for a specific sum of money and advise those preparing the plans and specifications as to specific costs where the project is located. Before the project is submitted for bidding, they make a complete cost estimate to make sure that the project is within the client's budget.

b. When a client has imposed a definite cost limitation, and where an architect or engineer knows or should have known that his client has limited funds, he is subject to severe penalties if, through his neglect, he submits an erroneous cost estimate. When an architect or engineer prepares plans and specifications that require the client to spend beyond his means, he risks not only all the payment for his professional services, but in addition may be held liable for any damages which the client may suffer by reason of his negligent estimate. It is just good business for an architect or engineer to know the cost of his project with reasonable accuracy.

c. One should not confuse engineers' estimators with the estimators employed by contractors and subcontractors. These will be discussed later. The engineers' estimator works with round figures; he hopes to be within five percent (5%) of the low bidder's price. However, he must be familiar with all trades. The contractor's estimators limit their pricing to work they do with their own forces and collect bids from subcontractors on the remainder. The subcontractor's estimators must be authorities on the pricing of work in their trade.

13. The Clerk of the Works

Architects or engineers also employ a clerk of the works. The duties of the clerk of the works will be described later.

2.03 THE CONTRACTOR

A. DEFINITION

1. The contractor is the person or company that the owner employs to

perform specific work. Obviously, the owner does not need the services of an engineer or a lawyer to enter into a contract. The engineer and lawyer are only advisors to the owner. They assist, advise, and represent him.

2. When an architect or engineer designs a project, he usually invites various contractors to submit bids or prices for performing the specified work. The contractor for a construction project has to estimate the costs of the job. The estimates must be extremely accurate. If a contractor's bid is too high, the work is awarded to another party and time and money are wasted. If the figures are too low, the contractor can lose a great deal of money.

B. SUBCONTRACTORS

1. Contractors can depend upon subcontractors or they can do the work with their own forces. The choice often depends upon the area. It stands to reason that in a large city, specialists can do work more cheaply than contractors who may do a type of work occasionally. For example, concrete floor finishing can be done two ways. A contractor can call the union hall, hire finishers and supervise the work himself, or he can hire a subcontractor. If he does the work himself, he saves the profit the subcontractor would make. However, the labor that he picks up at the union hall is not as efficient as the workers of the subcontractor. The subcontractor doing the same type of work all the time soon learns who are the good workmen, and he refuses to hire others. As a rule, it is cheaper for the contractors to sublet work than to do it themselves. Today the average general contractor building commercial and industrial projects sublets about ninety percent (90%) of his work.

2. Subcontractors usually work in cities and work for several contractors. In small towns with only one or two general contractors, subcontractors are brought in from the city. This is expensive and it is usually cheaper for the general contractor to hire local skilled labor.

C. THE ESTIMATOR

1. Any building is a dream until construction is started. The architect has a picture on paper, but it is only a picture until the contractor transforms that picture into a solid, three-dimensional structure. The estimator is the one who translates that picture into cold, hard dollars. Lines on a drawing or phases in a specification can be changed for the cost of an eraser, but when an estimator says he will furnish a building for a specific sum of money, it is a final action and the first step in the transformation of a dream into a solid object.

2. It is easy to understand why the estimator is the key figure in any construction business. When the estimator's bids are high, the time

spent estimating is lost. If the estimator figures too low, the firm will lose money. A bad mistake can put a firm out of business.

3. There are two (2) types of estimators. One type works on the estimating staff of the general contractor. The other group is associated with subcontractors and suppliers of materials. The chief function of the first involves taking figures from subcontractors and material suppliers. The second group is required to estimate the cost of doing work in a specialized field. Their scope is limited, but they must be experts in pricing the work in which they are involved. Together, they take the responsibility of translating the architect's concept into the very real matter of money.

D. ESTIMATING

1. By the Contractor

a. The preparing of a cost estimate is a detailed procedure, and the methods may vary in different offices. In general, the first operation after the contractor receives the plans and specifications is to analyze the project and determine the work that will be done by the contractor's own forces and the work that will be awarded to subcontractors. That, of course, is a basic decision.

b. For the contractor to be a low bidder, it is necessary to receive low bids from the subcontractors. Therefore, to receive as many bids as possible is to the firm's advantage; the firm has a greater choice of selecting responsible subcontractors with low prices. In actual practice, each contractor sends out postcards to all of the various subcontractors engaged in the trades that are required. If these subcontractors are interested, they submit bids to the firm.

2. By the Subcontractor

a. When a subcontractor receives a card from a contractor for work he would like to do, he must examine the project documents in order to establish the costs. The documents may be examined at the office of the architect or engineer, at the office of one of the general contractors bidding on the project, at a plan room, or on microfilm in the subcontractor's office.

b. Plan rooms are offices established in many cities for the purpose of giving estimators a central place to work while figuring their costs on jobs in the area. Some plan rooms are maintained by cooperative organizations consisting of subcontractors and material suppliers who contribute to the cost. Others are private companies which sell a service. The best-known of these is the F. W. Dodge Division of McGraw-Hill Information Systems Company.

c. The F. W. Dodge Company was established in 1891 by Frederick W. Dodge, a publisher of a small newspaper in Boston, when he began delivering daily Dodge Reports on the area's construction projects. In 1896, this new company merged with the U.S. Building News Company of Clinton W. Sweet in New York. Over the years, the company expanded throughout the United States, and in 1961 it was purchased by McGraw-Hill. The Dodge Reports are mailed to subscribers daily, giving specific details on construction projects according to the interests of the prospective bidders. This information allows subcontractors and other users to submit unsolicited bids to contractors whom a subcontractor may not have known were figuring the work. Today there are one hundred and sixteen (116) Dodge Plan Rooms located in thirty-nine (39) of the fifty (50) states.

d. After determining the quantities and quality of the materials required, the estimator places the information on an estimate sheet, along with any sketches required, and returns to the office for pricing. The estimate sheet differs for the various subcontractors. An example of one appears in the Appendix of this book.

e. For those who prefer the convenience of working in their own offices, Dodge mails rolls of microfilm containing the complete bidding documents for more than ninety percent (90%) of all United States projects that are competitively bid with an estimated cost of at least fifty thousand dollars ($50,000). Subscribers who receive microfilms project the images of the drawings back to original size and accurate scale on a special patented viewing table.

3. By the Material Suppliers

Some material suppliers will make a take-off of quantities and bid to the subcontractors at a lump-sum price for the material required. However, most material suppliers sell their materials at unit prices, the same as a store. The subcontractor is then responsible for the proper quantities.

E. BIDDING

1. Subcontractors obtain the price of materials they are required to buy, add material they are furnishing, add their field labor costs, add their shop labor including set up and loading trucks, add cartage, add travel time if required, and add fees for bonds and permits. They add up their costs and enter a percentage for overhead and profit. To this they add any taxes. This gives them their bid price.

2. It is important to realize that each contractor and subcontractor has a slightly different form and various short cuts for figuring prices. The important part is to be sure that all costs are included.

3. Shortly before the bids are due, subcontractors give their prices to the various general contractors they wish to quote. As general contractors are interested in quoting the lowest price possible, they take the

lowest reliable bid from subcontractors figuring each trade, add them up, and add a percentage for their profit. To this they add the cost of doing their own work and the profit. They then place their bid price on the proposal and give the same to the architects or engineers.

4. It should be realized that general contractors do not know until they receive the bids from their subcontractors, often an hour or less before bids are due, whom they will employ as their subcontractors. They do not know for sure even who is bidding on the various trades. Therefore, it is impossible for them to make deals or divisions in the trades different from those which appear in the specifications.

5. As all contractors and subcontractors are bidding on the same work, their prices should be almost the same. Of course, each contractor is anxious to be the low bidder. For those who are not, the cost of preparing their estimates is lost. Knowing other bids is a help, and many subcontractors, as well as contractors, use many ways to get this information.

2.04 OPENING THE PROPOSALS

A. On public work, the proposals from the contractor are received by the public agency, read aloud, and become public record. On private work, the bids are received by the architect or engineer. They are recorded and evaluated by the contract administrator and submitted to the owner. The contractor to be awarded the contract is selected in a conference between the owner and the architect or engineer.

B. The opening of bids is a most exciting time. To all but one contractor the weeks spent estimating and figuring are a total loss, and often contractors console one another with statements to the effect that the low bidder must have made a mistake. The joy of the lower bidder is often tempered with the thought that maybe the low bid was made possible by a mistake.

C. To the owner and architect or engineer the opening of bids signifies the completion of one phase of the work. One of the most disagreeable moments in the life of any architect or engineer is when it is found that the lowest acceptable proposal is well in excess of the client's budget. At this point in time, the pleasant relationship between the designer and the client may be completely destroyed. The very best the architect can hope for is long hours of rewriting specifications and revising drawings which will not be paid for. The owner can expect delays that could be costly.

2.05 BID PEDDLING

A. It is in the period between the time the general contractor is selected and the time the contract is signed that bid peddling takes place. By "bid peddling" we mean that the general contractor calls subcontractors other than low bidders for each trade; the low figure may or may not be revealed, but all subcontractors are asked to reduce their price. Each subcontractor is played against the other until the lowest possible price is obtained. Subcontractors who are hungry for business do reduce their price and are then forced to reduce the quality of their work. As the price the contractor will receive from the owner has already been determined, any reduction in a subcontractor's price goes directly to the contractor. Bid peddling is a profitable business for the contractor.

B. While the general contractor is usually blamed for bid peddling, others share the blame. Often subcontractors who find their bids are not low will offer to reduce their price without being asked.

C. In fairness it should be emphasized that not all general contractors engage in bid peddling and some consider the practice unethical.

D. Bid peddling is an old problem and has received considerable publicity in the trade and professional papers. As the cost of the project has been determined on a lump-sum proposal, bid peddling usually lessens the quality of the work and materials; it never improves it. The practice is a problem of the construction industry which the specifications cannot prohibit, but under some conditions they may be able to control it.

2.06 SIGNING THE CONTRACT

A. When the contractor is selected, a contract is drawn up. A contract is usually physically written by the architect or engineer; the owner is asked to have an attorney approve the same.

B. A building contract is between the owner and the contractor. The architect or engineer is simply a representative of the owner or the owner's agent, to act in his behalf, but is not one of the contracting parties.

2.07 STARTING CONSTRUCTION

A. NOTICE TO PROCEED

After the contract is signed, the contractor is given a notice to proceed with the work. This notice is usually given to the contractor when signing the contract but may be issued later if so permitted by the contract.

B. THE SUPERINTENDENT

1. After the notice to proceed is issued, a whole series of events takes place. One of the first is for the general contractor to hire or appoint a general superintendent. It is the superintendent's job to see that the subcontractors get on the job, do their work satisfactorily, get off the job, and let the next subcontractor start work.

2. The general contractor, in theory, does no work. The specifications are written with all productive work assigned to subcontractors. It is the general contractor's job to coordinate the work of the subcontractors.

3. In actual practice, some large contracting companies do considerable work with their own workers. In such companies, the general superintendent is a highly paid key executive, with direction of a hundred or more skilled workers and control over several thousands of dollars' worth of equipment. The general superintendent's job is to organize the work so that it can be performed in the most efficient manner, to keep the cost of construction within the estimate, and to hire foremen for the various trades.

C. THE CLERK OF THE WORKS

1. The clerk of the works is not a clerk as we usually define the term. This person is a trained construction engineer employed by the architect or engineer to enforce the terms of the contract. Quite often the position is occupied by a professional engineer. He represents the architect or engineer at the job site, and interprets the plans and specifications, gives assistance in solving the many problems that arise during construction, approves or rejects materials delivered to the job site, approves or disapproves the workmanship, and approves monthly payments to the contractor. The last-named item gives him the power required. He cannot physically force a contractor to do anything but can withhold payment for defective work.

2. The power of the clerk of the works is limited to enforcing the plans and specifications. To require work not specified is not permitted. However, some offices permit the clerk of the works to issue field orders and, in such a case, the contractor is paid for the extra work.

3. To the construction worker or the casual observer, the clerk of the works has a simple job. It appears that the task includes watching others work and complaining when the work isn't satisfactory. Actually, he carries enormous responsibility. By his actions or failure to act, he can involve an employer in expensive lawsuits. He must insist that the specifications be followed, but must also stay within the limits of the authority laid down. He must reject shortleaf pine if longleaf pine is specified, and must check the work of each trade and the coordination between trades to be assured that the work is as specified. Obviously, he cannot watch each batch of mortar being mixed or each electrical connection being made. Therefore, it is necessary to know where to look and how to spot-check and sample materials. However, he should refrain from giving orders to workers. The clerk who actually takes charge and shows the contractor's employees how to do a job assumes the responsibility for the results. For example, when he tells

the workers how to support and brace the concrete formwork, is not his employer responsible if someone is injured if it fails? In the eyes of the law, responsibility goes with authority.

D. THE OWNER'S REPRESENTATIVE

Sometimes the owners place their own representative at the job site, with the job of representing the owner in any dispute, checking upon the clerk of the works, and making sure defective materials or workmanship are not accepted. The representative is the owners' agent, and therefore does have the power to request the clerk of the works to issue field orders and also has the power to approve the orders.

E. SUBCONTRACTORS

At the same time as the superintendent and the clerk of the works are being assigned, the contractor's purchasing agent is busy awarding contracts to subcontractors. These awards must be made early enough to allow the subcontractor time to order and receive materials so as not to delay the work. If the trade is one that requires shop drawings, contracts should be awarded to allow the draftsmen time to do their work.

F. SHOP DRAWINGS

1. Definition

"Shop drawings" are drawings prepared by the contractor, the subcontractor, or his material supplier to supplement the design drawing made by the architect or engineer.

2. Method

a. After the contract has been awarded, shop drawings, if required by the particular subcontractor, are made to conform with the design drawings prepared by the architect or engineer.

b. The method of approving shop drawings is specified in the special conditions and may vary in detail. Usually two (2) copies of the drawings prepared by the subcontractor are submitted to the general contractor. The general contractor submits them to the architect or engineer. Some specifications specify that the subcontractor's drawings are to be submitted directly to the architect or engineer. This does save time; but the general contractor loses control by not being able to keep track of the submittals and approvals, and for this reason this procedure is not recommended.

c. The architect may approve or disapprove the shop drawings or may approve them with corrections. If the drawings are approved, they are so stamped and one (1) copy is returned to the subcontractor (through the general contractor if so specified). This allows the subcontractor to order and fabricate material with assurance. The subcontractor prints the copies required in the field and sends them directly to the architect or engineer, who stamps all copies approved and sends a copy to the clerk of the works and the remainder to the general contractor for distribution.

d. If the drawings are disapproved, the disapproved items are noted on the drawings and the drawings are returned to the subcontractor. The subcontractor is required to submit new drawings.

e. The purpose of approving drawings with corrections is to permit the subcontractor to start fabrication early. This type of approval is reserved for minor corrections. The prints are stamped "Approval as Noted" and the minor corrections are so marked. The prints are returned to the subcontractor, who places orders for the material, corrects the tracings, and returns the proper number of prints to the architect or engineer. The drawings are stamped approved. One copy is returned to the subcontractor for filing, one to the clerk of the works, and the remaining copies to the contractor for distribution.

3. Purpose

Shop drawings have a threefold purpose: to assist the subcontractor or material supplier in fabricating the material, to obtain the architects' or engineers' approval of the method or arrangement of the materials, and to give other subcontractors information to properly do their work.

4. Examples

a. *To assist the subcontractor*

(1) Let us suppose that a structural steel subcontractor obtains a contract to furnish and erect the steel work for a twenty (20)-story building. The structural engineer would show on his design drawings the size and location of the columns, the girders, the beams, the lintels, and the like. Details would also show the bracing and any unusual feature.

(2) The structural steel subcontractor is required to cut each piece of steel to a particular length, punch holes in the members for rivets or bolts, shop rivet or bolt the connection angles to the members and make other shop connections as required, paint the steel, deliver it to the job site, and erect it. To do this the steel subcontractor needs a drawing of each piece of steel showing its size and length, the size and location of any holes, and any copes or cuts. Also needed are erection drawings showing how to erect the steel and coordinate the design drawings with the detail shop drawings.

(3) Detailing the structural steel for a multistory building presents difficulties that the student might overlook. While the floor load

and design might be the same for several stories, the details would not be alike. As the columns become lighter as the height is increased, the length of the beams framing into these columns must be increased. In addition, wind bracing usually changes as the height is increased. Many more drawings are required to detail a structure than to design it.

b. *To give others information*

(1) Anchor bolts are furnished by the structural steel subcontractor to hold base plates to concrete piers or footings. The specifications often specify the placing of the bolts under "Concrete."

(2) The anchor bolts must be placed accurately, or the structural steel will not fit. The structural steel shop drawing shows the anchor bolt location and the column center lines.

(3) The general contractor receives the approved shop drawings for distribution and sends one copy to the concrete subcontractor.

(4) The concrete subcontractor receives shop drawings from the reinforcing bar supplier, and all subcontractors requiring anchor bolts, inserts, sleeves, or other items imbedded in concrete, and should also receive shop drawings for any cut-outs in concrete walls or recesses in slabs required by other subcontractors. In this case the purpose of the shop drawings is to assist the concrete subcontractor in forming the work, to assure the other subcontractors that the concrete work will be done in accordance with their requirements, and to assist the contractor in coordinating the work between the various subcontractors.

2.08   CONSTRUCTION

A. The clerk of the works inspects the work of each of the subcontractors during the progress of the work. If he finds material at the job site that does not conform to the specifications, orders must be given to have it removed, and if subcontractors are found to be performing work in a manner other than that specified, it is ordered corrected.

B. As there is no contract between the owner and the subcontractor, the clerk of the works has no direct authority over the subcontractor. In theory, the clerk of the works should report any deviation from the specifications to the general contractor for correction. In actual practice, the subcontractor usually is willing to make corrections requested by the clerk of the works.

C. In the event the subcontractor believes that the requirements by the clerk of the works are beyond those specified or beyond the scope of his contract, it is possible to appeal to the general contractor. If the general contractor's superintendent agrees with the subcontractor, the problem is usually referred to the general contractor's home office. Should the dispute involve the extent of the subcontractor's contract, the office will decide whether the work involved is in another subcontract, whether the subcontractor should be paid extra for doing the work, or whether the general contractor will do the work with his own forces. If the dispute involves an interpretation of the specifications, the general contractor can appeal to the architect or engineer. If the architect or engineer agrees that the specifications are at fault, it is possible to accept the work as constructed or issue a bulletin requesting a price for correcting the work. If the architect or engineer decides that the work demanded by the clerk of the works is covered in the specifications, the general contractor may be directed to make the required correction and submit a bill for the cost. Who should pay the bill would be a matter for arbitration.

2.09 COMPLETING CONSTRUCTION

When the last subcontractor has left the job, the superintendent notifies the architect or engineer that all is ready for a final inspection. At a specific time the owner's representative, selected personnel from the architect's or engineer's office including the clerk of the works, and selected personnel from the general contractor's office, including the superintendent, meet at the job site. They make a complete inspection of the facility. Any correction is listed. This list is called a "punch list." When the items on the punch list are resolved, another meeting is scheduled at which the keys, bonds, and pertinent papers are delivered by the contractor to the owner, and in turn the owner gives the contractor, through the architect or engineer, a certificate of completion. Final payment is due within a specific number of days after the date of acceptance of the building.

2.10 DEFECTIVE MATERIALS OR WORKMANSHIP

A. As a rule the specifications require the contractor to replace materials or workmanship that prove to be defective within a period of one (1) year. This does not mean that the contractor must replace broken windows, unplug drains, or replace burned-out light bulbs. The owner is expected to maintain the structure.

B. Normally, when defects are found, the owner calls the architect or engineer, who calls the contractor. The contractor calls the proper subcontractor or makes the repair with his own forces.

C. Some bonds and warranties extend beyond the one-year period. The procedure of obtaining the repair or adjustment remains the same.

THREE
Contract Documents

3.01 DEFINITION

A. The term "specification" by definition refers to the description of a product or a method. As we have previously learned, this can take the form of spoken words, models, drawings, a written description, or any combination thereof. Most modern specifications consist of drawings and a written description bound in book form to supplement the drawings. While together they form a specification in the defined meaning of the term, the general practice is to refer to the drawings as the "plans," and to the book as the "specifications."

B. To avoid confusion, we will adopt the common policy of using the term "specifications" to refer to the books of specifications only. The term "plans and specifications" will be used to refer to the complete specification as defined above.

C. A contract is a voluntary agreement, between two or more competent parties, for valid consideration, to do or abstain from doing, some lawful act. A contract may or may not be in writing.

D. The Contract Form is a written document stating the terms of the agreement, listing the other documents that form a part of the contract, and carrying the signatures of the parties to the contract.

E. The term "contract documents" refers to all records in connection with the work at any specific time. Prior to bidding, the project documents would consist of the drawings, the specifications, and the proposal form. As construction nears completion, the contract documents would consist of the drawings, the specifications, all addenda, the proposal form completed and signed by the contractor, the signed contract form between the owner and contractor, all bulletins, the contractor's reply to bulletins, all change orders, all field orders, and all field work orders.

3.01 (Cont.)

F. The contract documents should designate the quality, the quantity, and the location of materials, and the method by which they are assembled at the job site. They should contain a statement of the price to be paid and the time allowed to complete the work specified. It boils down to "what" goes "where," "when," and for "how much."

3.02 DRAWINGS

A. IMPORTANCE

1. The most costly part of the professional's task is preparing "working or construction drawings." These are graphic. They indicate arrangement of materials.

2. The following paragraph indicates the items that are usually shown on the drawing. To show less is to provide an incomplete drawing; to letter out items that could be typed in the specifications is a waste of time.

B. THINGS TO BE SHOWN

1. The location of the project on the site.

2. The location of all utility lines, roads, and elevations.

3. Plans show location and quantities of materials, equipment, and fixtures. They should also show the size of openings in the walls and floors and the interior finishes.

4. Overall dimensions and detail dimensions showing size and location of all items.

5. Elevations showing a graphic indication of physical appearance.

6. Details showing interrelation of materials, equipment, outlets, and the connections.

3.03 SPECIFICATIONS

The specifications describe what is to be furnished and how it is to be installed; the drawings designate where it should be placed. Specifications are made up of words and may be defined as "a description of the quality of materials and equipment to be used on a project and their application or installation."

3.04 ADDENDA

The Addenda consist of changes in the drawing, in the specifications, or in both before the contract is awarded. Each addendum is sent to each bidder prior to the opening of the bids. The bidder is required to acknowledge receiving each addendum and to include the price of the work involved to the same extent as if the work was originally shown.

3.05 THE PROPOSAL FORM

The Proposal Form is prepared by the architect or engineer and given to the bidders to fill out and return. The bidders state in the proposal form the price or prices they will charge for doing specified work. The proposal is not limited to one quotation. It may contain one or more specific jobs and several alternates. Only one of several proposals is accepted for a specific job. When the one is accepted, the others are automatically rejected.

3.06 THE CONTRACT FORM

The Contract Form is written by the architect or engineer or by the owner's attorney. It is an agreement between the owner and the one bidder selected by the owner. The contract states exactly what the contractor is to do and what is to be paid for the work. The contract, of course, refers to the drawings, the specifications, all addenda, and the proposal form.

3.07 BULLETINS

A "bulletin" is a request for a price for making a change in the contract. The contractor has a contract to perform a specific task for a specific amount of money. However, in a part of the specifications called "The General Conditions" the owner is usually given the right to make changes in the contract. If the owner wishes to make a change, the architect-engineer issues a bulletin, describing the change the owner wishes to make. The contractor analyzes the change and informs the owner through the architect-engineer the cost of making the change. This is an offer which the owner has the right to accept or reject. If the owner rejects the offer, the contractor is informed in writing and proceeds as if no bulletin had been issued.

3.08 CHANGE ORDERS

A. If the owner accepts the offer of the contractor, a "change order" is issued by the architect or engineer. The change order gives the contractor authority to proceed with the changes made to the contract by the bulletin. The price in the contract is revised accordingly.

B. If a method to determine the cost of extra work is a part of the contract, the change could be described in the change order and it would not be necessary to issue a bulletin.

3.09 FIELD ORDERS

A "field order" is an order issued by the clerk of the works, or his employers, in the field making changes in the contract that the contractor agrees to do at no change in the cost.

3.10 FIELD WORK ORDERS

A "field work order" is a change in the contract issued by the architect or engineer in the field when immediate work is required and there is not enough time to issue a bulletin. The contractor is usually reimbursed on a "time and material" basis which has been established in the proposal form.

3.11 ORDER OF IMPORTANCE

A. Obviously, all documents should be in agreement. However, through human error, there are times when they are not. It should be emphasized that the courts do not consider all documents of equal value. By general rule, that which is done last takes precedence. In the event of ambiguity, typed material will take precedence over printed material, and handwritten material will take precedence over typed material.

B. Conforming with the preceding article, a handwritten field work order would normally take precedence over any other document. Any field order would usually take priority over a change order, and a change order which involved a change in the contract would take precedence over the contract. The contract should include all items of the agreement and should under normal conditions take precedence over all items written before the contract was signed.

C. In the absence of any specific provisions to the contrary, words will take precedence over drawings. Hence, specifications will always govern if there is a disagreement between them and the drawings.

FOUR

The Main Divisions of the Specifications

4.01 GENERAL

A specification is divided into sections. These sections come under one (1) of three (3) divisions. The first division is called the Bidding Documents and consists of three sections entitled, The Invitation to Bid, the Instructions to Bidders, and the Proposal Form. The second division is called the Conditions and consists of sections entitled The General Conditions, The Special Conditions, The General Contractor's Work, and Alternates. The third division is called the Technical Division. While each of these divisions will be discussed in detail in future chapters, a brief outline of each is stated here to assist the student in understanding the entire book of specifications.

4.02 THE BIDDING DOCUMENTS

A. THE INVITATION TO BID

The Invitation to Bid is sometimes called the Advertisement. It can be a telephone call, a written letter, or a paid advertisement placed in a newspaper telling contractors that plans and specifications are ready for bidding. The law requires that some public projects must be advertised in the press when a project is ready for bidding. The purpose is to let all interested parties know about the work and to prevent favoritism. In private work the owner has the right to limit the bidding yet may choose to publish an advertisement, but the more common type of invitation is by letter or telephone. The invitation is simply a request that a contractor submit a bid on a project. It may or may not be included in the book of specifications.

B. THE INSTRUCTIONS TO BIDDERS

When there is no advertisement, the Instructions to Bidders is the first section in the specifications. It informs those interested in bidding when the bids are due, how to fill out the proposal form, and where to deliver it when it is completed.

C. THE PROPOSAL

The architect or engineer prepares the proposal form. This form is sent to the various bidders. The bidders fill in the blank spaces giving their prices for doing the specified work and sign the same. Legally the proposal is an offer. If the owner accepts the offer, a contract is made. The purpose of having the architect or engineer prepare the proposal form is to ensure uniformity; thus the price each bidder submits will be easy to compare with those of others, and the low bidders can be easily determined. It is easy to understand that if each bidder were permitted to prepare the proposal submitted, no two bids would be made on the same basis.

4.03 CONDITIONS

A. THE GENERAL CONDITIONS

The General Conditions, more correctly called the General Conditions of the Contract, describe conditions required on every individual construction project. They cover such items as insurance, ownership of drawings, royalties and patents, protection of the work, claims for extra cost, termination of the contract, and payments. As the General Conditions are always the same, they are usually printed. The American Institute of Architects sells a very excellent set of printed sheets, and these are used in most construction projects. The federal government and various state and local governments print their own documents for their use. Many large companies also prefer to print their own general conditions, each adapted to their own use.

B. THE SPECIAL CONDITIONS

The Special Conditions are sometimes called the Special Conditions of the Contract or the Supplementary General Conditions. They are similar to the General Conditions in that they deal with conditions of work. However, Special Conditions deal with specific stipulated items that apply only to the project under consideration. For example, a contractor estimating the costs for constructing a water treatment plant must know how to get the material to the job site. There is, or there is not, a railroad siding on the property where work is to be performed. The contractor should know whether there is a railroad siding and under what conditions it may be used for delivery of the material. This would affect the price. Such an item would normally appear in the Special Conditions, as each job at each building site would have different conditions. If, however, a single company had a single plant and an established policy for handling a contractor's freight, this information could appear in their printed General Conditions. The same information should be given about who will furnish water or electrical power. The contractor must know the working conditions in order to submit an intelligent quotation.

C. THE GENERAL CONTRACTOR'S WORK

A general contractor who has a contract with an owner has certain duties and obligations that he alone can perform. These can be placed in a separate section of the specifications. It is more common, however, to include the General Contractor's Work as a subsection in the Special Conditions.

D. ALTERNATES

An "alternate" is a request for a price for making a specific change in the contract documents. This will be described more completely in Chapter XI. Not all specifications have alternates, and if none are required, the section can be omitted. If one or more alternates are requested, these alternates should be specified in a separate section. Alternates can be simple or intricate. An example appears in the Appendix.

4.04   THE TECHNICAL DIVISION

A. The technical division of the specifications is the most important of the specifications. It specifies the actual work to be done.

B. The number of technical sections depends upon the type of project. A simple project could have only one (1) technical section; a large, complex project could have fifty (50) or more technical sections. Chapter Six will cover the technical division in detail.

4.05   ORDER OF WRITING

While the technical division is the last to appear in the book of specifications, it is the first to be written. The technical division will usually consist of several sections and make up the largest division of the specifications. If alternates are desired, the alternate section is usually written after the technical sections are complete. However, some alternates are so dependent upon some sections in the technical division that some alternates may be written when the specification writer is concentrating on those technical sections. When the alternate section is complete, the specification writer usually will write the General Contractor's Work and the Special Conditions. During the final stages of check, the Proposal Form and the Instructions to Bidders will be completed. The Invitation to Bid will be the last item written in the specifications before the bidding.

4.06 ORDER OF IMPORTANCE

The specification writer should make every effort to prevent a contradiction in the specifications. However, if there is a discrepancy between various sections, the general rule is that the typewritten sections will take precedence over the General Conditions, which are printed. It is also common practice to give precedence to statements in the Special Conditions over those in other sections of the specifications.

FIVE

Types of Specifications

5.01 GENERAL

If any two experienced specifications writers were asked to specify the same object, there would be a considerable difference in the wording and possibly a greater difference in the method. There are as many ways of specifying an object as there are specification writers. However, all specifications fall into one or more of six (6) general types, and these types are the subject of this chapter. The six types are: the Performance Specification, the Description Specification, the Brand-Name Specification, the Closed Specification, the Open Specification, and the Reference Specification. A Combination Specification is a specification containing two (2) or more of the above types in a single description.

5.02 THE PERFORMANCE SPECIFICATION

A. DEFINITION

A "performance specification" is one where the results of the product, rather than the product itself, are specified.

B. USE

1. The government may be interested in buying an aeroplane which can carry a fifty (50)-ton load at a height of forty thousand feet (40,000) flying four (4) times the speed of sound. The size, the power of the engines, and the weight are immaterial if these results can be accomplished. Such a product requires a performance specification.

2. Another example is where an owner needs a new roof on his building, wants the roof to last twenty-five (25) years, and doesn't care about

the number of plies of felt required or the type of bitumen used; this owner wants performance only.

C. EXAMPLE

"1. Fan

"The fan shall move not less than eight hundred and sixty cubic feet of free air per minute (860 cub ft/min) and shall move not less than seven hundred and eighty cubic feet of air per minute (780 cub ft/min) against a one-eighth inch ($1/8''$) static pressure."

5.03 DESCRIPTIVE SPECIFICATION

A. DEFINITION

The "descriptive specification" is, as the name implies, a description of a product.

B. USE

A descriptive specification is used where the architect-engineer wants more than a minimum performance. For example, in specifying a stone abutment for a bridge, the beauty of the material is equally as important as its performance. Structurally other materials might be better. To obtain the desired stone, a description would be necessary.

C. EXAMPLE

"1. Fan

"a. The fan shall be a wall-mounted, centrifugal type of fan of weather-proof construction made for outdoor use. It shall be of all-aluminum construction including aluminum centrifugal wheels and alumimum hardware. The metal in the fan shall not be thinner than sixty-four thousandths (.0064) of an inch.

"b. The fan shall be a direct-drive, propeller-type fan mounted on a ball bearing, totally enclosed, one-sixth horsepower ($1/6$ H.P.) motor supported by a rigid frame attached to the fan housing.

"c. The air inlet shall not be less than ten inches (10") in diameter."

5.04 BRAND-NAME SPECIFICATION

A. DEFINITION

A "brand-name specification" is where the desired product is specified by the name given by the manufacturer or by the manufacturer's name and the model number.

B. USE

The brand-name specification is used when the architects or engineers

5.04 B. (Cont.)

wish to use one of several specific products that they know from past experience will satisfy their needs.

C. EXAMPLE

"1. Fan

"The fan shall be size 10 as manufactured by the Static Air Fan Company of High, Texas; the Howell Lynn Ayre Company of Pretty, Miss.; the Rubb Burr Fan Company of Fountain, Penn.; or an equal approved by the engineer."

5.05 CLOSED SPECIFICATION

A. GENERAL

There are two types of closed specifications, the single-product and the multiproduct. Closed specifications are usually brand-name specifications.

B. SINGLE-PRODUCT SPECIFICATION

1. Definition

The "single-product, closed specification" is where only one product is specified by name.

2. Use

The owners may want a single product to be used. For example, their manufacturing plant may be equipped with one type of conveyor. The owners may be willing to pay a little more for a conveyor that matches their existing equipment to reduce their maintenance and their inventory of spare parts.

3. Example

"a. Fan

"The fan shall be model U R 1 - 2 as manufactured by the Howell Lynn Ayre Company of Pretty, Miss. No other will be accepted."

C. MULTIPRODUCT SPECIFICATION

1. Definition

The "multiproduct specification" is the same as a single-product specification except that more than one product is named.

2. Use

The owners may want competition in the bidding but to avoid the use of a product or products they do not like.

3. Example

"a. Fan

"The fan shall be model U R 1 - 2 as manufactured by the Howell

Lynn Ayre Company of Pretty, Miss. or by the Rubb Burr Fan Company of Fountain, Penn."

5.06   OPEN SPECIFICATION

A. "Open specifications" are the opposite of closed specifications. They are called "open" because all manufacturers whose products meet the performance or description specified may bid.

B. All performance specifications and all descriptive specifications are open specifications. Brand-name specifications are open specifications if in addition to the brand names a phrase such as "or equal" or similar wording is added after the brand names.

C. The phrase "or equal" means that the item specified by brand name is established as a standard and any manufacturer with an equal product may bid.

D. The examples in Articles 5.02 C, 5.03 C, 5.04 C, and 5.07 C are examples of open specifications.

5.07   REFERENCE SPECIFICATION

A. DEFINITION

A "reference specification" is where the item desired is referred to by a number corresponding to a number in a published specification.

B. USE

1. The government and various private companies print complete specifications on commonly used products. If these specifications are available, it is easier and usually more satisfactory for the specification writer to refer to them rather than write pages of specifications.

2. The specification writer should use only reference specifications that are well known by the trade and that can be easily obtained. Contractors would be justified in refusing to bid on a specification they didn't have and couldn't obtain in a short period of time. Inspectors are helpless to enforce a specification if they don't have a copy.

C. EXAMPLE

"1. Fan

"The fan shall conform to Federal Specification W-F-207 c."

D. DANGERS

Specification writers should always read the specification they are referring to. Many times the specifications that are published specify several types or grades of material in the same specification. In such a specification the grade as well as the specification number should be given.

5.08 COMBINATION

A. GENERAL

It may be desirable to use a combination of the above types of specifications. While it would be impossible to have a combination of an open and a closed specification, it is possible to have combinations of performance, descriptive, and reference specifications.

B. USE

A product may be required with specific physical characteristics and also may be required to perform to a particular standard.

C. EXAMPLE

"The fan shall move not less than eight hundred and sixty cubic feet per minute (860 cub ft/min) of free air and shall be a wall-mounted, centrifugal-type fan made for outdoor use. The motor shall be constructed to NEMA standards."

D. DANGERS

If a combination specification is used, extreme care must be used to make a specification that is possible to build. For example, if the performance specification for a fan is used, and a motor incapable of giving that performance was specified, it would be impossible for the contractor to complete the contract. Conflicts in specifications can result in court cases. One of the better-known cases is summarized in the following article.

E. CASE

1. This case, *MacKnight Flintic Stone Company v. Mayor, Aldermen and Commonalty of the City of New York* (160 N.Y. 73, 54 N.E. 661), took place in 1899. It is well known and the precedent for many of today's court decisions.

2. The contractor, MacKnight Flintic Stone Company, was awarded a contract to construct a prison and courthouse for the City of New York. The waterproofing specification was a combination type; the manner of the work to be done and the materials to be used were specified in detail. In addition the specifications stated that the contractor must leave the work in perfect order and guarantee the basement to be watertight for five (5) years from the date of the acceptance of the work.

3. The subcontractor used the materials specified and applied them in the manner prescribed. When the waterproofing was completed, the

inspector told the subcontractor he had done a good job. However, when the project was completed, the boiler room and the basement leaked. As a result, the city refused to make the final payment on the contract and the contractor brought action in the courts.

4. The contractor's position was that all work had been done according to the contract. He furnished the materials specified and applied them exactly as specified. On the other hand, the city claimed the specifications required that the boiler room be waterproof and the contractor had failed to conform.

5. The judge examined the specifications, which required that the contractor apply a specific number of plies of felt and cover each ply with a specific amount of tar. The contractor had had no choice. If he had applied more or less than was specified, he would have violated his contract. The result was a basement that leaked. The judge concluded that if the description specifications, when fully performed, did not provide a waterproof structure, the fault was with the city and was not the contractor's responsibility.

F. CONCLUSION

1. It is not true, however, that a performance specification is necessarily better than a descriptive specification. In another case where the specification stated, "The basement walls shall be watertight," the contractor applied no waterproofing whatsoever. It was a dry year and no leaking was discovered during the one (1)-year warranty period; however, shortly thereafter in a bad rainstorm the walls leaked badly. The owner suffered a bad loss but was unable to recover his money.

2. The student should realize after reading this chapter that an item, such as a fan, can be specified in many ways and that the best type of specification depends upon the product or method being specified. In this respect, experience is the best teacher.

SIX

The Technical Division

6.01 CONTRACTORS, SUBCONTRACTORS, AND SUPPLIERS

A. When a contract is awarded for a project, the person or company awarding and paying for the work is called the Owner; the one accepting the contract and agreeing to perform the work is called the Contractor. To fulfill the contract, the contractor has the choice of buying materials and hiring labor to assemble them, or of awarding contracts to others to do this work. Normally, he does the work he can do efficiently with his own forces and sublets the remainder to those who specialize in a particular phase of the work. A contractor who awards various parts of the work to others is called a General Contractor.

B. The contractors who specialize in one phase of the work and are employed by the General Contractor are called Subcontractors. Those who supply material for the project are called Suppliers. The supplier may have a contract with the General Contractor or with one of the subcontractors.

C. When the term "Contractor" is used, it means one who has a contract with the owner. Should the owner employ a contractor for some special work, for example plumbing, the contractor would be called the Plumbing Contractor. If he were employed by the General Contractor, he would be called a Plumbing Subcontractor.

D. The writer should use the correct terms when writing specifications. When referring to a subcontractor, the term to use is Subcontractor.

E. It should be remembered that the owner has a contract with the contractor. He, and he alone, has the legal responsibility to deliver a finished product to the owner; and he cannot avoid this responsibility by subletting any or all of the work. The subcontractor has a contract with the contractor only; his relationship with the owner is indirect. However, it is the subcontractor who buys the material, hires the labor, and does most of the work.

6.02   SECTIONS

A. The technical division of the specifications is divided into sections. The purpose of these sections is to assist the contractor in evaluating bids.

B. Usually a General Contractor is free to employ as many subcontractors as he pleases. Some contractors sublet nearly all of their work. Others do a large part of the work with their own forces. When General Contractors have a light workload, they often do the work themselves that they would sublet under normal conditions. When preparing specifications, the writer does not know what trade will be sublet and which trade the contractors will do themselves. Therefore, specifications are divided into trade sections. One section of the specifications should be written for each group of subcontractors.

C. Not knowing how the contractor will sublet his work, the specification writer assumes that the General Contractor will sublet all of the work and engage only in supervising the subcontractors. Therefore, the wording of the specifications should be applicable to both the General Contractor and the subcontractors involved.

D. Trade union regulations do not determine the breakdown of the specifications. The breakdown is determined by the work done by various subcontractors. A subcontractor may hire people from several trades to do the work of the subcontractor. For example, a Concrete Subcontractor may hire carpenters to build forms, hire reinforcing setters to place the reinforcing, hire steel workers to set anchor bolts, hire plumbers and electricians to place sleeves, hire laborers to pour the concrete and strip the forms, and then hire cement finishers to finish the slabs. The work is in one technical section because the contractor (and the architect and engineer) wants the erection of each phase of the work to be the responsibility of one subcontractor. If the formwork for concrete were built by one subcontractor and the concrete poured by another and a failure resulted, the subcontractor pouring the concrete could say the forms were not strong enough while the Form Building Subcontractor could claim that the loads were improperly concentrated in one area. An endless argument could result. Making one subcontractor responsible for the results in a particular area avoids this trouble.

E. The work performed by a group of subcontractors in any one area is fairly standard but may vary with geographical locations. In a large city, it is not difficult to find subcontractors to do all forms of work. In small towns, it may be hard to find subcontractors. Likewise, in different sections of the country different groups of subcontractors do different types of work. For example, in Southeastern Michigan roofing and sheet metal work go together. This is considered one trade. There are other sections of the country where roofing and sheet metal are separate. This applies to many trades.

F. It is extremely costly to the owner to have the work in specifications under a wrong trade heading. Let us suppose that the stone coping was put under the Roofing section. The Roofing and Sheet Metal Subcontractors would have to price that work, but they don't employ stone masons and don't have the know-how to do the work. As a result they ask for prices from other contractors who specialize in that type of work. The Stone Contractor figures the price of the work and adds a profit, the Roofing Contractor adds a profit, and the General Contractor adds a profit; as a result the owner pays three profits instead of two. Suppose that the stone coping costs the Stone Subcontractor three thousand dollars ($3,000). If the subcontractor bids directly, ten percent (10%) profit would be added and a price of three thousand three hundred dollars ($3,300) would be submitted to the General Contractor. The General Contractor would add this into the other costs and add ten percent (10%); the owner would then pay three thousand six hundred thirty dollars ($3,630) for the stone coping. If the price were submitted through the Roofing Subcontractor, the amount charged by the Stone Subcontractor would be the same, three thousand three hundred dollars ($3,300). The Roofing Subcontractor would add this to the costs and add ten percent (10%), and so the price to the General Contractor would be three thousand six hundred thirty dollars ($3,630). When the General Contractor's profit is added, the cost to the owner is three thousand nine hundred ninety-three dollars ($3,993), or three hundred sixty-three dollars ($363) more than should have been paid. It is just as costly for the owner to have materials in the wrong trade section as it is to over-design structural steel or electrical work.

G. Getting the work in the proper trade section is a most difficult job for the specification writer. It can be learned only by continuous writing over a period of time. As new products appear, new subcontractors start in business to install these products. Often established subcontractors take on new lines of work. It is a constantly changing field.

H. A suggested list of trade sections appears in the Appendix. It is printed to assist the student in writing classroom specifications. It can also serve as a guide for construction specifications. However, the writer should check local conditions and revise it where required.

6.03   THE CONSTRUCTION SPECIFICATIONS INSTITUTE

A. This chapter would not be complete without writing of the work being done by the Construction Specifications Institute, often referred to as the CSI.

B. The CSI was started because a group of specification writers were dissatisfied with the way specifications were being prepared by the various government agencies. As a result, in 1948, sixty-five (65) men interested in standardizing bidding procedures met in Washington and elected Mr. James Moore of the Hospital Construction Office in the Public Health Service to head the group as the first president. Specification writers in New York City learned of the improvement brought about by the group in Washington and asked to join their organization. New York became the first chapter in May 1951, followed by Chicago, Los Angeles, San Diego, Sacramento, San Francisco, Detroit, Boston, and Cleveland, until, at this writing, there are 123 chapters throughout the United States and Canada, with almost 11,000 members.

C. The purpose of CSI is to improve specifications. The lack of uniformity of the subcontractor trades in various sections caused this organization to take action. Architects and engineers of the country doing work throughout the nation have difficulty in producing specifications that are economical to the owner in areas where the local trade practices are unfamiliar. The CSI has attempted to set up a list of trades to be used nationwide. This list already has had some acceptance. The CSI hopes that by getting sufficient architects and engineers to adopt this list of trades, they can force subcontractors to change their bidding practices. For example, the CSI shows Roofing and Sheet Metal as one trade. They hope that, in areas where Roofing subcontractors and Sheet Metal subcontractors operate separately, combining the trades in the specification will cause some subcontractors to combine or to add additional facilities to handle both trades. Once this is done by a very few, the remainder will be forced to accept the same methods to stay competitive.

D. A uniform method of dividing trades will be helpful to the specification writer and the General Contractor. However, until subcontractors adopt that method of doing work, the results will be costly to the owner.

E. The trade division proposed by the CSI is shown in the Appendix.

6.04 SMALL ITEMS

It may not be necessary to write a complete section to cover a small work item which could be placed in another section. For example, if there were only two (2) stone sills in an entire building, it would not be necessary to have a separate section on stone work. This could be placed under Masonry and the Masonry Subcontractor could hire the proper union tradesmen to place the sills. Likewise, on a project involving the pouring of a small slab, the specification writer might find it advantageous to place the concrete finishing under Concrete rather than in a separate section. Economy is the key. If the amount of work in any trade section is too small to attract a subcontractor's bid, that work should be placed in another section of the specifications.

6.05 PURPOSE

A. The purpose of subdividing trades is primarily to assist the contractor in receiving the lowest bid from subcontractors. In populous areas where many subcontractors are bidding on a project, the General Contractor is not always sure what subcontractors are figuring the work. The General Contractor may send out cards requesting quotations from many subcontractors; however, there is no certainty that all of them will bid or that other subcontractors will not send in figures. It must be remembered that subcontractors, in order to protect their prices, often wait until the last hour to submit them by telephone. When a contractor receives thirty or forty (30 or 40) bids in the last two (2) hours of the bid period, there is not time to analyze them. Under such conditions, it is essential for the contractor to receive bids that can be readily compared. For that reason, the contractor asks each subcontractor to bid on one or more sections of the specification complete. The contractor can then receive comparative bids by telephone, record them, and determine the low bidder. Theoretically, the subcontractor is supposed to submit a price days before it is due, but it actually doesn't happen that way.

B. The question arises, isn't confusion or error possible as a result of last-minute telephone bids and no record from the subcontractor? The answer is in the affirmative. However, it must be realized that the contractor receives several bids from each trade. If one figure is considerably above or below the others, it is an indication that a mistake has been made and it should be checked. Contractors will call up subcontractors and inform them that their price is out of line. They know if the subcontractors aren't making any money, they can expect a hard time. There is no reason for the general contractor to conceal from subcontractors that their figures are too high or too low.

C. It is not the intention of the specifications to prescribe each subcontractor's work. Except in very unusual cases, the owner or the engineer does not care who performs the work; they are merely concerned that it be satisfactory. It is assumed that the contractor is knowledgeable, capable, and responsible, and if through experience the contractor can produce a quality product fast and cheaply, everybody gains.

D. An example of this occurred when an engineer specified a new airfield. The post holes for the miles of fence around the airfield were specified under "Excavating," and the placing of concrete around the posts under "Concrete." The remainder of the work was specified under "Fencing." Each subcontractor bid on the work specified in his section. After work was started in the field, the Fencing Subcontractor proposed to the General Contractor that he be allowed to dig the holes to place the fence posts, and to place the concrete in the ground. He would make no additional charge. He made this proposal because he was equipped with a mechanical post hole digger and concrete mixer on a single truck. He had an efficient crew that could place the work fast. He would not have to wait while one crew dug the hole before he could line the posts and secure them in place and then wait again while another crew came and placed the concrete. As the quality of the work would be better and the responsibility for the finished product under one subcontractor, the General Contractor and engineer agreed to make the change. The Excavating Subcontractor did not have the special equipment to dig the holes and had depended upon hand labor. The Concrete Subcontractor was set up to pour a large volume of concrete and the fence post operation was for him a costly annoyance. Upon request, the Excavating and the Concrete Subcontractors allowed a sizable reduction in their price to the General Contractor. However, in accordance with general practice, their reduction included their actual estimated cost; no reduction was made in their profit.

E. In many cases, permitting the contractor to select the trade divisions of the work is advantageous to all concerned. In the above case, the owner had a better and faster job, the engineer gained experience which would enable future clients to save money, the contractor saved considerable money, and the two (2) subcontractors were relieved of a responsibility at no loss in profit. It was fortunate for the engineer that the owner never learned the amount of money he could have saved had the specifications been prepared in a different manner.

F. There are many, even among practicing architects and engineers, who maintain that it is not the business of the specification writer to subdivide the specifications into trade sections. As we have previously stated, the primary purpose of dividing the technical division into sections is to enable each subcontractor to compile a complete and intelligent bid for the contractor without duplication of another subcontractor's work and to eliminate any expensive uncertainty as to the scope of one's work, thus reducing the owner's costs. In the above cases, the contractor did not know the names of the Fence Subcontractors or the Excavating Subcontractors that were bidding on the project until bids were received a few hours before his proposal was due. Under such conditions, the contractor had no opportunity to discuss a reduction in price prior to submitting his bid.

SEVEN

Preparing to Write a Technical Section

7.01 OFFICE PROCEDURE

A. Good specification writers are always busy, but the flow of work is uneven. There are periods when demands upon their time are relatively light and they have time to talk with salespeople, study and file catalogs, and visit jobs under construction. There are other long periods of time when their workload is almost superhuman. Deadlines must be met, and there are periods when they may be required to work on several jobs at the same time.

B. Specification writers cannot write the final draft of their specifications until the drawings are nearly completed. Their specifications then must be typed, checked, printed, collated and bound, and ready to issue by the time the drawings are printed.

C. The specification writers' work in preparing a specification is divided into six (6) separate steps: taking notes, preparing an outline, research, writing, checking the typing, and checking the collating and binding. Because they cannot wait until the drawings are completed, they start work on the sections least likely to be changed. For example, they cannot work on the Hollow Metal Work, Carpentry, or Hardware until the door schedule is complete; so they work on Masonry and Overhead Doors.

D. The following subchapters present the six steps in specification writing. The work on the various sections, however, progresses so that some sections are ready for final typing while others require research and still others have not yet been started.

7.02 TAKING NOTES

A. Each specification writer probably has a different method of taking notes. As a start, the following method is suggested, which can be altered as the specification writer gains experience.

B. The first step is to get a loose-leaf notebook. From the preliminary drawings or sketches compile a list of all the trades involved, listing a separate trade on each sheet. The trades are determined by checking the drawings with the list given in the Appendix. This list will change as the job progresses, and sheets may be added or removed as required. This notebook accompanies the specification writer in conferences with the owner, at meetings with the department heads, on visits to the job site, in talks with salesmen, and wherever the job is discussed. If the owner says he wants a pink bathtub in his office latrine, such a note should appear on the page headed "Plumbing." However, most notes are obtained by studying the drawings as they progress.

C. Some specification writers prefer cards to loose-leaf paper. This may be satisfactory for the experienced writer, but the beginner will find difficulty in handling the cards. They tend to become disarranged in the course of note taking and time might be lost in keeping them in order. In a conference it is necessary to locate the proper page or card quickly.

D. For rapid reference, some specification writers use differently colored paper for different groups of trades; others use index tabs. The main point is that all information should be recorded. A beginner who depends upon memory will soon find himself lost on any large project.

7.03 AN OUTLINE

A. GENERAL

Before starting the writing of any section of the specifications, the writer should prepare an outline of that section. The purpose of the outline is to organize the notes taken in preparation for the specification writing. The extent of the outline will depend upon the individual. Simple headings are ordinarily sufficient. A discussion of the various subsections required in a typical technical section follows.

B. THE FIRST THREE SUBSECTIONS

The first three subsections in each section are GENERAL NOTE, SCOPE OF THE WORK, and WORK NOT INCLUDED IN THIS SECTION. These are headings that will appear in the outline. The text under these headings will be added as the specifications are written.

C. SHOP DRAWINGS

1. General

If shop drawings are required, they should be specified in the technical section. The trades usually requiring shop drawings are listed as follows:

2. List

 a. Concrete (For reinforcing steel)

 b. Precast Concrete

 c. Stonework

 d. Incinerators

 e. Structural Steel

 f. Bar Joist

 g. Miscellaneous Iron

 h. Cranes

 i. Monorails

 j. Hydraulic Equipment

 k. Ornamental Metal

 l. Bank Equipment

 m. Cellular Steel

 n. Steel Decking

 o. Curtain Walls

 p. Metal Siding

 q. Cement Asbestos

 r. Metal Sash

 s. Hollow Metal Work

 t. Fire Doors

 u. Overhead and Vertical-Lift Doors

 v. Rolling Metal Curtains

 w. Slate, Marble, and Precast Terrazzo

 x. Wire Partitions

 y. Folding Partitions

 z. Movable Partitions

 aa. Metal Toilet Stalls

 ab. Laundry Equipment

 ac. Kitchen Equipment

 ad. Laboratory Furniture

 ae. Metal Casework

 af. Lockers and Shelving

 ag. Organs, Chimes, and Bells

 ah. Finish Hardware (A hardware schedule)

 ai. Theater Seating

 aj. Roads and Paving (Manhole covers and frames)

 ak. Flagpoles

 al. Swimming Pools (Hardware and equipment)

 am. Boiler House Equipment

 an. Plumbing

 ao. Heating, Ventilation, and Air Conditioning

 ap. Dust-Collecting Equipment

      aq. Fire Protection Equipment

      ar. Electrical Equipment

      as. Elevators and Electric Stairways

      at. Stage Equipment

      au. X-Ray Equipment

      av. Park and Playground Equipment

D. MATERIALS

Under this heading the specification writer lists all of the materials required to complete the work. The inexperienced writer should leave considerable space for adding items originally overlooked.

E. SAMPLES

The architect or engineer may wish to have the material supplier furnish him with samples of materials for approval before any material is shipped to the job site. The purpose is to save the delay that would occur if large quantities of material were rejected at the job site. Samples are usually required for marble or other materials when artistic qualities are required. The specification writer should be aware of this and consult with the architect or engineer.

F. FABRICATION, DELIVERY, AND STORAGE

The writer should try to visualize the entire process that the material specified takes from forest, mine, or quarry to the final product. If the materials require shop fabrication, this heading should appear; if there is any special requirement for the delivery of the materials, such as protection, crating or the like, a heading entitled "Delivery" should appear in the outline. Storage of material at the job site could be important. If under-cover protection is required, it should be so specified under "Storage."

G. INSTALLATION

1. In specifying the installation, writers should visualize the entire process from the delivery of the material to the final inspection. If they do not know how a particular product is installed, they should find out. It is impossible for specification writers to describe a process they know little or nothing about.

2. Though writers must specify everything they want, they shouldn't overspecify to the extent that they cause inconvenience to the contractor (and extra expense to the owner) without receiving some value. For example, it would be foolish to specify that the concrete must be conveyed in wheelbarrows; the contractor may prefer buggies. On the other hand it would be proper to require the subcontractor to use elephant trunks when pouring concrete into steep forms or through large vertical distances. Elephant trunks prevent separation of the ag-

gregates and affect the quality of the concrete.

3. Normally such things as scaffolds, runways for conveying concrete, or other temporary construction which does not affect the finished work are not specified. The condition of concrete formwork would affect the finished work and should be specified. Likewise, when there are two or more ways of accomplishing a task, but one is far superior to the others, it would not be wrong to specify the superior method. For example, it would be desirable to require the contractor to use a surveyor's level to set the screeds when unusual tolerances are required in a finished concrete slab. This method would allow the clerk of the works to make a rapid check before the concrete is poured and thus avoid trouble.

4. As the requirements for each trade are different, there can be no set rules of material installation. Writers must outline the procedure step by step.

5. In outlining the installation, attachments and other materials not listed will come to mind. These should be added under MATERIALS, to complete the list.

H. WARRANTY AND GUARANTEE

1. General

The word "warranty" and the word "guarantee" are frequently confused and misunderstood. Buyers are often misled when told "it's guaranteed" because they assume that a written guarantee protects them from any defects in the item purchased. This is not the case. The amount and time of protection must be explicitly stated to have an enforceable document.

2. Definition

a. A "warranty" or a "guarantee" is a verbal or written statement attesting to the quality of the product or that it will perform as required under specific conditions. Warranties and guarantees usually have a limited time and state exactly what will be done if the product proves defective.

b. A warranty is issued by the manufacturer of a product. For example, a purchaser of an automobile or household appliance may receive a warranty from the manufacturer of the product.

c. A guarantee is issued by someone other than the manufacturer. It is a pledge to fulfill the manufacturer's obligation in the event of default.

d. The difference between a warranty and a guarantee can be illustrated in the purchase of an automobile. The buyer receives a warranty from the manufacturer of the car and may also receive a guarantee from the dealer. If a defect occurs, the buyer returns the car to the dealer. The dealer makes the repair as a part of the guarantee. Should the defect be a battery or some item purchased by the manufacturer from a supplier, it would be replaced by the dealer. The dealer would return the defective part to the manufacturer who guaranteed it. The manufacturer would return it to the supplier who manufactured the battery and issued the warranty.

3. Value

The value of a warranty or guarantee depends upon reading it correctly and upon the integrity of the party issuing it, since the buyer can seldom afford to sue in the event of breach. Most misunderstandings arise because the buyer doesn't read or understand the terms of the document. The terms stated in the warranty or guarantee may limit the liability of the manufacturer or dealer to the extent that the warranty or guarantee is almost without value. The author remembers the disappointment of a childhood friend who ordered a gold ring by mail. The advertisement said that a written guarantee would be furnished with each ring. The ring was delivered with a guarantee declaring that the ring was "solid metal painted with a genuine gold-colored paint."

4. Construction Projects

The effect of warranties and guarantees is the same for a construction project. A contractor can guarantee the work of the subcontractors; subcontractors can warrant their own work and guarantee the products furnished by their suppliers.

5. Specifying

a. Usually warranties and guarantees are not furnished unless so specified. The overall guarantee furnished by the general contractor should be required by the "Special Conditions" or by the "General Contractor's Work." The warranties and guarantees to be furnished by the subcontractors should be specified in the technical sections.

b. Specification writers determine what products the manufacturers will warrant, the extent of the warranty, and the time it will remain in effect. They should specify the maximum warranty they can obtain from subcontractors in the various trades. It is unreasonable to expect a contractor or subcontractor to guarantee a product beyond the extent that the manufacturer is willing to warrant.

c. A subsection headed "Warranty and Guarantee" should appear in the outline for sections where they are required. This is usually the last subsection in the outline and in the technical section.

7.04   RESEARCH

A. GENERAL

When the writer has completed the outline it will be apparent what information is lacking and which items require research before starting a particular section. Constant research is a part of the specification writer's job. With rapid changes in products, technology, and building methods, even the experienced specification writer must continually research the various fields for new products.

B. REFERENCE SPECIFICATIONS

1. General

a. If a specification for the material the writer wishes to use has been published by a reliable source and is available to all; it should be used.

b. There are several organizations that publish standard specifications for materials. These specifications are used by the industry. They are well known, well written, and of such quality and in such detail that they cannot be equaled without considerable research and study.

c. The specification writer should avoid referring to specifications that are not in common use and are not readily obtainable by the bidders. The organizations that publish specifications acceptable to the industry follow.

2. The American Society for Testing and Materials

a. *History*

(1) The American Society for Testing and Materials was organized in 1898 by a group of seventy (70) men. It was formally incorporated into a national technical society in 1902. Its members are individuals, companies, technical societies, educational institutions, engineers, scientists, educators, testing experts, or research workers. It is a nonprofit corporation formed for the development of standards on characteristics and performance of materials, products, systems, and services and the promotion of related knowledge. With the aid of one hundred and twenty (120) main technical committees with approximately twenty-five hundred (2,500) subcommittees, over five thousand (5,000) standards, including test methods, definitions, recommended practices, and specifications, have been published.

(2) The standards published by the American Society for Testing and Materials are recognized as one of the best sources of dependable information to be found, and they are used extensively by most architects and engineers as reference specifications.

(3) These specifications are published in hard-bound books which are revised yearly. The 1974 set consisted of forty-seven (47) volumes, comprising over thirty-two thousand (32,000) pages with

over five thousand (5,000) standards. Members may buy the entire set for approximately one thousand dollars ($1,000). Individual copies vary in price from thirty-one and a half dollars ($31.50) to four dollars and a quarter ($4.25). The materials specified in each of the books follow.

b. *List of ASTM books*

(1) Steel Piping, Tubing, and Fittings

(2) Ferrous Castings; Ferroalloys

(3) Steel Plate, Sheet, Strip, and Wire; Metallic-Coated Products

(4) Structural Steel; Concrete Reinforcing Steel; Pressure Vessel Plate; Steel Rails, Wheels, and Tires

(5) Steel Bars, Chain, and Springs; Bearing Steel; Steel Forgings

(6) Copper and Copper Alloys (Including Electrical Conductors)

(7) Die-Cast Metals; Light Metals and Alloys (Including Electrical Conductors)

(8) Nonferrous Metals—Nickel, Lead, and Tin Alloys, Precious Metals, Primary Metals, Reactive Metals

(9) Electrodeposited Metallic Coatings; Metal Powders, Sintered P/M Structural Parts

(10) Metals—Mechanical, Fracture, and Corrosion Testing; Fatigue; Erosion; Effect of Temperature

(11) Metallography; Nondestructive Tests

(12) Chemical Analysis of Metals; Sampling and Analysis of Metal-Bearing Ores

(13) Cement; Lime; Gypsum (Including Manual of Cement Testing)

(14) Concrete and Mineral Aggregates (Including Manual of Concrete Testing)

(15) Bituminous Materials for Highway Construction, Waterproofing and Roofing, and Pipe; Skid Resistance

(16) Chemical-Resistant Nonmetallic Materials; Clay and Concrete Pipe and Tile; Masonry Mortars and Units; Asbestos-Cement Products

(17) Refractories, Glass, and Other Ceramic Materials; Manufactured Carbon and Graphite Products

(18) Thermal and Cryogenic Insulating Materials; Building Joint Sealants; Fire Tests; Building Constructions; Environmental Acoustics

(19) Natural Building Stones; Soil and Rock; Peats, Mosses, and Humus

(20) Paper, Packaging; Business Copy Products

(21) Cellulose; Casein; Leather; Flexible Barrier Materials

(22) Wood, Adhesives

(23) Petroleum Products and Lubricants

(24) Petroleum Products and Lubricants (II)

(25) Petroleum Products and Lubricants (III)

(26) Gaseous Fuels; Coal and Coke; Atmospheric Analysis

(27) Paint—Tests for Formulated Products and Applied Coatings

(28) Paint—Pigments, Resins, and Polymers

(29) Paint—Fatty Oils and Acids, Solvents, Miscellaneous; Aromatic Hydrocarbons, Naval Stores

(30) Soap; Engine Coolants; Polishes; Halogenated Organic Solvents; Activated Carbon; Industrial Chemicals

(31) Water

(32) Textile Materials—Yarns, Fabrics, and General Methods

(33) Textile Materials—Fibers, Zippers; High-Modulus Fibers

(34) Plastic Pipe

(35) Plastics—General Test Methods; Nomenclature

(36) Plastics—Materials, Film, Reinforced and Cellular Plastics; Fiber Composites

(37) Rubber—Test Methods

(38) Rubber—Specifications; Carbon Black; Gaskets; Tires

(39) Electrical Insulating Materials—Test Methods

(40) Electrical Insulating Materials—Specifications; Electrical Insulating Liquids and Gases

(41) General Test Methods (Nonmetal); Statistical Methods; Space Simulation; Particle Size Measurement; Deterioration of Nonmetallic Materials

(42) Emission, Molecular, and Mass Spectroscopy; Chromatography; Resinography; Microscopy

(43) Electronics

(44) Magnetic Properties; Metallic Materials for Thermostats and for Electrical Resistance, Heating, and Contacts; Temperature Measurement

(45) Nuclear Standards

(46) End-Use Products—Aerosols and Closures, Surgical Implants, Resilient Floor Coverings; Appearance of Materials; Sensory Evaluation; Forensic Sciences

(47) Index

c. *Designation*

Each standard has a designation number. The capital letter gives the general classification. The six designating letters are: A, ferrous metals; B, nonferrous metals; C, cementitious, ceramic, concrete, and masonry materials; D, miscellaneous materials; E, miscellaneous subjects; and F, end-use materials. The number following the letter is a sequential number, and the number following the dash is the year of the last revision. Thus, standard "A 29-67" indicates that it is a ferrous metal and the standard was last revised in 1967. The letter and the sequential number are permanently assigned; the number after the dash will change as the standard is revised. The letter "T" after the last number indicates that the standard is a tentative; such a standard is shown as "C 729-72 T." An "a" after the designation of the year denotes a second revision within the year and a "b" would denote a third revision. Thus, "B 19-73a" indicates that the standard was revised twice in 1973. Standards that have been reapproved without change are indicated by placing the year of last reapproval in parentheses as a part of the designation number, for example, "*C 4-62 (1970)." The asterisk preceding the designation indicates that the standard has been approved as an American Standard by the American National Standards Institute.

d. *Identification*

When using the ASTM Standards as a reference specification, it is best to give the title as well as the designation number: "C 45-25 (1960) Quicklime and Hydrated Lime," "D 225-65 (1970) Asphalt Shingles Surfaced with Mineral Granules," "E 146-68 Methods of Chemical Analysis of Zirconium and Zirconium-Based Alloys," or "F 288-71 Tungsten Wire for Devices and Lamps."

3. Federal Specifications

a. *General*

(1) The Federal Specifications are prepared under the direction of the Administrator of General Services of the United States Government. Their use by all federal agencies is mandatory.

(2) Because the Federal Specifications cover most items purchased by the government, the scope of these specifications is much greater than that of specifications of the American Society for Testing and Materials. However, for the limited number of materials they specify, the American Society has a better specification. It has been said that any material manufactured will conform to some Federal Specification and these specifications should not be used when a quality product is desired. Federal Specifications cover everything from peanut butter (Z-P-196 C) and artichokes (HHH-A-696 B) to a sphygmomanometer (GG-S-618 C) or a station wagon (KKK-A-00850).

b. *Numbering system*

(1) The Specification Number
The specification number used to designate a Federal Specification has three (3) component parts: The group for procurement to which the specification relates, the initial letter of the title of the specification, and the serial number determined by the alphabetical location of the title.

(2) The First Letter
The first letter states the group or classification according to the following list:

7.04 B. 3. b. **(Cont.)**

(3) List

A—Aircraft, Boats, and Ships*
B—Animals*
C—Animal Products
D—Arms (Small)
E—Artillery*
F—Boilers, Engines, and Tanks
G—Books and Printed Matter
H—Brooms and Brushes
J—Cable and Wire (Insulated)
K—Canvas Articles
L—Cellulose Products and Synthetic Resins
M—Ceramics
N—Cereals and Products
O—Chemicals
P—Cleaning and Polishing Materials
Q—Coal and Products
R—Coal Tar and Products
S—Cooking and Heating Apparatus, Furnaces, and Ovens (Nonelectric)
T—Cordage, Twine, and Products
U—Drugs and Medicines
V—Dry Goods and Notions
W—Electric Apparatus
X—Explosives
Y—Fruits
Z—Fruit Products
AA—Furniture
BB—Cases
CC—Generators and Motors
DD—Glass and Glassware
EE—Groceries
FF—Hardware
GG—Instruments
HH—Insulating Materials
JJ—Knit Goods, Netting, and Webbing
KK—Leather and Leather Goods
LL—Livestock, Poultry, and Marine Products
MM—Lumber and Timber
NN—Lumber Products
OO—Machinery
PP—Meats and Sea Foods
QQ—Metals
RR—Metal Products
SS—Minerals and Products (Nonmetallic)

TT—Paints, Pigments, Varnishes, and Products
UU—Paper and Products
VV—Petroleum and Products
WW—Pipe, Pipe Fittings, Plumbing Fixtures, Tubes, and Tubing (Metallic)
XX—Pumps
YY—Recreational Articles*
ZZ—Rubber and Rubber Goods
AAA—Scales
BBB—Suits and Uniforms
CCC—Textiles (Yardage)
DDD—Textile Products
EEE—Tobacco and Products*
FFF—Toilet Articles
GGG—Tools
HHH—Vegetables
JJJ—Vegetable Products
KKK—Vehicles
LLL—Wood Products
MMM—Adhesives
NNN—Laboratory Equipment and Supplies
OOO**
PPP—Packaging and Packing
*No Federal Specifications have been prepared for this group.
**Reserved for future use.

c. *Changes*

A specification that has been issued may be changed in either of two (2) ways: by issuing a new specification or by issuing an addendum. When a revised specification is issued, a small letter is placed after the number. Thus, specification HHH-A-69b indicates that the specification was revised twice. When an addendum is issued to the specifications, the number of the addendum is added in parentheses following the specification number. Thus, specification KKK-A-851 (1) indicates that one addendum has been issued to the specification. Addenda are used when the change is minor and the cost of printing a revised specification is not justified.

d. *Issuing agencies*

The government agency preparing the specification is indicated by the use of two zeros preceding the serial number and by an abbreviated agency designation. Thus, the specification for Aluminum Alloy Sheets, Plates, and Shapes is QQ-A-002502 (3) (Navy-Ships). It indicates that the specification was prepared by the Navy, Bureau of Ships. The number P-D-00200b (GSA-FSS) for a deodorant indicates that the specification was written by Federal Services Administration Federal Supply Service.

4. Military Specifications

The government also publishes military specifications which are completely separate from Federal Specifications. They are used extensively by the Department of Defense but are not well-known and are seldom used by others. The letters MIL always precede a military specification. Thus, specification MIL-F-52308 is a military specification for a filter element.

5. American National Standards Institute

a. *History*

(1) In 1916, the American Institute of Electrical Engineers took the initiative and invited the American Society of Mechanical Engineers, the American Society of Civil Engineers, the American Institute of Mining and Metallurgical Engineers, and the American Society for Testing and Materials to cooperate with it in establishing a national coordinating agency. An organization meeting was held on October 19, 1918, to which the War, Navy, and Commerce departments of the government were invited; they adopted the name, the American Engineering Standards Committee. By 1928, they had outgrown their committee structure and the American Standards Association was formed. This new association adopted over three thousand (3,000) national standards, and their specifications became a standard reference for most architects and engineers. In 1969, the name was changed to the American National Standards Institute.

(2) The necessity may not be realized until we consider conditions prior to the First World War. At that time, each manufacturer set his own engineering standards. Each company used bolts having threads of a different pitch and design. When the government tried to purchase interchangeable parts for guns, tanks, ships, etc., from those other than the original supplier, it discovered that the manufacturer had no single standard for machine parts nor standard machine tools designed to make parts to a single standard. The result was untold production delays. The American Engineering Standards Committee started the standardization in piping process equipment and other such fields. Herbert Hoover, as Secretary of Commerce under President Calvin Coolidge, supported the group, and under the American Standards Association, thirteen hundred (1,300) engineers worked on the War Standards Committee to produce one hundred and sixty (160) American War Standards aimed at increasing industrial efficiency for war production.

b. *Designation*

(1) American Standard specifications are designated by a letter followed by a number with a dash and the date of issue of the specification. B18.5-1952 is a specification for round-head bolts issued in 1952.

(2) The following list is the classification for American Standard specifications.

A. Civil Engineering and Construction
B. Mechanical Engineering
C. Electrical Engineering
CS. Commercial Standards
D. Automotive
G. Ferrous Metals and Metallurgy
H. Non-ferrous Metals and Metallurgy
J. Rubber
K. Chemical Industry
L. Textile Industry
M. Mining
MH. Materials Handling
N. Nuclear
O. Wood Industry
P. Pulp and Paper Industry
PH. Photography and Motion Pictures
S. Acoustics, Vibration, Mechanical Shock, and Sound Recording
X. Office Equipment and Supplies
Y. Drawings, Symbols, and Abbreviations
Z. Petroleum Products

6. The American Association of State Highway Officials

a. The specifications of the American Association of State Highway Officials are considered standard for designing roads, parking lots, or similar installations. The specifications published by each state for road and bridge construction are also valuable reference specifications.

b. The designation for the AASHO is similar to that of the ASTM, a letter for the classification, a specification number, and the year. Thus, specification T 99-57 is a specification for testing the moisture-density relations of soils using a ten-pound (10-lb) hammer and an eighteen-inch (18″) drop.

C. SOURCES OF INFORMATION

1. Watching

a. The best way to learn construction is by watching construction projects, or, even better, working on a project. Talking with skilled workmen, if permitted by the contractor, noting their maximum working tolerances, and learning the relationship between quality workmanship and cost is the most valuable experience that a specification writer can obtain. There is no substitute for field experience.

b. The specification writer should train by observing existing construction. If there is a crack in a terrazzo floor, the writer should find the reason; where walls have cracked adjacent to doors, he should determine what could have been done to prevent it; and if he sees spalled stonework, he should determine whether the fault was the selection of the materials or the method by which it was laid. By simple observations, one can avoid the mistakes of others.

2. Experiments

Most professional architectural or engineering firms do not have extensive research facilities, but the specification writer can learn from a few simple experiments. If a salesman says his paint is better than the one being used, a sample of each product can be obtained, applied to pieces of the material, and examined after being exposed to the weather. The correct flooring may be determined by installing samples of several types of flooring where they will receive equally hard usage. If an advertiser says a material will not absorb water and it will float forever, try it.

3. Textbooks

Textbooks are an excellent source of information for beginners. The correct name for each component part of an engineering project must be learned. Texts written for beginning plumbers should not be overlooked. A specification writer who is going to specify plumbing work should know at least as much as a beginning plumber.

4. Building Codes

The purpose of a building code is to set a minimum standard of construction that provides for the safety of the people in a specific area. Building codes are issued by the local government and vary greatly even in adjacent towns. They often change every few years. Before starting a project, any specification writer should be familiar with the building code for that area. The writer should remember that the code specifies a minimum quality and anything above that minimum must be specified in detail.

5. OSHA

The Occupational Safety and Health Act was signed into law by President Nixon on December 30, 1970. Before that time, the state and local governments wrote and enforced the building codes. OSHA standards should be studied to ensure that there is no violation of the act in the specifications. Because of the importance of this act, a more detailed explanation of the act appears in Chapter 24.

6. Associations

a. *General*

Manufacturers of similar products have formed associations. The purpose of these associations is to encourage the use of their products in preference to others. Many of these associations publish excellent technical literature and handbooks. The value of their books and pamphlets lies in their impartiality. Since they are published by the association, they do not favor any one manufacturer.

b. *Representatives*

(1) Many of these associations maintain local representatives in the large cities. These people are paid by the associations and are available to students as well as to professionals. The information they have on a product is the most up-to-date and accurate of any source.

(2) The following is a selected list of better-known associations with their home offices. There are many other such well-known associations.
   (a) Portland Cement Association—Chicago, Illinois
   (b) Concrete Products Association of Michigan—Detroit, Michigan
   (c) Structural Clay Products Institute—Washington, D.C.
   (d) National Lime Association—Washington, D.C.
   (e) American Institute of Steel Construction—New York City
   (f) Steel Joist Institute—Washington, D.C.
   (g) Gypsum Association—Chicago, Illinois
   (h) Vermiculite Institute—Chicago, Illinois
   (i) Southeastern Michigan Roofing Contractors Association—Detroit, Michigan
   (j) Aluminum Window Manufacturers Association—New York City
   (k) West Coast Lumbermen's Association—Portland, Oregon
   (l) Western Pine Association—Portland, Oregon
   (m) Southern Pine Association—New Orleans, Louisiana
   (n) Metal Lath Association—Cleveland, Ohio
   (o) Acoustical Materials Association—New York City
   (p) Marble Institute of America—Mount Vernon, New York
   (q) Asphalt Institute—College Park, Maryland

7. Experienced Users

If the specification writer can find a person who has used a product for a period of time and is satisfied with it, it is a good recommendation. However, the beginner should discount a list of users supplied by a salesman. No material supplier is going to list a dissatisfied customer, and even the poorest manufacturer can find someone who is satisfied with his product.

8. Professionals

a. Other professional architects or engineers are a good source of information and most of them will be helpful to the beginner. However, there are many differences of opinion among architects or engineers; what one specialist may claim to be best, another condemns and would not use. One person who has had experience with a product may condemn its use, while another with equal experience describes it as the only product on the market which can reasonably and properly be specified.

b. The beginner must realize that an engineer who has once had a disastrous experience with a material probably will never specify it again, even though the product may have been redesigned. The specification writer should not, without further investigation, accept one person's condemnation as a reason for not using a material. The appearance of a roofing application was severely criticized by an architect unfamiliar with a particular product. An investigation showed that the final application of the coating had never been applied because the owner went into bankruptcy before the project was completed, the subcontractor receiving only a partial payment for the work that had been performed.

9. Sales Agents

a. In the course of work, the specification writer will meet many salespeople. Some know their product and its limitations, their competitors' products and their limitations, and something of the trade's practices in the field. Such people will even advise the specification writer that the product they sell is not the best for a particular application and will assist the writer in selecting another. The specification writer will find in this group a few quality-minded people who can be depended upon to place the good of the project above making a sale. Such people are invaluable in keeping the writer informed of the latest developments in the product line and advised as to how to improve his specifications.

b. Most sales representatives know their product and are able to advise the writer as to the advantages of using that product in preference to others. These people are valuable to the writer, but the writer must remember that there is often a difference between talk and field performance.

c. There are a few salesmen who can be a source of trouble. These salesmen quote one price to the engineer while the project is being specified and a higher price to the contractor when the product is being purchased. There is the salesman who waits until the day before bids are due to walk into the specification writer's office and say, "You know when I advised you to specify my product, I forgot to tell you that my product requires an extra transformer which we don't furnish." There is also the salesman who, after the bids have been received, calls your office and says, "I know you wanted a complete pump, but the number you used from our catalog was only for the shaft. We are low bidders and the pump proper and motor will be extra." Fortunately, the latter type of salesmen are few in number. In time they are no longer welcomed in an architect-engineer's office and probably go into other types of selling where they do not have to depend upon repeat business.

d. It will take time for the beginning specification writer to learn how to question salesmen and how to separate fact from talk. The novice will find that the salesmen with the fastest and most positive-sounding answers are not always the most reliable. The new writer will also find that first impressions are not always accurate and that one should always be suspicious. Knowing whom to call to get specific and reliable information is an asset to any specification writer.

10. Manufacturers' Catalogs

a. The advantage of a good catalog is that the information there is ready to be used whenever the writer needs it.

b. A manufacturer's catalog is a silent salesman. A good catalog gives the basic information about a product. With catalogs from various manufacturers, the specification writer can compare the advantages of each product and in the privacy of the office select the proper one required.

c. A specification writer lives with catalogs. He should assemble as many as possible, be familiar with their contents, and have them ready for use when required. The ability to find data on a specific product fast is one of the qualities required in a competent specification writer.

d. Manufacturers' literature is useful but must be properly used. The specification writer must learn to separate facts from misleading information.

e. There are many good catalogs. There are many others that are lacking the simple information that a writer needs. Madison Avenue advertising agencies appear, at times, to be unable to comprehend that an architect or engineer may be more interested in the size and construction of a bathtub than in a picture of a semi-nude about to enter one.

11. Filing System

a. Any catalog is useless if one is unable to find it. The maintenance of a good filing system is essential to a specification writer. Filing is not easy. It is a tedious job, and the writer may, at times, be tempted to assign it to some inexperienced clerk. Beware! Hours of time can be lost in trying to find misfiled information—and often when the writer can ill afford it.

b. In an attempt to solve the filing problem, the American Institute of Architects in 1920 established a filing system for the rapid classification and retrieval of manufacturers' catalogs. This system was standard in most offices, and many advertisers had the AIA file number prominently displayed on the first page of their catalogs. Many specification writers did not like this system because there was no relationship between the AIA numbering system and the section in the specification where the product would be specified. The "Data Filing Format," Part Two, of the *Uniform Construction Index* was first published in 1972 by the American Institute of Architects (AIA), the Construction Specification Institute (CSI), the Associated General Contractors of America, the National Society of Professional Engineers (NSPE), and others working together. It now supersedes the AIA documents. The Data Filing system is based on the premise that there is one correct place for each catalog to be filed. Each product is assigned an appropriate number which is identical with the Specification Format of the Construction Specification Institute. The *Uniform Construction Index* can be purchased from the AIA, the CSI, or the NSPE.

c. The author has his own method of filing, which may be helpful to some. The first step is to determine whether the catalog is worth filing. Many manufacturers would be surprised at how fast their expensive artwork reaches the wastebasket if it doesn't contain useful information. Except when under the extreme pressure of time, the author writes the filing number on each catalog on the day it is received. Allowing catalogs to pile up for weeks compounds the work and often tempts one to throw away the entire lot. A very few valuable catalogs of products in common use are filed under the proper heading in the author's desk, and duplicate copies are requested for the general files. Filing by number is not difficult and can be assigned to a file clerk or typist who is not busy.

12. Sweet's Catalogs

a. Having a complete catalog file is good, but keeping it up to date can be a time-consuming job. Many years ago, some people made a living by distributing manufacturers' catalogs. The manufacturers would pay men a small fee for placing their catalogs in an architect's file. By handling a large number of different manufacturers, these men could make a living. They visited the architect or engineer's office and offered to place his files in order, discarding old information and replacing it with new. As this service was free, most architect-engineers welcomed it.

b. Shortly after the turn of the century, a man named Clinton W. Sweet, while making catalog deliveries in Boston, noticed that most architects and engineers had poor filing systems and that many catalogs got lost or were misfiled. He was continually meeting professional men who were spending too much time looking for simple information. Along with Henry Desmond, the first editor of his *Architectural Record* magazine, Sweet set up a system for prefiling, indexing, and binding catalogs. The idea was slow to develop, but when the two men finally persuaded a few manufacturers to bind their catalogs together, the first *Sweet's Catalog File* appeared in 1906 as a single volume. That same year the new catalog service was purchased by the F. W. Dodge Company. Frederick W. Dodge founded this firm as a construction project information service in 1896 when he started to deliver daily reports on new Boston-area projects to local businessmen by bicycle. In 1961 Dodge merged with McGraw-Hill, Inc., and in 1968 changed its name to McGraw-Hill Information Systems Company.

c. The Sweet's Catalog Service now provides five separate files of catalogs to cover different construction markets: architectural (general building), industrial construction and renovation, interior design, light construction (residential and light commercial building), and Canadian general construction. In addition, it offers *Sweet's Showroom Guide,* an illustrated sourcebook of furniture, portable lighting, and accessories for the interior design market; and *Sweet's GuideLines,* a program designed to help manufacturers prepare the complete and effective information on their construction products needed by designers, specifiers, and purchasers. *Sweet's Catalog File* is indexed by manufacturer's name, type of product, and trade name. Every year new files are furnished free of charge to the most active architects, engineers, corporate builders, general contractors, government offices, and interior designers.

13. Master Specifications

a. *Definition*

"Master specifications" are specifications that have been written for a technical section of a specification without reference to any particular project. Their purpose is to guide and assist the specification writer who is preparing specifications. They are not reference specifications and should not be used as such. The use of reference specifications is usually limited to materials; master specifications are written to cover the entire trade.

b. *General*

Many architectural and engineering offices have tried to establish a set of technical specifications that can be used from job to job. Few have been successful. With changing methods and materials and with field conditions changing on every job, the amount of work required to keep master specifications in proper condition is justified only in extremely large offices.

c. *Corps of Engineers' "Guide Specifications"*

(1) The government is large enough and does enough construction work to make such a system practical. Therefore, the Corps of Engineers of the United States Army publishes *Guide Specifications.*

(2) The Guide Specifications are an excellent source of information and, if used properly, they can be advantageous to the beginning specification writer.

(3) As the name implies, they are to be used as a guide for writing specifications. They should not be copied verbatim. They are well-written and complete; but because they are written for no particular project, they have to be excessively long to cover all possible conditions. As they are for nationwide use, no attempt is made to include a meaningful scope of work or a division of trades.

(4) The Corps of Engineers, Specifications can be extremely useful in checking for possible omissions. By comparing the specifications he has written with the Corps of Engineers' Specifications, the beginning specification writer can discover where his specifications are weak.

(5) The second subsection of each section of the Corps Specifications is entitled "Applicable Publications." Under this heading, reference specifications are listed that appear throughout the body of the specifications. They list letter suffixes, amendments, and dates indicating the latest revision. Throughout the remainder of the specifications, the letter suffixes, amendments, and dates indicating specific issues are omitted. The purpose is to save printing costs when a revision is made in the reference specifications. When revised reference specifications are issued, only the "Applicable Publications" subsection is changed in the *Guide Specifications.* In using the *Guide Specifications,* the subsection on "Applicable Specifications" may be omitted from the writer's specification; however, the reference

specification used throughout the text should be revised by adding suffixes.

14. Other Specifications

When writers do not know a great deal about specification writing, they often refer to other specifications. In large offices this practice is encouraged. However, it is a dangerous practice to copy such specifications verbatim. There are many more poor specifications than there are good ones, and while a specification might be adequate under some conditions, it might not be so under other conditions. Most specifications are written for specific projects. When beginners copy a specification already used for one project without making any adjustment, they may be requiring a lot of expensive things from the contractor which are not needed on the new project.

15. Previously Written Work

Experienced specification writers generally rely on their previously written specifications. They keep a file of their previous work as a reference. When they start a project, they remember similar work on other projects. They also remember their mistakes and troubles that developed because of the way they described certain items. It is through these sad experiences that specification writers learn their business. As a result, their specifications improve throughout the years. It is for this knowledge that experienced specification writers can demand salaries considerably above those paid to writers with less experience.

16. The Construction Specifications Institute

Membership in the Construction Specifications Institute should be considered a requirement for anyone engaged in specification writing. The Institute maintains an office and staff in Washington, D.C., to assist writers. Members regularly receive information that is invaluable to the specification writer. They publish a magazine entitled "The Construction Specifier." It was first published in 1949 as a quarterly. It is now published monthly and is mailed to all members. This magazine is written for specification writers by specification writers and contains book reviews, court decisions involving specifications, and advertisements directed toward the specification writer. Specification data sheets are also sent to members. They consist of single sheets on new products and changes in existing products. They are furnished loose-leaf for easy filing and contain concise data on the product. Some local chapters also distribute papers on subjects of special interest. All chapters have meetings where writers discuss their problems among themselves and with members of the construction industry. The data sheets are a prime source of information.

17. The Clerk of the Works

The Clerk of the Works can be and usually is the specification writer's greatest critic. His job is to enforce what the specification writer writes. Poor specifications lead to arguments as to intent and make his job much harder. However, after using a specification, he should be able to spot weakness in wording and to recommend changes. With his knowledge of field erection, he may be able to suggest changes that would reduce cost without sacrificing quality. The specification writer should make every effort to be on friendly terms with the Clerk of the Works and listen to his criticism and suggestions and resolve to make the next specification a little bit better.

EIGHT

Basic Decisions

8.01 GENERAL

Before a specification can be started, a few basic decisions must be made regarding the method of binding the final specifications, the covers, the format, the numbering of pages and subsections, and the method of reproducing the specifications. Unless specification writers are the heads of their departments or running their own businesses, the chances are that these basic decisions will be made for them. Even those who run their own businesses will have clients who insist upon having a specific format. For that reason, writers should be familiar with the advantages and disadvantages of each method.

8.02 BINDING

A. FASTENERS

1. There are various methods for securing specifications in covers. Most specifications are bound with wire staples, brass paper fasteners with washers, two pronged paper fasteners, and spiral binders.

2. Wire staples are preferred by many and are excellent for small specifications. They are not recommended for large specifications because the staples in such cases must be longer and of a heavier gauge, making them more difficult to remove.

3. Round-head split-prong brass paper fasteners with washers make a more secure binding for large specifications. They are inserted through holes in the paper, a brass washer is placed over the ends, and each of the prongs is bent in opposite directions against the washer and paper. They are easy to remove and pages can be inserted without

much trouble. They are inexpensive. However, holes must be punched in the paper before it can be bound, and it takes time to place the washers on the fasteners and to bind the pages. In addition, the ends are exposed, so that they can catch against other papers. For this reason, books using such fasteners cannot be easily filed. Moreover, the ends may scratch desk tops and other fine surfaces. This difficulty may be overcome by using special covers.

4. Two-pronged paper fasteners are made in two parts—the prongs and the holders. The prongs are made of slightly deformed soft metal. The center part, or back, is approximately three-eighths of an inch ($3/8''$) wide. The two ends are about an eighth of an inch ($1/8''$) wide and pointed. To use the fasteners, the ends are bent at right angles and inserted through two holes in the paper. The prongs are then inserted into slots in the holder and bent flat against the holding device. The prongs are held in place by sliding rings. The prongs are manufactured in various lengths for various thicknesses of books and for top- and side-bound specifications. Many architects and engineers prefer them because they are easy to apply and easy to remove and they withstand heavy usage. As in the case of the brass paper fasteners, holes must be punched in the paper. The prongs have the additional disadvantage of being limited to two (2) holes, which renders the fasteners less secure.

5. Spiral bindings are made of steel wire and plastic. Both types make a very secure binding. They have the advantage of letting the pages lie flat when the book is open. However, a spiral machine is required to place or remove pages and they require a special punching of the paper.

B. PAGE BINDING

Most specifications are bound on the left-hand-margin side and are opened like a book. This gives a longer binding, which will stand harder usage; however, some prefer a top binding. The top binding allows more typing on a single page because no margin is required at the left of the page.

8.03 COVERS

A. Specifications receive rough treatment at a job site and a cover helps protect the pages. If wire staples, brass paper holders and washers, or two-pronged paper fasteners are used, the covers should be made to enclose the fasteners and prevent damage to desk tops or other surfaces.

B. To be practical, covers should be either heavy enough to resist bending and creasing, or light enough to roll without cracking. Heavy covers require a spiral fastener or a gummed-tape binding to form hinges to give the flexibility necessary for opening the bound specification. Lightweight covers should be of a tough, flexible, medium-weight paper. Heavyweight glazed linen is another satisfactory material.

C. Usually the name of the architect or engineer is printed on the cover. Various offices attempt some degree of individuality in the covers and the style of printing their name. Some offices use different colors to distinguish between different specifications when divided contracts are issued on a single project, but this requires a stock of various-colored covers. It is easier to select a single color and standardize on the printing. As no harm can be done by colors or styles of printing, individuality is not discouraged. An architect or engineer is free to select the most extreme designs and colors without any detriment—other than to give the contractors a chance to chuckle at the idiosyncrasies of the professions.

8.04 NUMBERING PAGES

A. Specification pages should be numbered. The purpose is twofold: to assist in the proper assembling of the pages after printing, and to warn the reader if a page is missing. With pages that are not numbered, it would be impossible for a bidder to know if he had read the entire specification. Likewise, it would be difficult to prove that a bidder received the entire specification.

B. Continuous pagination throughout the specification is preferred by some. However, this has several disadvantages. One is that the pages cannot be numbered until the entire specification is typewritten. The typist must then replace each sheet in the typewriter to record the page number. Also, if at the last minute a page is added, as often happens, many pages have to be renumbered.

C. The more common method is to number each section individually. This means that each section starts with page one (1), and the section number appears with the page number. Thus page 6-1 is page one (1) of section six (6). This method allows each section to be written independently of the other sections and a final typing of the table of contents to make sure the final pages of a section are not missing.

D. There is no generally uniform position for page numbers. Some place the numbers in the upper right-hand corner; some place them in the lower right-hand corner; and some in the middle at the bottom of the page.

E. In a busy office where several specifications are published monthly, it is advantageous to have the project number typed on each page to prevent mixing loose papers from two or more projects.

8.05 NAMES

A. GENERAL

1. There has been no established practice for naming the various parts of a specification. While most offices refer to the various parts of a specification as "sections," there are a few who refer to them as "divisions." Likewise, the subsections or subdivisions are sometimes called "main headings."

2. In an effort to establish a uniform standard, the following designations are suggested.

B. DESIGNATIONS

1. Divisions

The term "division" refers to the main division of the specification. See Chapter IV.

2. Sections

A specification is divided into "sections," sometimes called "trade sections." Each section is written to enable subcontractors to quote prices on complete sections. Sections are subdivided into subsections, articles, paragraphs, and subparagraphs.

3. Subsections

The main headings within each section are called "subsections."

4. Articles

The headings in any subsection are called "Articles." A subsection may be complete within itself or may be divided into two (2) or more articles.

5. Paragraphs and Subparagraphs

If an article is subdivided, each part is called a "paragraph." Likewise, each paragraph may be divided into two or more subparagraphs.

8.06 NUMBERING SUBSECTIONS

A. Because of the need for ready reference, it is necessary to establish some form of numbering system within each section. This can be accomplished by consecutively numbering each subsection throughout the specification, numbering each line of type on each page or consecutively numbering each subsection in each section.

B. The first method has the obvious disadvantage of upsetting the numbering system of a large part of the specification every time a subsection is added and requiring the specification to be completely written before typing.

C. Numbering each line of each page has advantages but requires a lot of

8.06 C. (Cont.)

extra typing and is unsightly. The writer knows of a case where the engineer had the line number printed on the master in small digits spaced to line up with his typewriter. His system failed completely when his machine required repairs and was replaced with another using slightly smaller type.

D. Consecutive numbering of each subsection has so many advantages that it is used by most offices. The articles under each subsection are numbered or lettered and the paragraphs under each article are also numbered, as are the subparagraphs. If there is only one article or paragraph under the heading, the number is omitted.

8.07 NUMBERS AND LETTERS

A. GENERAL

The use of numbers or a particular combination of letters and numbers is left to the individual office; and each office usually has an established method for numbering sections and subsections. Sections may be numbered using arabic or roman numerals. Subsections should also be numbered, and there is a definite advantage to incorporating the number of the section in the number of the subsection.

B. COMMON SYSTEMS

While no specific numbering system is used throughout the profession, there are two systems which are generally used: the decimal system and a system of numbers and letters called the "outline system."

C. THE DECIMAL SYSTEM

The decimal system consists of using arabic numerals for sections and numbering the subsections consecutively throughout the section, using the section number as the first digit. Thus the subsections in section 6 would be 6.01, 6.02, 6.03, etc. The article in each subsection would carry the number of the subsection. Therefore, the articles in subsection 6.03 would be numbered 6.03.01, 6.03.02, 6.03.03, 6.03.04, etc. Likewise, the paragraphs carry the number of the article and are numbered 6.03.04.01, 6.03.04.02, 6.03.04.03, etc. This system has the advantage that each paragraph can be easily identified by numbers. It has a disadvantage of being difficult to follow during the writing of the specification.

D. THE OUTLINE SYSTEM

The outline system is similar to the decimal system and sections and subsections are numbered in the same manner. The articles, however, are indicated by using capital letters. Thus, the articles would be lettered A, B, C, etc. Any reference to a specific article would carry the subsection number and the article letter. In a similar manner, the paragraphs in each article are numbered with arabic numerals and the subparagraphs are lettered with small letters. Thus, subparagraph 8.04 C. 3. e. refers to subparagraph e in paragraph 3 in article C in subsection 8.04 in Section VIII. There is a section written in this manner in the Appendix. The advantage of having a positive numbering system will be appreciated when writing addenda and bulletins.

8.08 THE FORMAT

A. GENERAL

1. With the exception of the specification writer and typist, it is doubtful if anyone reads an entire specification from cover to cover. The estimator for the general contractor will read the SPECIAL CONDITIONS and the GENERAL CONTRACTOR'S WORK in detail. He will probably read the SCOPE OF THE WORK and the WORK NOT INCLUDED in each of the sections. The general contractor's estimator will also read some sections completely to determine if they should be sublet and from whom to request quotations. On work to be sublet completely, the estimator cares little about the details. The type of electrical outlet the electrical subcontractor will supply is of no interest to him.

2. Subcontractors are interested in the sections they are figuring. They read these in detail and sometimes read about the related work. The remainder of the specification is useless to them.

3. Material suppliers are interested only in one subsection or article describing the material they intend to furnish.

4. The Clerk of the Works, or inspector, is interested in different parts of the specification at different times. When a load of reinforcing bars is delivered to the job he is interested only in the paragraph specifying the bars, nothing else.

5. The masonry foreman is interested in the bond, the joints, and workmanship clauses. The accepted materials are at the job site when he comes to work. Why should the specifications of these materials interest him?

6. Since the specifications are used only as a reference book, the various subsections relating to particular materials and products must be easily and quickly located.

B. THE SECTION

1. Table of Contents

The table of contents will refer the reader to the proper section in the specifications. However, a breakdown of each section into subsections, articles, and paragraphs in the table of contents is costly and seldom used. Most people will locate the section and scan the pages looking for the proper item. For this reason, the various subsections and articles should stand out from the text. The practice of writing a succession of paragraphs with no headings dividing the subject matter into related clauses is undesirable.

2. Type

a. As most specifications are typewritten, the use of italics or different type faces is impossible for the most part. With most typewriters, the only method to make titles stand out is by the use of capital letters, by underlining, and by double spacing of letters.

b. Each section should be started on a separate page and have the section number and trade heading. Generally this title is centered on the page, and it is commonly typed in capital letters and underlined thus:

<u>SECTION V</u>
<u>MASONRY</u>

or

<u>S E C T I O N 5</u>
<u>M A S O N R Y</u>

C. SUBSECTIONS

1. General

a. Subsection titles that are indicative of the following text are decidedly helpful to estimators and superintendents and should be adopted for all specifications.

b. Examples of various methods of heading subsections are shown, using a simple sentence that could head each section of the specification.

2. Examples

a. *Style I*

5.01   GENERAL NOTE
The accompanying General Conditions of the Contract and the Special Conditions herewith shall apply to and form a part of this section and have the same effect as if repeated in full herein.

b. *Style II*

5.01   The accompanying General Conditions of the Contract and
GENERAL   the Special Conditions herewith shall apply to and form a
NOTE   part of this section and have the same effect as if repeated
           in full herein.

c. *Style III*

5.01 GENERAL NOTE
The Accompanying General Conditions of the Contract and the

Special Conditions herewith shall apply to and form a part of this section and have the same effect as if repeated in full herein.

d. *Style IV*

5.01 THE GENERAL CONDITIONS of the Contract and the Special Conditions herewith shall apply to and form a part of this section and have the same effect as if repeated in full herein.

e. *Style V*

5.01 GENERAL NOTE
The accompanying General Conditions of the Contract and the Special Conditions herewith shall apply to and form a part of this section and have the same effect as if repeated in full herein.

3. Comments

a. Style I is used by many because this method saves space. However, it appears crowded and cramped. Not setting the number off to the left and not skipping a line between the title and the text serve to de-emphasize the title.

b. Style II brings the title out in the margin for emphasis and in case of reference, but is difficult to type and is seldom used.

c. Placing the title in the right-hand margin as shown in Style III is preferred by many. However, subheads in the right-hand margin lose force when one realizes that English reads from left to right. It is more natural to read the text after the heading.

d. The attempt to make the first words of a paragraph serve as a heading, as in the fourth style, by capitalizing selective words indicative of the subject matter is a handicap in writing and a hindrance in reading. It may serve to condense the volume of the specifications, one of the arguments advanced in its favor; but this is offset by the necessity of cleverly wording the paragraph so that the first words comprise the title.

e. Style V is used by the author. It gives the title prominence; the block-form, single-spaced text has a uniform, neat appearance and is easy to type. The skipped line and indentation may add a page or two to the book of specifications, but it is clearer and easier to read, time-saving in reference, and generally attractive in appearance. Brevity in specifications should be obtained by using fewer well-chosen words, not by crowding the typewriting.

D. ARTICLES

The dividing of subsections into articles can be important, and it is desirable to make the various articles easy to locate. The supplier furnishing one specific material should not be required to read an entire specification to find the requirements for that material. The style of type for articles should differ from that used for subsections, using lower-case letters with the title underlined with a solid line.

E. PARAGRAPHS AND SUBPARAGRAPHS

Articles are subdivided into paragraphs and paragraphs are divided into subparagraphs. However, the information written in various paragraphs or subparagraphs is not necessarily less important than that in the subsections or articles. For that reason, a heading when used should stand out from the text, but less prominently. One method is to use broken lines under paragraph headings and dotted lines under subparagraph heads. A sample section written in this manner appears in the Appendix.

8.09 APPEARANCE

A. GENERAL

Specification writers should give thought to the appearance of their specifications and spend the time necessary to train their typists. A good-looking set of specifications will give the client the proper impression, whereas sloppy specifications have the same effect as slovenly drawings.

B. FORMAT

While some formats present a poor appearance, there is nothing that detracts from a specification more than the lack of consistency in following a format. Once a format is decided upon, it should be followed throughout the book of specifications. However, it is the responsibility of the specification writer to present a rough copy with the proper titles, where required, so the typist can follow the agreed-upon format.

C. HEADINGS

1. The specification writer should number each article under each subsection; however, if there is only one article, placing the number one (1) in front of the article has no meaning. The same holds for paragraphs or subparagraphs.

2. The specification writer has the option of placing a title for each article or omitting them. However, if one article in any subsection is given a heading, the remaining articles in that subsection should have headings.

D. TIPS FOR INSTRUCTING TYPISTS

1. The typists should be instructed never to place a heading on the last line of a page. A heading should always be above the text. There should be at least one line of the text following the title, or better, the title should appear on the following page. While printers' rules require the same number of lines on successive pages, this rule need not be

followed in specifications, as the typing is generally on one side of the paper only and irregularities are not objectionable.

2. Unequal lengths of lines will give a page a ragged look. A good typist will keep the lines of a paragraph approximately equal, except when this leads to excessive hyphenating.

3. When a subsection is continued on the following page, the typist should place the subsection number (and the article, paragraph, or subparagraph number if they are involved) before the word "continued" at the top of the next page. This enables the typist to follow the numbering system without having to refer to former sheets. It also gives the reader a ready reference.

8.10 TYPISTS

A. A carefully written specification can be ruined by poor typing. It is unwise, even dangerous, to have specifications typed by an untrained person. One whose knowledge of punctuation and spelling is limited will be likely to make costly errors. A misplaced comma can seriously affect the meaning of a sentence, and the accidental omission of the word "not" could be costly, to say the least. The specification writer is expected to check the typing; however, in the last-minute rush to get a project out for bids, the tendency is to accept poorly arranged pages rather than demand retyping.

B. A well-trained typist can be an asset to any specification writer. A typist who asks questions when the rough copy is not clear, checks spelling, and turns out attractively arranged pages is a jewel that will save a specification writer many hours of time and trouble. The final effect and the assured accuracy are worth a highly paid typist.

NINE

Writing a Technical Section

9.01 GENERAL

A. When all general and specific information has been assembled for a section, the writer is ready to write that technical section in its final form. By "writing" we do not mean that the specification writer writes each section in longhand. This would involve unwarranted and unavailable time. Obviously some short cut must be found.

B. Various specification writers use several different methods. Some work from a master specification and cross out the parts that are not applicable. The results of this type of specification depend on the quality of the master specification. At best it would be a very general specification, and this method cannot be recommended. An even worse practice is to copy an old specification written by someone else, where the exact conditions for which the specification was written are unknown. Such a specification, in all probability, would not include all of the conditions that must be taken into account for the new job.

C. A most satisfactory method is to start with the outline previously prepared. By assembling applicable paragraphs from books, manufacturers' catalogs, other specifications, and similar sources, most of the information can be made ready. It is sometimes desirable to have the typist copy paragraphs or items from books when they cannot be reproduced on a copying machine. By stapling, pasting, or taping this material in the proper order, deleting words or phrases not applicable, adding words, sentences, or paragraphs where required, and making modifications as necessary, proper subsections can be developed. This process is repeated until the section is complete.

9.02 THE FIRST SUBSECTION

A. PURPOSE

1. The first subsection in each section of the specification should read exactly the same. Usually entitled "General Note" or "General Conditions," this first subsection explicitly incorporates the General and Special Conditions into all the work specified in that section. This can be done in a simple statement such as, "The General and Special Conditions are a part of this section of the specifications," or in a more formal statement, such as, "All work performed under this heading shall be governed by Section II, the General Conditions; Section III, the Special Conditions; this specification; and the general and detail drawings."

2. The purpose of this subsection is to make each subcontractor responsible for the items specified in the General and Special Conditions. There is a practical and legal reason for this.

B. PRACTICAL REASONS

1. There are various conditions in the General and Special Conditions that apply to the subcontractors and might affect their costs. From the point of view of the specification writer, it is easier to make statements that apply to several subcontractors in the Special Conditions than to repeat the same statement in each section of the specifications. For example, if the Special Conditions provided that the general contractor supply the hoist to be used by all trades, and the subcontractor was unaware of this, his bid price might be higher than it needs to be.

2. As a subcontractor bids only upon a specific section in the specification, unless the General and Special Conditions are in some manner tied into the estimate, it would be unreasonable to expect the bidder to follow these conditions. This would be particularly true in the case where a contractor breaks a book of specifications and sends only the section the subcontractor is to price. This is not an uncommon practice, and the subcontractor's bid should not be dependent upon something the subcontractor has not read or does not know exists. The General Note warns the subbidder that there is more involved than what is stated in the subsection.

C. LEGAL REASON

1. Cases

a. *Common law*

Prior to 1916 common law provided no way for a third party to enforce a contract of which he was not a part. For example, if A manufactured a defective product which was sold to B, and B resold it to C, C could take no direct action against A. If C did take legal action, such action would have to be taken against B, as there is no "privity of contract" between A and C. This is shown in the case of *Winterbottom v. Wright* in 1842 in England.

b. Winterbottom v. Wright

An English contractor had a contract with the Postmaster General to provide stagecoaches and maintain them in repair for the purpose of carrying the royal mail. A defective stagecoach broke down, upset, and injured the driver. The Court of The Exchequer denied the driver any rights to recover from the contractor since there was no "privity of contract" between the driver and the contractor. The agreement was between the contractor and the Postmaster General.

c. MacPherson v. Buick Motor Company

(1) In 1916 an undertaker, Donald C. MacPherson, was injured in an accident resulting from a disintegration and collapse of a wooden wheel on his Buick automobile while traveling at a speed of eight (8) miles per hour. MacPherson had purchased the car from a Schenectady retail dealer and had driven it less than five hundred (500) miles.

(2) The defective wheel had been purchased from the Imperial Wheel Company by the Buick Motor Company. Evidence showed that Buick could have discovered the defect by an inspection before they sold the car to the Schenectady dealer. This inspection had been omitted.

(3) MacPherson took action directly against the Buick Motor Company. The defendant claimed there was no privity of contract between MacPherson and Buick. Justice Cardozo, for the New York Court of Appeals, judged the defendant liable; four other judges concurred.

(4) The "MacPherson doctrine" was widely accepted in the courts throughout the nation. While this case was limited to a product that could produce bodily harm if the construction was defective, other decisions broadened the scope. The case of *Fentress v. Van Etta Motors and Ford Motor Company* illustrates this.

d. Fentress v. Van Etta Motors & Ford Motor Co.

William E. Fentress purchased a Mercury automobile made by the Ford Motor Company from defendant distributor Van Etta. The plaintiff sued for damages to his car when it was wrecked in an accident resulting from defective brakes. No other property was damaged; no persons were injured. The Appellate Department of the Superior Court of California held the manufacturer liable.

e. *Broadening the law*

The law has been broadened to apply to most subcontractors. Privity of contract is no longer a satisfactory defense and action can be taken directly against the negligent party.

2. Subcontractors

It is possible for a subcontractor to be financially stronger than the contractor who employs him. For example, the smallest general contractor could employ the Bethlehem Steel Company to fabricate and erect structural steel. It is also possible that an owner may wish to take legal action directly against a supplier or a subcontractor for failure to perform in accordance with the requirements in the General or Special Conditions of the contract. Subcontractors in the past have successfully defended themselves in the courts from complying with those requirements when no reference was made to the General or Special Conditions in the section they used while preparing their quotation. The General Note robs the subcontractor of this defense.

9.03 THE SCOPE

A. GENERAL

1. The second subsection in each section is entitled "Scope of the Work." As the title implies, it is a statement of the work to be done.

2. "Work Not Included In This Section" is the title given to the third subsection in each section. In this section is listed work that adjoins the work specified and the limits of the work in each trade.

3. The second and third subsections are called the "scope subsections." As they establish the extent of the work in each section, they are most important. Each estimator must know what work is to be figured and the exact limits of that work in order to submit an intelligent quotation. The extent of work will have a greater effect upon the price than upon the quality of the material or workmanship. If not properly written, the scope paragraphs will cause more trouble than any other part of the specification.

4. There are those who contend that work omitted from the "SCOPE OF THE WORK" is not a part of the contract even though the material and workmanship are specified elsewhere. There are often legal grounds for such a belief.

B. EXAMPLE #1

"1. Scope Of The Work

"All ceilings, walls, wood floors, stairways, in all rooms, corridors, halls, vestibules, and closets on the interior of the building, and all exterior surfaces of wood or steel on the exterior of the building shall be coated with two (2) coats of paint."

2. Comment

This at first glance would appear to be a very complete scope for the painting subcontractor. Let's analyze it. According to that statement, the subcontractor would not be required to paint the structural steel after it was erected or a miscellaneous iron not exposed to view; would not be required to paint any material in pipe tunnels or pipe chases; would not be required to paint all material between the suspended ceiling and the slab above, the sprinkler system, or any exposed piping. Any one of these items could amount to a large sum of money.

C. ALTERATION WORK

While the scope offers a problem in new work, an alteration project is many times more difficult. All work shown on the drawings for a new project must be done by someone; on an alteration project the full scope might not be known. There are those who contend that the statement to remove a wall does not include removing the piping buried in that wall. The contractor could be justified in asking extra money to cover any additional expense if the existence of the pipe were unknown. This does little to save the specification writer from embarrassment, because that contingency could have been avoided with a few words. However, on government projects there have been many decisions favoring the contractor even though the pipes were in plain view. The judges take the view that the specifications must be complete. Even though work is implied and necessary to complete a particular task, the contractor can assume that others will do work not specifically included in the "Scope."

D. METHOD OF WRITING

In order to protect themselves, specification writers write the "Scope Of The Work" to include every possible condition and then under the "Work Not Included" they list the exceptions to the scope of the work. In this manner any item which is not explicitly excluded is part of the work. If, for example, the specification writer forgot to omit the painting of galvanized pipe above the ceiling, deleting it when the omission was discovered would result in a deduction in the contract price, which the owner would welcome.

E. EXAMPLE #2

"1. Scope Of The Work

"Unless otherwise specified, the contractor or his subcontractor shall furnish all materials, tools, equipment, appliances, transportation, labor, and supervision required to paint all surfaces of the building, including surfaces as they are exposed during the construction period.

"2. Work Not Included In This Section

"a. Aluminum, concrete, copper, galvanized iron, glass, masonry, slate, stone, stainless steel, resilient flooring, terrazzo, ceramic tile, plumbing, and electrical fixtures need not be painted.

"b. The water heater specified in Section LXXXI, the lockers specified in Section LXI, the laboratory furniture specified in Section LIX, finished hardware specified in Section LXIV, and electrical equipment specified in Section LXXXV will be prefinished in the shop and will not require painting in the field.

"c. The shop coat of paint for structural steel is specified in Section XXI.

"d. The shop coat of paint on miscellaneous iron is specified in Section XXII."

F. PROTECTION

There are several advantages to writing the "Scope" subsections as shown in Example #2. It is fair to the contractor, as he knows exactly what is or is not to be painted. The specification writer is protected because any omission in the "Work Not Included" would not be at an extra cost. The reference to other painting is helpful.

G. WORK NOT INCLUDED

1. As the worst mistake a specification writer can make is to omit work from the specification, the specification writer writes a general, all-inclusive "Scope Of The Work." The "Work Not Included In This Section" must be carefully written and becomes one of the most important subsections.

2. It should be noted that the title of this subsection is not "Work By Others." That subsection appears in the "Special Conditions." The "Work Not Included In This Section" means that the work under this heading is not to be done, is to be done by the owner, or other contractors, or is specified elsewhere in the specifications.

3. Placing the section number where adjoining work is specified is a help to the specification writer, as well as to the reader. The writing of a specification on a large project can take several months, and it is impossible to remember all of the details, particularly when two or more specifications are written simultaneously. The reference section allows the writer to make a quick check before the specification is published. In Example #2 the statement that the shop coat of paint is specified in Section XVI is a check, and the specification writer should turn to that section and check to make sure it is so specified.

9.04 OTHER SUBSECTIONS

A. The completion of the remaining subsections consists of taking the outline and information compiled and rewriting it in standard English form.

B. The information to go in each particular subsection is not discussed here in detail. Details of various materials and construction procedures are published and it would be of little value to repeat such extensive information here. However, there are general principles that should be followed, and these principles are discussed in subchapter 9.05.

9.05   GENERAL PRINCIPLES

A. CARE IN WRITING

Engineers are assumed to be skilled in their field; however, their technical knowledge is of little value if they are unable to communicate effectively. The technique of specification writing depends upon the application of a few basic principles of English grammar, word usage, and composition that are learned in school. It is mandatory that the specifications be precise in wording and punctuation, and in that respect specification writing is similar to legal work. Other types of writing need not be so precise, but in specifications a misplaced comma can result in a lawsuit. So, unless specifications are properly written, the careful work so laboriously designed into the project may be entirely forgotten when a misunderstanding arises. Specification writers have little defense, if what they write can logically be construed to mean something other than the owner's intent. Few will forgive careless work when it costs them money.

B. CLEAR SUBSECTIONS

1. The Four C's

    a. Each subsection in each section of the specifications should be clear, complete, concise, and correct. Of these the most difficult to obtain is clearness. What may be very clear to the writer could be difficult for a foreman in the field to understand; the intent the writer wished to convey can, under some conditions, produce an entirely different idea in the mind of a judge reading the document.

    b. The courts are filled with cases where there is an honest difference of opinion concerning the meaning between the party writing and a party reading the specification. There are many more cases where the intent of the writer was clear, but the wording left legal loopholes. Some contractors, particularly those working on projects for the federal government, depend upon their attorneys rather than the superintendent to protect their business.

2. Cases

    a. *General*

The ease with which a misunderstanding can develop is illustrated in the following examples.

b. *Church case*

(1) The specifications stated, "The church shall be built in three sections. Bids will be received for completing the front third of the church only. A temporary tight wall shall be constructed at the end. This partition will remain in place while bids are taken and the center portion is constructed."

(2) It was the architect's intention to construct and place into use the altar and the front seats in the nave. Later the nave would be completed and still later the narthex and the towers. However, some contractors considered the front of the church to be that facing the street and prepared proposals for building the towers and the narthex. Fortunately, the misunderstanding was revealed a few days before bids were due. However, several contractors were required to prepare new estimates and considerable time was lost when the bid date had to be extended.

c. *Wall Case*

A second case did not turn out so well. The specifications included the following sentence, "No paint is required on exterior walls." The intent of the writer was to omit painting the outside of the building. The contractor maintained that no paint was required on the interior surface of outside walls. While the engineer maintained that it was unreasonable to paint three sides of a room and leave the fourth unpainted, the contractor's interpretation of the specification prevailed.

d. *Legal principle*

An ambiguous clause in a contract differs from a similar clause in a specification. It is assumed that when two (2) parties negotiated a contract, the wording was mutually agreed upon, and the judge tries to find the intent of the parties. In specifications, the writer's intent means little. The contractor had nothing to do with the choice of words and had to take what was written and determine the meaning. As a result, any reasonable interpretation of the specifications, proposed by the contractor, would be supported by the courts. It is a general principle of law that in the case of ambiguity, the courts do not interpret the meaning in favor of the party who wrote the ambiguous statement.

C. SPECIFIC SUBSECTIONS

1. Cost

a. Each subsection of a specification should be a clear and accurate description of the technical requirements for a material, product, or method of installation. Vague specifications are certain to increase the cost of the project, as contractors are forced to bid higher to protect themselves against unfavorable interpretations. Architects or engineers must know what they require and describe in writing precisely what they want. To do this, they must make a thorough analysis of the material or method of installation before writing about it. Good practice requires that the specifications state exactly what is satisfactory, so that the estimator can properly price what is wanted and the clerk of the works can reject that which is unsatisfactory without danger of a lawsuit. Serious problems of interpretation will decrease the architect-engineer's profit and add to the cost for the owner. Litigation and arbitration are both expensive and time-consuming and often delay the work.

b. Honest contractors welcome a tight specification. They are able to price their material and labor accurately, without considering contingencies that often occur with vague specifications. A few contractors might deviate from or attempt to evade a well-written specification. If such an attempt is made, the architect or engineer must be totally inflexible and insist on compliance with the letter and intent of the specification.

2. Example I

a. The following example is one where the writer tried to be specific but left a loophole that cost the client a great deal of money.

b. The specification was for the repainting of a large office building interior. As the building was occupied, the painting had to be done at night and on weekends, which meant premium pay for the workers. One of the requirements in the "Scope Of The Work" was that "All surfaces of all doors shall be painted with two (2) coats." The painting of the hardware was deleted in the "Work Not Included" subsection. The contractor while estimating this job realized that "all surfaces" included the bottom edge of the door. To paint the bottom edge of the door required that each door had to be removed, painted, and rehung twice, once for each coat. With the hundreds of doors involved, this was an expensive process and not usually done unless so specified. To be on the safe side, the contractor called the architect, who said, without conferring with the specification writer and possibly without understanding the work involved, "'All' means 'all.' Follow the specifications." So the contractor included the price of removing and replacing the doors in his quotation. When the actual work was being performed, the clerk of the works did not require the contractor to remove the doors; this put a tidy sum of money in the contractor's pocket. A few words could have protected the owner. If painting the underside of the doors was the intent of the writer, the words "The work includes the bottom edge of all doors" would have warned the clerk of the works to require the removal of the doors. If the intent was to omit the bottom edge of the door, such a statement in the "Work Not Included" subsection would have saved the owner considerable money.

3. Example II

a. While writing the "Scope" sections, the writer should be careful not to limit the work by unnecessary words. If the intent is for the contractor to paint all doors, the statement should not read, "All wooden doors shall be painted," even if all the doors shown in the door schedule are wooden. There is always the possibility that a draftsman might change a door material at the last minute without telling the specification writer.

b. The following is an example of the danger of the writer unwittingly limiting the scope.

c. The specification was for a roof on a new building. Among other things the specification stated, "Flashing shall be provided where the roof joins vent stacks, air exhaust ventilators, and parapet walls." The contractor claimed an extra payment because one of the ventilators was an air intake. He was required to flash the air intake, but a lot of time was lost. The argument could have been avoided if the specification writer had written, "Flashing shall be provided where the roof joins a vertical surface."

D. ACCURACY

1. Unless covered by a statement to the contrary, the owners will be held responsible for the accuracy of the information they furnish to bidders. Misleading information is sufficient grounds for the contractor to collect additional compensation or damages if extra costs result.

2. The most costly type of error is one of omission. All materials and their installation must be specified.

3. Incorrect spelling, the omitting of words or whole lines of type, and similar errors in typing can have serious consequences. Mistakes of this nature may completely change the intent of the subsection.

4. Mistakes in typing numbers are very difficult for a proofreader or one not familiar with engineering to catch. For example, 2'4" could in error be typed 214" and .10% could be typed 10%. Spelling out numbers is one way to avoid this type of error. Placing the figure in parentheses after the words, "two feet four inches (2'4")," makes it easier to read. Mistakes in typing both the letters and numerals should be obvious to the proofreader.

E. BEING FAIR

1. General

a. The specification writer should be fair to both the owner and the contractor. It is in the best interest of both that the writer specify the desired standards of quality for materials and workmanship without imposing harsh and unfair conditions on the contractor. The architect or engineer's first responsibility is to safeguard the interests of the owner; however, as a professional, he shouldn't be unfair to the contractor by forcing him to assume responsibilities which should be assumed by the owner or the engineer.

b. The contractor is required to take considerable risk. Such normal things as weather, changing labor rates and material prices, soil conditions, and strikes are the hazards of the business; and it is not fair to saddle this party with specifications that are vague or subject to a unilateral interpretation by the architect or engineer. Such specifications can also lead to a misunderstanding with the owner, who may insist upon standards beyond those intended by the designer.

c. If specific difficulties or hazards are known to exist in the performance of the work, all available information should be furnished to the bidder. Concealing information could result in a lawsuit. If the existing conditions are unknown to the engineer, he should so state. This would allow the contractor to include a price for any contingency in the cost estimate. Some architects and engineers believe that requiring the contractor to visit and examine the location is all that is necessary. The courts have held otherwise. In several cases, it has been held that a contractor should be reimbursed if misled by fallacious statements in the specifications, (See *Christie v. United States,* 237 U.S. 234, *Hullerbach v. United States,* 233 U.S. 165, *United States v. Utah,* and others.)

d. It is unfair to the contractor to indicate that there is no obstruction in part of the excavation when a large concrete substructure covered with earth exists; and allowing the contractor to visit the site does not relieve the owner from the responsibility of disclosing its existence.

e. If the extent of hidden obstructions is not known to the owner, it would be proper for him to so inform the contractor and require him to assume the risk. The contractor would then include protection in the bid price. In most cases, it is cheaper for the owner to investigate existing conditions before sending the project out for bids, as the contractor, if he assumes the unknown risk, usually bases a price on the worst possible conditions.

f. Where the obstruction is clear to anyone visiting the site, the law is not as clear. On private work most architect-engineers take the position that the contractor, if free to visit the site, is responsible for the obvious existing conditions. The government does not follow this line of reasoning. Various contracting officers have ruled that if an obstruction is not shown on the drawings or indicated in the specifications, the contractor has been misled even though it was required that the contractor visit the site and the obstruction was in plain view.

2. **Examples**

   a. The specifications required that the contractor remove a wall to construct an addition. Radiators were hung on the wall in plain view. The local contractor visited the site several times before submitting a bid. After starting the work, the contractor submitted a claim for additional payment for removing the radiators and the piping in the wall. Ruled, even though the wall could not be removed without removing the radiators, the specifications should have included the specific removal of the radiators and piping. The additional cost was paid.

   b. Among other things in a contract to renovate an old building for the army, the specifications said, "The contractor shall examine the windows in the building and replace all broken or cracked lights with new glass." Approximately half the windows in the building were broken. The plans showed the four elevations of the buildings and two (2) of the windows were marked broken. The contractor claimed an extra for repairing all but the two windows noted on the plans. The ruling was in favor of the contractor. In the opinion of the contracting officer, the contractor was misled by the drawings into believing that only two windows were broken and did not need to count the windows at the job site.

   c. The "Scope Of The Work" required the contractor to examine approximately twenty (20) buildings located on a map of the site, remove the existing roofing, and replace it with new roofing as specified. Bids would be received on a unit price basis. On one (1) building, pipe supports supported a waterpipe a foot above the roof. A unit price was taken for the pitch pockets around the supports but no mention was made regarding the piping. It was ruled that the contractor was misled because the specifications did not mention the existence of the piping.

3. **Comment**

   a. Fairness applies to both the owner and the contractor. Certainly the owner should be expected to pay for items hidden from the contractor at the time of preparing the proposal. Likewise, the contractor shouldn't expect the owner to pay twice for items or conditions the contractor was aware of during the bidding period. The author knows personally of the first and third cases previously referred to. The second case was told to him by the contractor involved, who didn't expect to collect. He had been doing work adjacent to the building involved and knew the condition of the windows. He mentioned this case to the author to prove that it pays the contractor to question every point in the specifications.

b. Rulings similar to the above have, no doubt, cost the government millions of dollars. What is more, they encourage contractors to work with lawyers and study the specifications for any possible loopholes and to fight every point. Contractors can almost always show some discrepancy between actual conditions and those indicated in the bidding information, and controversies often result. The time lost in processing unjust claims is enormous. Governmental paperwork is one reason why many good and honest contractors refuse to bid on federal projects.

F. TOLERANCES

1. General

a. The contractor who builds a structure two hundred feet and two inches (200'2") long when the plans call for it to be two hundred feet (200'0") long could normally expect that the structure would be accepted. It would be substantial performance. However, if the building extended two inches (2") on another's property, he could find himself in difficulty. While a couple of inches' tolerance would be reasonable in a building, the engineer who specified a thirty-two (32) gauge metal would be justified in rejecting a thirty-one (31) gauge or a thirty-three (33) gauge even though the difference in thickness could be as little as seven thousandths of an inch (.007"). The standard of tolerance that would be acceptable from a contractor depends upon the practices of the trade involved. An engineer who specified a fifteen-inch (15") I-beam would be expected to accept a beam fourteen and seven-eighths inches ($14^7/8$") deep because that is within the rolling tolerance established by the industry. An engineer who wishes closer tolerances should specify that no variance will be accepted.

b. Any size specified has a tolerance, even Johanneson Blocks. If not explicitly forbidden, a reasonable addition or deduction in the material is implied, since the specified measurement may not conform to the trade regulations and since the precision of any measurement is dependent upon the means of measurement.

2. Concrete

a. The specifications writer who writes, "All concrete used on the project shall have an ultimate compressive strength of three thousand pounds per square inch (3,000 lb/sq in.) twenty-eight (28) days after pouring" may believe this is a mandatory requirement for the contractor to furnish nothing less than the strength specified. However, any lawyer in court could force the writer to admit that what was specified would be impossible to obtain in the field or consistently in the laboratory if no tolerance were implied. Tolerance means a plus or minus. Many writers do not realize this.

b. The intent of the writer was, of course, to establish a minimum strength of concrete. One could accomplish this by writing, "All concrete shall have an ultimate compressive strength of not less than three thousand pounds per square inch (3,000 lb/sq in.) twenty-eight (28) days after pouring."

3. The Word "Exact"

a. Even the word "exact" when used on a drawing implies a rather large tolerance, as is shown in the following case appealed before the Armed Services Board of Contract Appeals, which reversed a decision by the contracting officer.

* b. The alignment of surfaces supported by structural steel shapes was critical. The drawings pictorially showed the critical dimension with the word "exact" underneath. The contractor provided ordinary structural shapes, fabricated to the usual shop tolerances, and the frames were set inaccurately. The frame was off seven-sixteenths of an inch (7/16") and not within the range of accuracy needed. The contractor was required to take corrective measures and claimed an extra fee.

c. It was held that the word "exact" with a dimension has little meaning without indicating the specific tolerance.

4. Other Words

The words "clean," "smooth," "level," and "straight" usually imply tolerances the same as "exact," and they will be discussed later in the chapter.

G. TESTING

1. A specification should not specify anything that cannot be enforced. Otherwise the contractor who furnishes a cheap product has the advantage, realizing that the product cannot be properly tested; the contractor who wishes to conform to the intent of the specifications is penalized.

2. Requiring testing by the contractor in the presence of the clerk of the works or by an independent laboratory is a good practice. The requirements should be realistic and meaningful but not unduly burdensome and expensive. The same testing would not be specified for two (2) cubic yards of concrete as it would for a thousand (1,000) cubic yards. Testing is expensive, and five hundred dollars ($500) of testing on a fifty-dollar ($50) product could not be justified unless it was absolutely essential.

* Reported in *The Construction Specifier.*

H. STOCK SIZES

It is always desirable to use stock sizes when preparing a specification. Stock sizes are usually selected because there is a common demand for the item and it is a good product. Non-stock sizes are usually more expensive, and the product is often not as good.

I. Twice-Told Tales

1. It is a poor practice to repeat information in the specifications that is already shown on the drawings. If the information is identical, no harm results, but too often the information shown on the drawings and that described in the specifications do not agree. This results from lack of cooperation between the drafting room and the specifications department. While the documents may be in agreement during the progress of the work, changes and errors in making them can result in differences in the final product that will later create trouble.

2. To prevent conflicts the draftsmen and the specification writer should agree in advance as to what should and what should not be shown on the drawings. In general, the drawings should show what can be illustrated graphically, and the specifications should include that which can be more easily described in words. Simply stated, the specifications should define what is to be placed and describe how it should be placed, and the drawings should show what goes where and how much.

3. Some offices do not permit draftsmen to letter notes on drawings. However, there are times when short notes on the drawings are desirable. There is no harm in having the structural engineer show the design stresses on the structural drawings. It places the responsibility for the correctness where it belongs and eliminates the possibility of errors in communications.

4. The specifications should never state the number of items required; that information should appear on the drawings. Errors in numbers can be costly because the specifications govern when discrepancies occur, and the contractor is justified in furnishing only what is specified.

5. The author knows of a case where the specifications read, "A water-closet shall be furnished in each latrine." The contractor argued that he was required to furnish only one water-closet in each latrine even though the drawings called for more than one in most cases. For this reason, specifications avoid singulars when specifying materials. The sentence "Water-closets shall be furnished and placed where indicated on the drawings," would not be incorrect, even in the case where one was all that was required.

9.06 STYLE

A. PHRASEOLOGY

1. The students who have completed the required English courses in college should have little difficulty in properly expressing their thoughts in words. The same rules of grammar, sentence structure, punctuation, and spelling apply to specifications as to any other written document. However, there are differences. Whereas a creative writer spends more time selecting the proper figures of speech and euphonic sounds, the specification writer spends similar time expressing his ideas in clear, precise, and unequivocal language. Style is secondary. If it suits the purpose to start several sentences with the same word, the specification writer does so. Above all, a specification should be exact in its meaning. The ordinary reader is not looking for nor expecting fine style or clever nuances in such a document.

2. The purpose of a specification is not to immortalize the writer; if well done, the writing will be forgotten when the structure is finished. The specification is written for the reader and should be written so that a person can understand every word. Writers should remember that the reader may be a tradesman in the field, an estimator, or an owner. He should also remember that the reader could be a judge in court who may have little technical knowledge but remarkable knowledge in the meaning of words.

3. It should be unnecessary to say that a specification writer must use correct English, although it is often lacking.

4. As specifications are instructions to the contractor, they should give orders. Like military orders, they should be definite and mandatory. To be mandatory, they must be imperative. Therefore, the writer should always use the imperative "shall" or "shall be" when referring to work by the contractor. In this way the specifications can be followed and enforced. Never use vague and indefinite terms like "will," "is to be," or "are to be." Always say, "The contractor shall . . . ." The term "must" is not used. If that term is used in some cases, it implies a degree of compliance—that some things are more important than others in completing the contract, which is not the case.

5. The terms "will" and "will be" are used in a statement that some material or part of the work will be furnished by the owner, or someone other than the contractor. "The owner will" is a standard clause in most specifications. This is not based on consideration of grammar but is a helpful distinction between the commitments of the owner and the obligations of the contractor.

B. ARTICLES AND PARAGRAPHS

1. Subsections, articles, and paragraphs should be logically arranged in

order that the reader might anticipate what comes next. This should be done when preparing the outline. The next step is to arrange the work within each article or paragraph. Each article or paragraph should cover one subject only. It can be confusing to the reader to specify a material, its delivery, its storage, and its installation in one long paragraph. This also leads to sloppy thinking and poor writing. At one time a long, rambling article was the accepted method of writing specifications, but that method is now outmoded.

2. Under the heading "Materials," each material used should be specified in a separate article or paragraph. Under "Delivery," each type of delivery should be specified separately. Where two or more similar materials are to be delivered in the same way, it would be correct to specify their delivery in the same article. The same would be true of storage. For example, the storage of brick and concrete block could be specified in one article; storage of lime and cement, in another.

3. In specifying the installation, each operation should be specified in a separate article or paragraph and the paragraphs should follow in the order in which the work takes place in the field. For example, the building of the formwork should be specified before the pouring of the concrete.

C. SENTENCES

1. Type

Effective communication requires a precise explanation of ideas. For a specification to be precise, it must be clear to the reader, consistent in its use of words, and free from ambiguities; it also must contain complete and essential details. Clarity is best achieved with concise and short sentences written in plain words. When a sentence becomes too long or involved, it should be rewritten and made into two or more short sentences. The style and tense should be consistent throughout. Hyphens, commas, and semicolons should be used sparingly. Short sentences offer less chance for misinterpretation.

2. Mood

The indicative mood, passive voice, is the traditional language of specifications. Sentences like, "The waterproof coating shall be spread with a three-knob brush," or "Two coats of varnish shall be applied on all wood floors," offer small chance for a misunderstanding.

3. Grammar

a. *General*

It shouldn't be necessary to tell college students that correct grammar should be used throughout a specification. However, there are two (2) common mistakes that often appear in a student's specification.

b. *Agreement between the subject and the verb*

The sentence, "One of the six ventilators *are* on the job site," is incorrect. It should read, "One of the six ventilators *is* on the site." Plural verbs should not be used with singular subjects.

c. *Parallel construction*

"Heating, Ventilation, and Air Conditioning" should read, "Heating, Ventilating, and Air Conditioning."

4. Complete Sentences

All sentences should be complete in accordance with the rules of grammar. Broken or telegraphic-type sentences with prepositions, articles, and other small words omitted are usually not clear. The short-form specifications will be discussed in greater detail in a later chapter. Writers must realize that at some time they may be forced to defend their writing in court. What they have written will be judged by dictionary definitions and established grammar. A specification writer could be made to look rather foolish on the witness stand defending incomplete sentences on the grounds that he wished to save the typists from typing a few additional words.

5. Articles

Articles are a part of the English language. They shouldn't be omitted. For example, "Contractor shall paint exterior of building" should read, "The contractor shall paint the exterior of the building." The omission of articles leads to awkward composition.

6. Pronouns

Pronouns save repetition of the subjects when used correctly. They can also make the sentence more readable. The sentence, "Furnish all concrete, deliver the concrete to the job site, pour the concrete in the forms, and finish the concrete," is awkward. "Furnish all concrete, deliver it to the job site, pour it in the forms, and finish it," reads better. The sentence, "Concrete should not be poured when it is colder than thirty degrees Fahrenheit (30°F)," is ambiguous. Does the thirty degrees Fahrenheit refer to the temperature of the air, the temperature of the forms, or the temperature of the concrete before it is poured?

7. Things to Avoid

a. Avoid stilted language. Keep sentences short and precise.

b. Avoid pronouns that do not refer to specific nouns.

c. Avoid compound, complex sentences that ramble through several subjects.

d. Avoid elaborate sentence structure.

e. Avoid sentences that require involved punctuation.

D. WORDS

1. General

a. It happens more often than not that the one who decides the intention of a specification is someone other than the original writer. He can be a judge with no engineering background or understanding of technical words other than the dictionary definitions. For this reason it is important to use the exact meaning of words; otherwise more than one interpretation is possible. Unfamiliar words, words having more than one meaning, and unusual technical and trade expressions should be avoided. If a word can be interpreted in more than one way, it is necessary by the use of other words to restrict its meaning or to use a more accurate substitution.

b. The following is a list of words frequently used in specifications. Their correct use will reduce ambiguity.

2. List of Words

a. "All"—"Any"

(1) "All" is one of the most useful words in a specification, and it should be used liberally. The sentence, "The contractor shall furnish and install all of the masonry required to complete the work," leaves no room for debating on what is to be done or if it is included in the contract.

(2) "Any" implies a limited number to be selected by the reader.

(3) It is incorrect to say, "The contractor shall repair any defective piping." One should say, "The contractor shall repair all defective piping."

b. "Amount"—"Quantity"

"Amount" should be used in connection with monetary units. "Quantity" refers to the number of objects, volumes, and the like. In an estimate, "amount" refers to the cost, and "quantity" refers to the number of various units.

c. "And"—"Or"

The words "and" and "or" have entirely different meanings. "And/or" is sometimes used in legal documents but is undesirable in specifications because it is an indefinite expression and indicates lack of certainty.

d. "Balance"—"Remainder"

"Balance" and "remainder" are not synonymous, although they are sometimes used interchangeably. "Balance" is a device for weighing a mass; "remainder" is what is left.

e. "Bidder"—"Contractor"

One refers to "the bidder" before the contract is signed. After the signing of the contract, the bidder becomes the "contractor." We write, "The bidder shall mail his proposal to the architect," and "The contractor shall complete all work as shown on the drawings."

f. "Clean"

"Clean" is a word often used in specifications. It is such an indefinite term that it can be interpreted in several ways. "Clean sand" might mean an absence of fine particles to one person and an absence of organic materials to another. "Broom clean" and "surgically clean" are terms often used to define the extent of cleanness required. The only exact method of specifying cleanness is to specify the percentage and types of foreign particles permitted and their size in terms of microns.

g. "Either"—"Both"

The word "either" implies a choice. "Lights shall be placed in either room," does not mean the same as "Lights shall be placed in both rooms."

h. "Inflammable"—"Flammable"

The meaning of the two words is the same. However, some people think "inflammable" is the opposite of "flammable." It would be helpful to those who lack the advantages of an education if the word "inflammable" was not used. Using the words "flammable" and its opposite "nonflammable" would make a clearer specification to some persons.

i. "Level"

The word "level" when used as an adjective is a superlative. The expressions "dead level," "completely level," "true level," and the like degrees of level have no meaning. Levels, like dimensions, must be given a tolerance to have a definite meaning. This can be expressed in fractions of an inch in ten feet (10'0") or in inches over the whole project.

j. "Remove and Replace"

These words are often used. They mean that the item is to be removed and then the same item is to be replaced. If the intent is to replace with new material, the specification must so state.

k. "Resistant"—"Resisting"

"Corrosion-resisting" is preferred to "corrosion-resistant."

l. *"Smooth"*

"Smooth" means freedom from projections and offers a wide range of interpretation. It is a term often used. If smoothness is important, the degree of smoothness should be specified. It should not be confused with "warp."

m. *"Straight"*

"Straight," like the word "level," is a superlative. It cannot be qualified. If straightness is important, the limits that the work can vary from a straight line should be specified.

n. *"Will"—"Shall"*

"The owner will . . ."; "The contractor shall . . ."

E. PUNCTUATION

1. As has been said before, sentences whose meaning can be completely changed by incorrect punctuation should be avoided. It should be needless to say that the punctuation used should be correct.

2. That even a comma cost someone thousands of dollars is illustrated in the following statement taken from the specifications of one of America's largest architectural firms. The first is the way it was intended and the second the way it was written.

3. "All water piping, condensate piping, and steam piping below the ceilings shall be painted."

4. "All water piping, condensate piping and steam piping below the ceilings shall be painted."

5. As a result no water piping or condensate piping between the ceilings and floor slabs was painted. The intent of the writer was to paint all piping except the insulated steam piping above the plaster.

F. TENSE

Most authorities recommend the same verb tense throughout the specification.

G. ABBREVIATIONS

Even common engineering abbreviations are often misunderstood by workers and nontechnical people. As the amount of typing saved in the entire specification would be negligble, abbreviations are hardly worth the trouble they cause. Spell it out and be safe.

H. DEVELOPMENT OF A STYLE

The aim in writing specifications is to have a clear presentation rather than an elegant and impressive style. The student should study how sentences can be expressed more intelligibly, constantly striving for clarity.

There are many more poor specifications than good ones, and there is always room for improvement.

9.07 THE CHEAP SHALL BE FIRST

A. WILLS

When an attorney draws up a will, he first enumerates the minor bequests and then says, in substance, "The residue of my property I bequeath to . . ."

B. ORDER

1. In writing specifications, the same procedure is followed. Where different kinds of materials are used for the same or similar purpose, they are listed, under "Materials," the least expensive first, followed by the next least expensive. The most expensive is specified last. Under "Installation," in each section, the placing of the materials applicable to that section should be specified in the same order, from least expensive to most expensive.

2. Where the location of the materials to be used is shown on the drawings, such information should not be repeated in the specifications. However, where the specification writer is required to locate materials, he should follow the same rule as the lawyer writing a will. He lists the location of each material except the most expensive. For that he says, ". . . shall be used in all other areas."

C. EXAMPLE (Resilient Flooring)

"1. Materials

"a. *Asphalt Tile*

"All asphalt tile shall . . .

"b. *Linoleum*

"All linoleum shall be . . .

"c. *Vinyl asbestos tile*

"All vinyl asbestos tile shall be . . .

"d. *Vinyl flooring*

"All vinyl flooring shall be . . .

"e. *Cork flooring*

"All cork flooring shall be . . ."

"2. Installation

Under this heading, the installation of each of the materials would be specified in the same order.

"**3. Use**

"a. Asphalt tile shall be used in the classrooms and offices.

"b. Linoleum shall be used in the corridors.

"c. Vinyl asbestos tile shall be used in the kitchen and cafeteria.

"d. Vinyl tile shall be used in the science laboratories.

"e. All other resilient flooring shall be cork."

D. REASON

1. The student should note that if this method is consistently followed, some flooring will be specified for every part of the building, while any other plan obliges the specification writer to check each area most carefully to be sure that all space is provided for.

2. By including any unidentified space to be covered by the most expensive flooring, any correction could be made at a later date at no additional cost to the owner.

E. "EXCEPT"

The word "except" can be a troublesome word. To specify "all work except" and then omit the exception is a common error. By following the principle of "The cheap shall be first," the word "except" is omitted.

9.08   BEGINNERS' TROUBLES

One of the greatest weaknesses in beginners' specifications is the overdetailed descriptions of work they know well and inadequate descriptions of unfamiliar work. Architects or engineers cannot explain a job to a tradesman unless they know it first. The student should research an entire section before beginning to write it.

9.09   DO'S AND DON'TS

A. DO

1. Be definite.
2. Use correct English and use words with precise meanings.
3. Limit each paragraph to one subject.
4. Be sure the specifications agree with the drawings and all applicable codes and ordinances.
5. Use only good English.
6. Cover each subject completely.
7. Check manufacturers to be sure all specified items are available.
8. Be definite, as in a military order.

B. DON'T

1. Don't specify requirements vaguely.

2. Don't repeat information contained on the drawings.
3. Don't use "weasel-worded" sentences with hidden clauses and abstract meaning.

9.10 SUMMARY

Beyond the general information given here and what can be found in English language handbooks, it is hardly possible to tell more definitely how to write a technical section. Constant practice and experience are required. These develop one's ability to write good specifications.

TEN

"Or Equal"

10.01 THE PERNICIOUS WORDS

Every year one can read many published articles condemning the use of the words "or equal." Practically the entire construction industry has condemned their use. Without a doubt no one phrase in specifications has been subject to such severe censure. And yet the term continues to be used. Why?

10.02 DEFINITION

A. The phrase "or equal" is used in a brand-name open specification. The product is specified by a brand name or names and then followed with the words "or equal." The purpose is to establish a standard by naming a brand and then to permit the use of any product equal to that standard brand.

B. This leads to the necessity of judging whether or not a product is equivalent, and to the question of who should be the judge, the architect or engineer, the contractor, the subcontractor, or the material supplier. The expression "or approved equal" is sometimes used, apparently with the idea that the word "approved" solves the difficulty. It does nothing of the kind. The problem of who is to give the approval is still unsolved.

C. One way to solve the problem is to define whose approval is required. This could be done by a statement in the Special Conditions to the effect that when the phrase "an approved equal" is used, it means approval by the architect or engineer, as the case may be.

D. An easier and more common way is to use the phrase "or an equal approved by the architect or engineer." However, the statement can place a hardship on the contractor when dealing with an arbitrary or unreasonable architect or engineer.

10.03　OPEN OR CLOSED SPECIFICATIONS

A. GENERAL

The use of the phrase "or equal," or one of the variations previously described, determines whether or not a brand-name specification will be a closed or an open specification. The choice of using an open or closed specification is important, as it affects all of those involved in a building project.

B. THE ARCHITECT OR ENGINEER

1. Type of Specification

Specification writers or their employers usually determine the type of specification to be used. If they decide to use a brand-name specification, they are faced with problems. A single-product specification is usually not in the best interests of the owner, since it eliminates competition.

2. Closed Multiproduct Specification

a. Should specification writers use a multiproduct specification, they are faced with the selection of the products they will accept before writing the specifications. Naturally they specify products which have proved satisfactory to them or have a good reputation. Usually they specify several materials or brands. Sometimes there is so wide a range of products that to list them all would be impractical. However, when they omit the names of perfectly good makes, they curtail competition and bring upon themselves an avalanche of subcontractors and material suppliers inquiring the reason for the omission of their products. Do the specification writers consider them equal? Why are they not listed? If the salespeople do not receive satisfaction, they may go to the architect or engineer or even to the owner with the story that they have a superior product to the one specified. They can save the owner money, but they are not permitted to bid because of a despotic, capricious, ignorant specification writer.

b. When a closed specification is used, specification writers should know what they are doing and be prepared to defend their choice of product, or products. They should make every effort to sift fact from sales talk and ascertain and determine whether a particular brand name has the quality required for the product involved. They should be sure that the brands they specify will perform equally well.

3. Open Brand-Name Specification

    a. If specification writers decide to use an open brand-name specification, they are also faced with several problems.

    b. If they specify one product "or an equal approved by the architect or engineer," they will be faced with the same avalanche of subcontractors and material suppliers wanting to know if the architect or engineer considers their product equal, and if so how this information can be given to the contractor.

    c. If writers specify several products with "an equal approved by the architect or engineer," they must be sure the brands they name have the same quality and are competitive in price. A specification reading "a Lincoln, a Ford, a Volkswagen, or an approved equal" has little meaning.

    d. When several products are named in an open specification, some people will interpret the "or equal" as a product that has no feature worse than any of the products named. The result may be a product that has the worst features of all the various products named.

    e. Specification writers must remember that the contractor reads the phrase "or equal" as "or cheaper." To most contractors, a product at one-half the price is twice as good. By using any form of the phrase "or equal" they may get the product they specify or something cheaper; it won't be higher priced.

    f. Another problem comes after the bids are received and the contract is awarded. The subcontractor who cut a price to the general contractor may be looking for a way to recuperate the loss. This subcontractor may be quite insistent on getting a cheaper product approved. In government work the burden of proof would be on the specification writer. The writer could be required to prove that a product submitted for approval by the contractor is not "an equal."

C. THE CONTRACTOR

The contractor is faced with a different kind of problem when reading "or equal." When a subcontractor submits a price and states the intention to use a product equal to that specified, what should the contractor do? The contractor who uses the figure submitted risks being forced to pay a higher price to another subcontractor if the proposed product is not satisfactory; and the contractor who does not accept the low bid might lose the contract. One is never sure that some other contractor is not using that price. As a rule, most contractors will refuse to accept prices from subcontractors on a conditional basis.

D. THE SUBCONTRACTOR

Subcontractors are faced with a similar problem. They may have every reason to believe a product or method is equal to that specified, and bid accordingly. If they have miscalculated, they are put to extra expense; if not, they are still burdened with considerable work in proving that the substitute is an equal.

E. THE MANUFACTURER

Manufacturers spend great sums of money in advertising and hiring salesmen to persuade architects or engineers to specify their product. They know that being specified is the key to selling and staying in business. Manufacturers of high-grade building products are usually successful in having their products named in construction specifications. However, with the use of the term "or equal," inferior products often appear on the job because some salesman sold a below-standard product to an uninformed specification writer who accepted a salesman's fiction for established facts. The practice of undercutting quality as well as price and selling it as an equal has caused many quality-minded manufacturers to wonder about their policy. Some have solved the problem by making two or more grades of the same product—one to "sell" to the architect or engineer, and the cheaper product to sell to the contractor as equal.

F. THE OWNER

1. General

a. At this point, the student is probably wondering why the term "or equal" in any of its forms is ever used. The answer usually is that the owner insists. Strange as it may seem, there are owners who do not fully trust the architect or engineer and set up specification standards for the architect or engineer to follow. This is particularly true when the owner is the government. On government work, the architect or engineer must write an open specification or be able to prove that the product is one that can only be produced satisfactorily by a specific company.

b. The owner is the one who makes a project possible and it is the architect or engineer's duty to serve the owner's best interests. When the owner requests an open specification, it is the duty of the architect or engineer to explain what is involved, and if the owner insists, the architect or engineer must follow instructions or turn down the project. It must be remembered that the owner's money is involved, and the specification writer should have good reason why a manufacturer of a product not specified but equal to the one specified should not be permitted to bid.

2. Advantages

a. There are some advantages to the term "or equal," and if architects or engineers know their products, there is no reason why it cannot be successfully used.

    b. If architects or engineers write a closed multiproduct specification, they should search the entire field and name all of the products that will satisfy the owner's needs. If they fail to do this, they may exclude a product equivalent to the one specified that could save money for the owner. This means that the architect or engineer must spend valuable time researching all products and determine which meet the owner's needs. The fear that some specification writers might not do this is the reason many owners insist on the "or equal."

    c. By using an open specification, architects or engineers can use their full research time investigating the limited number of products submitted by the contractor. This gives the owner the opportunity of having the best product at the best price.

10.04 HAVING CONTRACTORS LIST SAVINGS

A. LISTING DEDUCTIONS

    1. Some architect-engineers have tried to solve the "or equal" problem by using only closed specifications and then providing space in the proposal form for the contractor to list any materials he would like to substitute, and the deduction in price if the substitute would be accepted. This has the advantage of requiring all contractors to bid on exactly the same products and facilitates comparison of the various quotations.

    2. Many salesmen try to persuade the specification writer to use this type of specification providing that only their product is named. Their argument is that such a specification gives the specification writer a chance to compare prices with other products, and that it will also prove that their superior product costs very little more than their competitor's inferior products. They may point to other jobs where the contractor did not list any other product as less expensive.

    3. This method may prove to be very expensive to the owner and may be the reason it is not approved by many corporations or the government. When a single product is specified, the contractors often accept only bids on that specific product and do not list deductions. Why should they? All contractors will be bidding on the same product and the award will usually go to the low bidder. After signing the contract, the contractor can still make suggestions to save the owner money. Being only interested in getting the job, it is not to the contractor's advantage to spend time with products which may or may not be approved if this contractor is awarded the contract.

    4. The bidder submitting a high bid on the specified products might lose the contract even though listing deductions which bring the price

below the low bidder. The owner might use these suggested deductions to obtain a still lower figure. The owner can ask the low bidder to submit a new proposal on the other bidder's suggestions. Ethics are often ignored where large sums of money are involved.

B. LISTING ADDITIONS

In an effort to overcome the contractor's reluctance to list savings, another method has been tried. Instead of listing substitutions for particular products, the contractor submits a bid using alternate methods to those specified to establish the price. This method has a limited advantage where cost is critical and the owner is looking for every means of saving on costs. It cannot be recommended on average or above-average work because it leaves an unlimited opening to the contractor and could involve an endless amount of work for the architect-engineer justifying decisions to the owner. Consider the architect-engineer's amount of extra work and loss of control of the project if the owner accepted a contractor's suggestion to remove all cut stone and substitute poured concrete.

10.05   DESCRIPTIVE SPECIFICATIONS

A. We have previously stated that the descriptive specification is an open specification. This is true since everyone may bid who can manufacture the product as specified. In actual practice, however, manufacturers are not going to change their standards to meet a single specification; and if they did, the cost would be prohibitive. For that reason a descriptive specification in many cases is in actual practice a single-product specification.

B. Many an inexperienced specification writer has fallen into a trap laid by a clever salesman. "Don't use our name," he will say, "write an open specification; let anyone bid. We welcome competition. Let me show you how." He will then produce a descriptive specification of the product that appears to be open. It sometimes takes considerable study to find those phrases, hidden in the volume of words, that exclude all of the salesman's competitors. Innocent words like "the water trough shall be copper" could exclude all other competitors if the remainder of the trade uses stainless steel for the same part.

C. Clever specification writers can use the above method when they want to exclude one or more manufacturers and still appear to have an open specification.

10.06   PERFORMANCE SPECIFICATIONS

The performance specification could become a de facto single-product specification if there were only one product made that could meet the performance specified. When the performance of a product is specified, any proposed item must be tested to ensure that the product performs as required. In many cases, the cost of testing exceeds the value of the product. For this reason, performance specifications are seldom used to specify inexpensive products. Performance specifications will be discussed in more detail in Chapter Thirty.

10.07   CONCLUSION

As we have said previously, each type of specification has its advantages, and the specification writer must learn under what conditions each type is best. This is not easy. Specification writing is not an easy job. It requires a lot of careful thought and thorough analysis to sift through a producer's literature, to recognize real value, and to distinguish value from showy advertisements or high-pressure sales pitches.

ELEVEN

Options and Alternates

11.01 OPTIONS

A. DEFINITION

When the term "option" is used in a specification, it means that the contractor has the option, or choice, of using any one, of two or more, products or methods. An example of an option follows.

B. EXAMPLE

"1. Pipe

"All pipe shall be standard weight, three-quarters inch ($^3/_4$") galvanized iron conforming to Federal Specification WW-P-406b(1). All pipe shall be taper-threaded at both ends.

"2. Pipe Fittings

"All pipe fittings shall be malleable iron screwed fittings conforming to Federal Specification WW-P-521e.

"3. Option

"At the option of the contractor, pipe with beveled ends and welded pipe fittings may be substituted for the pipe and fittings specified provided they are equal in all other respects."

C. INTERPRETATION

The option illustrated in the foregoing example means that the estimator should figure the cheapest way of performing the work. It should be obvious that pipe with screwed fittings would be more expensive. The contractor will be required to balance the cost of the more expensive fittings with the reduced labor cost to arrive at the best price.

D. LENGTH

Usually options involving products can be expressed in a single sentence. There are times when optional methods can involve several pages. For example, in specifying the finishing of concrete many engineers consider the absorption method and the dry tamp method equal. If an option were specified, each method would have to be described in detail. This would add several pages to the specification.

E. USE

The option is used when two materials or methods are equally priced and where the selection would depend upon the particular preference of the contractor. It would be useless to specify an option when it is known in advance that all the bidders will select the same material or method. There would be no purpose in specifying a building to be faced with common brick and then include an option for marble.

11.02 ALTERNATES

A. DEFINITION

An alternate differs from an option. An "alternate" is a request for a price for substituting one material or method in place of another or for adding to, or deducting from, the scope of the project. For example, the specification may state, "The contractor is requested to state the deduction in price if trap rock herein specified is omitted and rice-size emery is substituted in lieu thereof." Another example is, "The contractor is requested to state the amount to be added to his bid if the north wing of the building is increased to four stories as shown on the drawings." Of course, a separate drawing would be made showing the alternate.

B. PRICE

1. Unlike the option, the owner receives a separate price for the work required by each alternate. Any bidder, if he chooses, may refuse to bid on any or all alternates, or he may bid on one or several alternates without bidding on the original specification.

2. When the bids are received, the owner and architect or engineer compare them and decide which alternates will be accepted. When the contract between the owner and the contractor is written, it includes the alternates that were accepted.

C. ADDITIVE AND DEDUCTIVE ALTERNATES

1. Definition

There are two types of alternates, additive and deductive. An "additive" alternate is one which, if accepted, will increase the consideration in the contract. A "deductive" alternate is one in which the consideration will be decreased.

2. Examples

a. An example of an additive alternate is when a four-story building is specified and an alternate is requested for adding a fifth floor.

b. An example of a deductive alternate is where a five-story building is specified and an alternate is requested leaving off the fifth floor.

3. Advantages of Each

a. In theory, a four-story building should be the same price regardless of how the bids are taken. However, there is evidence to show that it is cheaper to use an additive alternate than a deductive alternate. The reasoning is that a contractor bidding on a five-story building would figure the price on a completed structure consisting of cost plus a percentage for overhead and profit. The same contractor, in figuring the alternate, may deduct only the cost of the fifth story from the total bid, and may not deduct the overhead and profit. However, when figuring a four-story building, the contractor includes the cost plus overhead and profit for the four floors, which is less than the computation of the contractor who figured on the basis of a five-story building and deducted only costs for the fifth floor. Of course, this is not true of all contractors. However, enough contractors do figure this way to make some owners insist on using additive alternates only.

b. A deductive alternate is preferred by most architect-engineers. It makes it possible for the plans to be completed for the project as planned. A simple note can inform the contractor which parts are to be omitted by the alternate. For an additive alternate, the plans and elevations are drawn for the smaller project and additional drawings are required to show the alternate.

D. USE OF ALTERNATES

1. There are many reasons for specifying alternates. When a board of directors, a city council, or any other governing body appropriates a specific amount of money to construct a building, an architect-engineer has to design this building to cost less than the amount appropriated. If it costs more, the bids will be rejected, and the plans and specifications will have to be revised and the project readvertised. This costs the architect-engineer considerable money and causes unwanted delay for the owner.

2. While the architect-engineer can estimate the cost with some degree of accuracy, there is no way of determining the lowest bid in advance. The architect's fee is usually based upon the final contract price, so it is advantageous to have the low bid at or just below the amount

of the appropriation. By using alternates, the chances of doing this are increased.

3. For example, the architect-engineer may know that if conditions are right and contractors are looking for work (their prices will be low), a building with an imported marble facing might come within the appropriations. However, to be safe the architect asks for alternates using native marble, local stone, and brick, feeling sure that the building with a brick facing will be less than the appropriations. When bids are received, the architect can select the alternate nearest the amount appropriated.

4. Alternates may be asked on an almost unlimited number of items. However, the writer should use considerable care in selecting alternates and should limit their number. A large number of alternates indicates that the architect-engineer does not know what is wanted, and this could be the reason for some contractors refusing to bid.

E. ALTERNATES ON GOVERNMENT WORK

1. It is possible that the low bidder on the base bid may not be the low bidder on the alternate. It is also possible, when there are numerous alternates, to have several bidders each of whom could be considered a low bidder depending upon which combination of alternates is selected. Because of this circumstance, favoritism for one of the bidders is sometimes the reason why an architect chooses a particular combination of alternates.

2. To prevent unfavorable publicity, some governmental agencies have established a procedure that works fairly well. The base bid is composed of the most expensive alternates and only deductive alternates are used. The alternates are arranged in order so that the first alternate is the least objectionable to the owner and the last is the most objectionable. If the lowest bid is more than the amount appropriated, the first alternate is considered. If the low is still above the appropriation, the second alternate is considered. This continues until a bid below the appropriation is obtained. It is possible that the low bidder on the base contract may not be the low bidder when the alternates are figured, but this method is fair to all bidders.

F. PRESENTATION

1. All alternates should be combined in a separate section of the specifications. As the alternates often apply to more than one technical section, this section is usually placed after the General Contractor's Work and ahead of the technical sections.

2. It is also desirable to refer to the alternates in the technical sections affected by the alternates. A single sentence in a subsection entitled "Alternate" is all that is required. The purpose is to alert all sub-bid-

ders. It is not uncommon for estimators to read only the section involving the trade they are figuring; they should be informed that additional estimates are required.

3. Alternates are usually numbered, and each alternate should be described completely. For example, "Alternate I consists of omitting exterior marble and substituting limestone in lieu thereof." This would be followed by a specification for the limestone and any difference required in the setting. If an already specified wing of a proposed building is to be eliminated, it is not only necessary to tell of the omission; it is also necessary to describe in detail how the opening at the wing will be closed. An example of an alternate section is in the Appendix.

G. DANGERS

1. General

Extreme care must be used in specifying deductive alternates to be sure that the owner will have a complete, workable project. There are examples where last-minute alternates were added that caused considerable embarrassment to the engineer.

2. Example I

On the day a five-story project was issued for bids, an additional item was placed in the proposal form requesting a price for "omitting all construction above the fifth floor except a three-foot parapet wall." Just before the signing of the contract it was discovered that the low bidder had included an open stairwell running to the roof and had omitted the roofing from the project.

3. Example II

A factory building project was issued for bidding with an alternate to omit the two north bays and place the wall in a new location as shown on the drawings. The architectural drawings were neatly drawn and the specifications carefully worded. It was a bidder who discovered that the electrical service entrance and the transformer for the entire plant were located in the north bays!

11.03 PURPOSE OF ALTERNATES

There is little reason to ask for an alternate if the intent is to use the least expensive product or method. An option will accomplish that. The purpose of an alternate is to compare prices of various products or methods, so as to allow either the best products for the owner's money or the highest allowable bid for the architect or engineer.

TWELVE

Short-Form Specifications

12.01 LENGTH OF SPECIFICATION

A. The question most often asked is, "How long should a specification be?" The answer: "As long and detailed as necessary to obtain the product desired at the lowest cost." This, of course, is an incomplete, oversimplified answer.

B. Actually there is little need to emphasize short-form writing to most students. The student, having a limited knowledge of building products, is required to limit his writing or to copy the work of someone else, which he may not completely understand. The student should never try to add words or sentences for the purpose of adding length to a specification. There is no substitute for knowledge of a product, and superfluous wording is easily detected.

12.02 WHAT DETERMINES THE LENGTH

* **A. AN EXAMPLE**

    1. The Department of the Army in 1875 wrote the following complete specification for a chapel to be constructed at Fort Sill, Oklahoma.

    2. "To be constructed of flat rubble stone walls of lime mortar. Rough plastered inside. Main roof timbers dressed and chamferred on corners for trusses. Rest of roof sawed, not dressed. Timbers oiled. Remainder white-washed. Windows to have rubble arched heads. Stone breaks will do for this purpose. Doorway same construction. All the woodwork to be shipped, framed, ready to put up, including

* Reprinted from the January 1961 *Construction Specifier,* with permission from the Construction Specifications Institute.

floors, roof, doors, and windows. Stone to be quarried and erected with lime burned at Sill by extra duty-labor."

3. Today the same chapel would require over a hundred (100) pages of specifications. Why? We must assume that one hundred (100) years ago the foregoing specification was sufficient to give the contractor the information he required. There was an understanding by both parties of what was wanted. It probably never occurred to the contractor to omit the glass from the windows because it wasn't specified.

4. Today there are many products on the market, many more grades of the same product, and many different ways of installing these materials. However, the biggest difference is the bidding procedure. Today a contractor cannot promise the owner more than is specified and still be the low bidder. There is too much competition. The courts hold that the owner can expect no more than is specified in the contract documents. For that reason, specifications have had to increase in length and detail to protect the owner.

B. COST

1. The cost of a project has some effect on the length of a specification but not to a great degree. Some architects and engineers who are not directly involved with specification writing fail to realize this. An inexpensive building using many different materials can require a much longer specification than a simple, expensive project. For example, a specification for a multimillion-dollar runway for an airfield could be shorter than a twenty thousand-dollar ($20,000) addition to a clubhouse. The reason is that the airfield pavement could be specified in six (6) technical sections: Excavating and Backfilling, Concrete, Sealing Joints, Painting, Electrical Work, and Sodding and Seeding. The clubhouse addition could have as many as twenty (20) trades. So the length of a specification is determined chiefly by the number of sections rather than by the cost of the project.

2. By rights the householder who is building a three hundred-dollar ($300) driveway to his garage should be protected from poor concrete and workmanship to the same extent as the corporation placing a multimillion-dollar air strip on a landing field. If this were done, the householder would have to pay considerably more for the driveway. The money that would be spent in writing a long specification, typing it, printing it, and hiring inspectors in the field could be better utilized in increasing the depth of the slab or by adding reinforcing.

3. For this reason, the architect-engineer often looks for a means of shortening specifications on small projects while still protecting the owner from the contractor. This need has opened the way for short-form specifications.

12.03 SHORTENING SPECIFICATIONS

A. GENERAL

Everyone is in favor of shortening specifications without reducing the content. With the exception of the controversy over the phrase "or equal," more has been written about this subject than any other. However, specifications seem to be increasing rather than decreasing in length. How can the length of specifications be shortened?

B. REDUCING TRADES

Specifications can be reduced in length by reducing the number of trades. However, this is beyond the specification writer's control. The number of trades required is determined by the drawings. Probably no designer would change a drawing to shorten the specification.

C. REDUCING SUBSECTIONS

1. The number of subsections in a short specification can be reduced only by reducing the amount of work required. For example, the requirement for shop drawings could be omitted on a small job without necessarily reducing the quality of the final product.

2. Some specification writers have proposed omitting the "General Note," the "Scope of the Work," and the "Work Not Included" subsections and starting each section with the "Materials" subsection. Their argument is that the contract is with the general contractor only, and that the specifications should ignore any subcontractor relationship. Such specifications can be written, and they do reduce the work of the specification writer. In previous chapters, we discussed the reasons for including these subsections; to omit them, except on extremely small jobs, would not be in the best interest of the owner.

D. REDUCING WORDAGE

1. Reducing wordage offers the greatest possibility for shortening specifications. Eliminating a few words in a sentence by rewriting may not result in a saving in time; however, if the student learns to reduce thoughts to short, simple sentences, the result will be a short, clear specification.

2. A common cause of long specifications is repetition. It is not uncommon to see several pages of descriptive matter copied from a federal or ASTM specification. A simple reference would not only be shorter but would be protection against errors in copying.

3. Unnecessarily long specifications are sometimes the result of taking old specifications and adding new, more applicable sentences. If this process is repeated a few times, the result is a long and often confusing specification. The time element, of course, is the cause of this.

It is easier for the specification writer to read and alter existing work than to rewrite.

4. Using guide specifications also contributes to long specifications. Guide specifications must be generally worded to cover many possible conditions. In the rush, many writers copy all of the wording and add additional sentences to cover a specific condition, whereas rewriting the specification completely would have resulted in a shorter and clearer specification.

12.04 WRITING SHORT-FORM SPECIFICATIONS

A. DEFINITION

There is a difference between shortened specifications and short-form specifications. We define a "shortened specification" as one condensed by eliminating excessive wordage. By a "short-form specification," we mean one where symbols are substituted for phrases that are repeated throughout the specification. This will reduce the length of the specification to some extent. Short-form specifications were very popular about ten (10) years ago. They are not too popular today.

B. EXAMPLE

1. General

The short-form specification starts with an explanation of terms, stating that the following symbols are substituted for words and that this is done to reduce the wording. The following is an example.

"2. Symbols

"a. : means the words 'shall be'
"b. -   "   "   "   'or an approved equal'
"c. #   "   "   "   'pounds per square inch'
"d. ;   "   "   "   'shall conform to'
"e. ASTM   "   "   'American Society for Testing and Materials'
"f. :,   "   "   "   'and watertight'

"3. Materials

"a. Concrete: 3000# ultimate strength.
"b. Steel; ASTM A 15-58T and A 305-56T.
"c. Forms: wood, steel-, amply strong:,"

C. COMMENT

1. It should be obvious to the student that such a specification, while short and explicit, is subject to easy error. A simple symbol mistyped could cause mistakes in meaning. With a large number of symbols, the specification could also be difficult to read.

2. There is nothing illegal about such specifications. However, the typing saved in a short-form specification when compared with a carefully worded specification amounts to only a few pages; and the added work in writing, proofreading, and interpreting is increased to the extent that most offices find that the short form offers little or no saving.

12.05   CLEARNESS

The most important requirement of a specification writer is to be clear. Clearness should never be sacrificed for length. Often when those in authority insist upon short specifications and trouble develops, they then demand to know why some obscure point was not covered.

12.06   WHY GOOD SPECIFICATIONS ARE LONG

A. The inexperienced writer has no difficulty in reducing the wording of existing specifications. When some clever contractor is able to circumvent the intent, the particular circumstance is explicitly covered in all of the writer's future specifications to clarify the meaning. After a few years, and many embarrassing experiences, the writer develops a longer specification that covers most loopholes and gives the clients exactly what they want. This is why experience is so important and why experienced writers can demand high salaries.

B. There is a general belief that contractors dislike long specifications and raise their price accordingly. This is true where specifications contain broad and polemical statements. However, well-written specifications are welcomed by the contractor. The time required to read as much as an extra page of specification is small in comparison to that lost in trying to construe the meaning of incomplete or vague description.

THIRTEEN

Contracts

13.01 OBLIGATION

There is no one method of securing quotations that is superior to others. In the building industry, certain types of work require specific types of bidding procedures. In some cases, the pressure of time may make it advisable to award separate contracts for the foundation work, the structural steel work, and various types of equipment so that the work may get under way prior to the completion of the architectural design. At times, "partial contracts" are preferred when there is a particular need to control the selection of contractors. The architect or engineer is expected to advise the client as to the type of contract most advantageous for the client. To do so, the architect must know the advantages and disadvantages of each type of contract.

13.02 TYPES OF CONTRACTS

A. GENERAL

There are six (6) different types of contracts that are commonly used in construction. They are the fixed-price contract, the cost plus a percentage contract, the cost plus a fixed fee contract, the cost plus a fixed fee with a maximum price contract, the cost plus a percentage with a maximum price, and the unit price contract.

B. THE FIXED-PRICE CONTRACT

1. General

The fixed-price contract states that for a specific sum of money, the bidder will agree to do a specific amount of work. The bid form is turned over to the contractor by the architect or engineer, and the contractor says in effect, "I will do the amount you have outlined for a certain fixed sum of money." This is called a "fixed price contract." It has some very definite benefits. It is the most common type of contract. At the present time, over ninety percent (90%) of the contracts are fixed-price contracts.

2. Advantages

a. The chief advantage of a fixed-price contract is that the owners receive the lowest possible price. Competition ensures this.

b. Another advantage to the owners is that the time involved is usually stipulated and the owners know in advance exactly what they are buying, the amount they are paying, and when they will get it.

3. Disadvantages

a. There are some disadvantages. The time involved is considerably longer than it would be for some other types of contracts. The reason for this is that the plans and specifications have to be completed before the project can be advertised for bids. One cannot take bids until the contractors know in detail what they must do and can estimate the price. Where the total time to perform a project is more important than price, other types of contracts are better. The main loss of time is in completing the contract document. It is to the advantage of a contractor with a fixed-price contract to finish the work as soon as possible (without overtime). A slow job costs the contractor money.

b. The quality of work will be poor. On this type of contract, price determines who is awarded the contract, and a contractor is required to "cut corners" to be the low bidder. A contractor cannot afford to furnish a product above the minimum specified.

4. Example

a. In a fixed-price contract, the offer submitted by each bidder will contain wording similar to that in the following paragraph.

b. "We the undersigned agree to construct a . . . . in accordance with the plans and specifications dated . . . . prepared by Walker, Home and Lever, Architects and Engineers, for the sum of . . . . ($. . . . .).″

C. COST PLUS PERCENTAGE CONTRACT

1. Use

The "cost plus a percentage contract" is selected when the cost of a project is immaterial and the owners desire the best materials and workmanship.

2. General

a. The cost plus a percentage contract is one where the contractor agrees to furnish a product and charge the owners all of the direct costs plus a stipulated percentage of the direct costs to cover the overhead and profit of the contractor.

b. It is important in this type of contract to specify the items that are included in the direct costs and in the overhead and profit.

c. It is also important that a method be established for the owners to audit the contractor's expenses. The contractor should be required to establish proper accounting procedures.

3. Advantages to the Owners

a. The cost plus a percentage contract makes it desirable for the contractor to use the most expensive materials and methods of installation. The greater the cost, the more money the contractor makes. For this reason, the owners get the very best of materials and the most expensive workmanship.

b. The owners are in full control. They may change their minds as to their requirements, they may destroy work they don't like, or they may double or triple the requirements. These changes are accepted by the contractor. The contractor makes money on additions and does not lose actual profit on reductions, though the anticipated profit is less.

c. Work in the field may be started before the plans and specifications are completed. The contractor does not have to know very much about the structure to establish a percentage to cover the overhead and profit. The contractor can therefore accept a project without seeing the plans.

4. Disadvantages

a. The main disadvantage of this type of contract is the excessive cost. For this reason, few cost plus a percentage contracts are awarded.

b. There are several reasons for excessive cost on this type of contract. One is that it is to the contractor's advantage to increase the cost. The contractor is encouraged to use inefficient (time-wasting) labor and expensive materials.

c. At best, labor will not be efficient. It doesn't take long for the laborer to realize that he is working on a cost plus contract. The worker isn't pushed hard and just automatically slows down. Contractors are apt to place the fast workers on fixed-price construction. This alone can raise the cost, and the contractor has no inducement to discourage this.

5. Example

a. The wording in the following subparagraphs is an example of an offer submitted by a subcontractor on a cost plus percentage contract.

b. "We the undersigned agree to construct a project for the Dull Tool Company. We will charge the Company our direct costs plus a fee of ten percent (10%) of the direct costs to cover our overhead and profit.

c. "Overhead shall include the cost of all salaried office personnel, all office equipment and supplies, all office telephone calls, the use of the contractor's small tools (for the value of less than $25 per tool), and all items not chargeable to the job.

d. "Direct costs shall include the cost of all materials; the rental of all tools, apparatus, and equipment of more than twenty-five dollars ($25) in value; the cost of auxiliary materials less the resale value of same; transportation costs; the salaries of all salaried personnel employed exclusively at the job site; the hourly wages of all labor; and supervision and taxes on the above."

D. COST PLUS A FIXED FEE CONTRACT

1. General

a. The "cost plus a fixed fee contract" is the same as a cost plus a percentage contract except that the consideration for the contractor consists of an agreed-upon fixed sum of money rather than a percentage of the cost. This means that the fee for the contractor will remain the same even though the final cost of the project is twice or half the estimated cost.

b. As this is a combination of the above types, it has some of the advantages and disadvantages of the above two (2) types of contracts.

2. Advantages and Disadvantages

a. The plans have to be under way so the contractor has some idea of the amount of work required to enable him to establish a fee, but the contractor doesn't have to have completed plans.

b. The owner still gets quality construction, but the contractor cannot afford delays that will keep the job going longer than expected.

c. The cost will be lower than cost plus percentage because the contractor gets no percentage of additional costs.

d. The contractor will try to hurry the job. The sooner he finishes, the more money he makes.

e. Labor will be driven harder because the contractor wants to finish the project.

E. COST PLUS A FIXED FEE WITH A GUARANTEED MAXIMUM

1. Another type of contract is a "cost plus a fixed fee with a guaranteed maximum." A contractor entering into this type of contract agrees to build a structure on a cost-plus-fixed-fee basis, and also agrees that the structure will not cost more than a specified amount of money. In this respect, this type of contract is similar to the fixed-price contract.

2. The fact that the owner is obligated to pay only a specific sum of money is the chief advantage of this type of contract. The owner has the privilege of making minor changes in the plans, excluding those that would bring the cost of the project above the amount agreed upon.

3. The disadvantages to the owner of this type of contract are the same as those of the cost plus a fixed fee, with some additional disadvantages of the fixed-price contract but to a lesser extent. The plans must be almost finished.

F. COST PLUS A PERCENTAGE WITH A MAXIMUM PRICE

The "cost plus a percentage with a maximum price contract" is similar to the cost plus a fixed fee with a guaranteed maximum. The difference is that the contractor is paid a percentage of the cost of the structure rather than a fixed fee. As the owner is protected by the maximum price and as a fixed fee is usually determined by the maximum cost, the owner may save money if the cost is less than the maximum. It does, however, give the contractor an inducement to calculate the costs as close as possible to the maximum; and this could be to the owner's disadvantage.

G. THE UNIT PRICE CONTRACT

1. Definition

The "unit price contract" is one where the actual amount of work is unknown; so the bidder charges the owner a specific amount of money for each unit or type of work. For example, the contractor may agree to excavate, drive piles, and place a foundation for a specific project. As the soil conditions are not known, the amount of work cannot be established in advance. In such a case, the contractor can bid a price per cubic yard for excavating, another price per cubic yard for backfilling, a price per foot for driving piles, a price per square foot for building and stripping forms, a price per ton for furnishing and placing each size of anchor bolt required, and a price per cubic yard for furnishing, placing, and finishing concrete.

2. Advantages

a. The advantage of a unit price is that it allows the owner to receive competitive prices from several contractors when the extent of the work is unknown.

b. It also allows the owner the freedom to make changes in the volume of work required while the job progresses without changing the contract.

c. In addition, it permits the owner to control the amount of money that will be spent. The owner knows the cost of any specified work in advance and can stop work at any stage.

3. Disadvantages

a. There are several disadvantages to the unit price contract. One is the high cost. For protection, the contractor is required to bid for the most expensive process within any unit. For example, the contractor's cost for placing a one (1) by ten (10) form around single footings would not be the same as for building and bracing wall forms; the cost of placing a ton of three-eighths inch ($^3/_8''$) reinforcing bars in a wall would be more than for placing a ton of one-inch (1") round bars in a footing.

b. It is very possible that there will be additions with this type of contract. If the details of the project are not known in advance, there is always the possibility of requiring work for which there has been no preestablished unit price. For example, in the before-mentioned case, if sleeves were required in the foundation, negotiations would have to be conducted to establish a price.

c. The cost of inspecting is greatly increased with this type of contract. The clerk of the works not only has to inspect the quality of the work but must also make sure the contractor does not do work that is not required. However, the greatest expense to the architect-engineer and, of course, indirectly to the owner is the cost of checking quantities. The clerk of the works will require assistance to check the contractor's delivery of materials and take measurements. These measurements must be accurate, as they determine the cost.

4. Use

a. Because of the disadvantages hereinbefore stated, the unit price contract is seldom used in construction projects; however, it is the most common type in production manufacturing. The manufacturers of a product can only estimate their sales volume for a model year. Therefore, it is to their advantage to receive bids and award contracts on a unit price basis. See Chapter Twenty-nine.

b. Contracts for piling are often awarded on a unit price basis as previously described. Maintenance-type contracts, where the budget is limited, are also awarded in this manner. They allow the engineer to use the entire appropriation in the most advantageous manner. As an example, when a government appropriates a specific sum for the repairing of a road, the engineer, after receiving the unit prices, can determine exactly the extent of the repairs permitted by the budget.

c. Paving contracts are often awarded on a unit price basis because it is difficult to administer them on any other basis. Because of the large area involved, a very slight difference in thickness can mean many tons of material. The price per ton for bituminous concrete or the price per cubic yard for Portland cement concrete is easier to control.

5. Preparing Proposals

a. *Quantities*

It should be obvious that the volume of work affects the unit price of the work. For example, the cost per foot for placing one hundred feet (100 ft) of pipeline would be greater than that for placing one hundred (100) miles even if the specifications and conditions of work were exactly the same. For this reason, proposals for unit prices usually contain an estimated quantity and an assurance that the quantities will not vary more than a specific percentage above or below that quantity.

b. *Number of items*

The number of items in a unit price proposal depends on the complexity of the project. The fewer items there are, the easier it is to administer the proposal. However, as we have previously stated, the bidder must figure the most expensive unit price for any operation. Therefore, the more items, the less the cost. For example, if a price per ton of reinforcing bars in place is requested, the contractor is required to guess the size of the bars involved and their location. The cost of placing and supporting small bars on roof forms would be considerably more than that of placing bars in a footing on the ground. For self-protection, the contractor must add a contingency factor to any quotation. If separate prices are requested for furnishing each size of bar and support, the contractor could quote an exact price on the material and would be required to figure a contingency only on the labor. If separate prices were requested for placing each size bar in footings, walls, beams, and slabs and separate prices obtained for placing steel on each floor above the ground, accurate prices could be obtained. However, the bidding schedule would be too long to be economically administered. Experience is required to make a unit price proposal sufficiently long to obtain advantageous prices and short enough to administer.

6. Example

a. *General*

The bidding schedule appears as a part of the proposal form and the instructions for completing it should appear in the Instructions to Bidders. The following example is taken from a proposal to replace an existing dirt road by constructing a concrete road with sewers and curbs. Since drawings are furnished, the extent of the completed project is known. Unit prices were requested because the total appropriation was inadequate to do all of the work required, and the road commission wanted as much pavement as possible. The unit price permits the commission to spend all of the money appropriated to the best advantage and then extend the scope of the work if additional money is available at a later date. The quantities in the schedule are for price comparison only.

b.*" Bidding schedule*

" (1)   Basic .... $_____
" (2)   Excavating 78,000 cub yd @
        $_____ per cub. yd. .... $_____
" (3)   Backfilling 26,100 cub yd @
        $_____ per cub yd .... $_____
" (4)   Storm Lines 11,560 ft @
        $_____ per ft .... $_____
" (5)   Catch Basins 58 @
        $_____ each .... $_____
" (6)   Subbase 24,000 cub yd @
        $_____ per cub yd......................... $_____
" (7)   Base 116,000 sq ft @
        $_____ per sq ft .... $_____
" (8)   Curbs 11,520 ft @
        $_____ per ft .... $_____
" (9)   Pavement 5,260 ft   @
        $_____ per ft .... $_____
"(10)   Sawing Joints 1,740 ft @
        $_____ per ft .... $_____
"(11)   Filling Joints 17,580 ft @
        $_____ per ft .... $_____
"(12)   Sodding 15,000 sq ft @
        $_____ per sq ft .... $_____
"(13)   Total .... $_____ "

c.*" Measurements*

" (1)   "Basic" includes all labor, material, and other items for the project except those included in items (2) through (12).
" (2)   One (1) cubic yard of excavating includes clearing, grubbing, and other work required to remove twenty-seven (27) cubic feet of soil, clay, rock, or other material regardless of type, neatly piling material that is suitable for backfilling, and disposing of the remainder from the site of the work.

" (3) One (1) cubic yard of backfilling consists of backfilling an excavation of twenty-seven (27) cubic feet with acceptable earth previously removed from the excavation and stored at the site. It also includes the compaction of the soil as specified.

" (4) One (1) foot of storm line includes placing a sand fill as specified, digging the bell holes, and placing and sealing twelve inches (12") of storm drainage pipe all as specified.

" (5) One (1) catch basin consists of furnishing all materials and labor to build a catch basin as shown on the drawings and specified.

" (6) One (1) cubic yard of subbase consists of furnishing twenty-seven cubic feet (27 cub ft) of the subbase material specified and placing the same as shown and specified.

" (7) One (1) square foot of base consists of furnishing, placing, and compacting one hundred and forty-four square inches (144 sq in.) of base material as specified to the thickness shown on the drawing.

" (8) One (1) foot of curb consists of furnishing and placing twelve inches (12") of the curb illustrated on the drawings and specified. The price includes the joints as shown.

" (9) One (1) foot of pavement consists of placing twelve inches (12") of concrete roadway of the width and thickness shown on the drawings, complete as specified.

"(10) One (1) foot (1'-0") of sawing consists of sawing twelve inches (12") of concrete to the depth and width shown on the drawings, all as specified.

"(11) One (1) foot (1'-0") of joint filling consists of filling twelve inches (12") of expansion or contraction joints with the hot rubber as shown on the drawings and specified.

"(12) One (1) square foot of sodding and seeding consists of furnishing and placing one hundred and forty-four square inches (144 sq in.) of sod adjacent to the curbs and seeding the same all as shown and specified."

H. COMMENT

1. While it is possible to negotiate a fixed-price contract, usually the owner receives quotations from several bidders, selects one, and awards a contract. While it would be possible to take bids on cost-plus contracts, the contract is usually awarded by negotiations with a single contractor selected by the architect-engineer after consulting with the owner.

2. On fixed-price and unit price contracts, the architect-engineer has little difficulty maintaining control during construction, but the cost-plus-type contract demands a very close relationship between the owner, the contractor, and the architect-engineer. The architect-engineer is supervising the spending of the owner's money and frequent visits with the owner are required. At the start of the project, the architect-engineer must have a clear understanding of the extent of

authority given. The architect-engineer must insist that all correspondence from the contractor to the owner come through him. If he permits the contractor to work directly with the owner, he is headed for trouble. Unfortunately, the architect-engineer cannot control the actions of a despotic owner. When an owner issues orders directly to the contractor, the contractor is encouraged to take any problems directly to the owner, and the architect-engineer is in an untenable position.

13.03 ARCHITECT-ENGINEER CONTRACTS

A. GENERAL

While the writing of specifications deals with contracts between the owner and the contractor, the architect-engineer is also concerned with the contract he has with the owner. Normally this contract is a variation of the "cost plus a percentage with a guaranteed maximum," although fixed-fee and "cost plus a percentage" contracts are not uncommon.

B. VARIATION

In the variation of cost plus a percentage with a guaranteed maximum, the architect agrees to produce contract documents and supervise the construction for a percentage of the estimated cost of the structure and agrees that the cost of the project will not exceed a specific amount. This, of course, limits the architect-engineer's fee.

C. FIXED FEE

1. The owner who decides to award the contract on a fixed-fee basis prepares a "Statement of Work." After examination of this document, the architect makes an offer. If rejected, the owner may make a counteroffer to the architect-engineer, who may accept, reject, or make another counteroffer. This process of offer and counteroffer is known as "negotiation."

2. It is not ethical for an architect-engineer to bid on a project. Architects and engineers provide services and it is always possible to provide less service for less money. Architects or engineers are required to design the best product of which they are capable for a cost within the owner's stated budget. To do this, the architect must expend considerable professional judgment. For the owner to select this service on price alone would not be in his best interest or in the best interest of the profession. It would be similar to a person taking bids from various physicians for an operation.

D. COST PLUS A PERCENTAGE

Where it is difficult for an architect-engineer to establish the amount of work required by the owner, a "cost plus" contract may be desirable. In this type of contract, the owner usually pays the architect-engineer twice the amount of the payroll plus all blueprinting and other direct costs.

13.04 SUBCONTRACTORS

A. When the owner awards a contract to a contractor, it starts a whole series of other contracts; the contractor awards a contract to each of his various subcontractors, who in turn award contracts to each of their suppliers, each of whom awards contracts to their material suppliers. The architect-engineer is not usually involved with these contracts except for "cost plus" work. In this type of work, the clerk of the works should follow up the subcontracted work to protect the owner.

B. While the contractor may have a "cost plus" contract with the owner, it is not necessary for the contractor to have "cost plus" contracts with his subcontractors. In fact, the contractor's contract with the owner may require the contractor to receive fixed-price bids from three (3) or more subcontractors for each trade. The clerk of the works is involved in the selection of subcontractors when several alternate subcontractors for each trade are submitted by the contractor.

13.05 PARTIAL CONTRACTS

A. DEFINITION

1. The issuance of single contracts as against that of partial contracts has been debated in the trade press, on the convention floor, and before legislative assemblies. The mechanical and electrical contractors have campaigned for partial contracts. The success of their program is shown in the fact that over half a dozen states in the union have laws requiring partial contracts on all state-financed construction.

2. Basically, there are two (2) systems of competitive bidding: the single or overall general contract method and the partial contracts method.

3. A partial contract is where more than one contractor is employed to do work on a single project. Each contractor is a prime contractor and has a contract with the owner to do specific work on the project. An example is where the owner employs one contractor to place the foundations and another to build the superstructure.

4. When bids are to be received on partial contracts, the architect-engineer prepares separate contract documents for each phase of the project and issues to each group of bidders only the specific documents they wish to bid upon. The bids on each phase may or may not be due at the same time. There is no reason why the same type of contract should be used for the various phases of the work. It is necessary to coordinate the scope of each proposal to make sure that there are no conflicts.

B. ADVANTAGES

1. General

Under specific conditions, however, it may be advantageous to the owner to have partial contracts with several contractors rather than a single contract with one general contractor. A few reasons follow:

2. To Raise Money

An owner may not be able to finance an entire project. Money is sometimes difficult to obtain when a project is in the planning stage; it is easier to borrow when construction is under way. In such a case it might be advantageous to the owner to award one contract for the foundations and, after obtaining additional funds, to award another contract for the superstructure.

3. To Save Time

a. Completing a project by a certain time may be of primary importance. When the foundation work is awarded ahead of time, the physical work in the field can proceed while the architect or engineer is completing the remainder of the drawings.

b. Shop drawings for structural steel are a time-consuming process. The length of each beam and column must be determined accurately. Hack saws are not normally one of the steel erector's tools. In addition, every rivet hole must be located in every beam, girt, purlin, truss, and column. The number of man-hours consumed in making structural steel shop drawings is often greater than the time it takes to design the steel framework. To save time, it is sometimes desirable to award the contract for the structural steel ahead of the contract for the other building work.

4. To Increase Competition

A substantial number of the better mechanical and electrical contractors categorically refuse to bid through any general contractor, because they fear that their bids will not be handled ethically or in the same degree of fairness as they would be by an owner. To understand this fear, the student should realize that while some general contractors are conscientious and award subcontracts to the lowest sub-bidder in each category, the vast majority of general contractors have no thought of operating in such a manner. Instead, when they are awarded a contract, they start shopping the bids that have already been received from subcontractors. When work is not plentiful, this shopping results in an auction in reverse, and the point is reached where the subcontractor in order to cut the price must also reduce the quality of performance. As a result, the marginal operator who specializes in cutting corners gets the work. This results in many qualified mechanical and electrical contractors refusing to invest the money necessary to make an estimate where the chances of receiving a profitable contract are small.

5. To Obtain Better Contractors

As many of the better-equipped mechanical and electrical contractors will not bid upon projects through general contractors, except when they are starving for work, the divided contract enables the owner to make a selection from more and better contractors.

6. To Give the Owner More Control

In some building projects the value of mechanical and electrical work is greater than the value of the building work, for example, in a power plant, or in a chemical manufacturing plant. In such cases, it would be undesirable for a general contractor to award the largest part of a contract to an unqualified subcontractor simply because he submitted a low price. When proposals come directly from the contractors who will do the work, the owner can better evaluate the bids and more intelligently select the contractors.

7. To Reduce the Price

Many owners believe they can save money by issuing partial contracts to several contractors rather than by issuing a single contract to a general contractor. This supposedly has been proven many times by taking bids both ways on the same project at the same time. The lower initial price, which is obtained by the elimination of the general contractor's markup on the price of the subcontractors' work, appeals to many owners. However, an owner who has undergone the resulting agonies of long delays, bickering, and claims and counterclaims, can understand that the theoretically lower initial bid price is not always to an owner's advantage.

C. DANGERS

1. Administration

As previously explained, partial bids require separate contract documents for each contract awarded. This means extra work for the architect or engineer, who must print additional drawings and write completely different specifications for each contract. It also means separate bid forms and contracts. In addition, the specification writer must carefully coordinate the work in each contract. Where several specifications are involved, this can result in considerable work, and failure in any part can result in serious difficulties. The specification writer must make sure that all work is covered somewhere and that the same work does not appear in two contracts. It isn't enough to specify that each contractor's work must stop at some point. Some contractor should be responsible for the connection between the individual contractors' assignments.

2. Lack of Control

a. When one contractor's work can be completed before the second contractor starts work, there is no lack of control and no reason why partial contracts cannot be awarded. However, when two (2) or more contractors are working on a single project at the same time, the results are chaotic if there is no overall supervisor. There is usually no cooperation between the different contractors. Each contractor works when ready on the part of the project that is most convenient. Inadequate direction leads to friction between the contractors, resulting in delays and extras. For example, the mason unloads and stacks his brick in the most convenient spot because there is no warning that it is in the way of the electrical contractor. Once the trucks are gone, the mason will not assume the cost of moving the brick to a more convenient location; nor would the electrical contractor, who would wait until the walls were constructed, thus using the brick. The holdup of the electrical work would hold up contractors who needed electricity to run their power tools.

b. In a single contract, the general contractor has an effective control over the subcontractors. The general contractor can, and does, coerce the subs into cooperation. At the start of the job, this contractor will sit down with all the subcontractors and work out a construction schedule to be followed. Refusal to follow the schedule can result in withholding payment, fixing back charges, or making unfavorable reports to surety companies which have bonded the subcontractors. It is the abuse of this power that subcontractors often object to; but from the owner's point of view, a single contract is a better way to control a project.

3. Time

It is almost impossible to enforce a time schedule with several partial contracts. This is due to the fact that portions of the building constructed by one trade depend for their support, tie-in, and performance upon the portions constructed by other trades. When such subcontractors are supervised by separate contractors, the responsibility for any delay can usually be shifted from one contractor to another. A general contractor is financially interested in an efficient job. The faster he can complete a job, the lower the cost of supervision and overhead. The power to coordinate the work of subcontractors and prevent delays lies with the general contractor.

4. Field Problems

a. With a single contract there are clear lines of responsibility; this is the key to administrative efficiency in any business undertaking. Conditions that diffuse areas of responsibility weaken the efficiency of job planning and thereby cause problems of construction that could have been anticipated beforehand. Coordination of efforts of the various trades and skills involved on any construction job is obviously crucial to completing the project on schedule.

b. If three (3) or more contractors are working on a project with no overall supervision, chaos usually develops, and even though trying to keep from becoming involved, the architect-engineer will be in trouble. Claims and counterclaims, requests for extras, and complaints from one contractor about another contractor will plague the architect or engineer from the field, while demands that the project be speeded up and the site be cleaned up will come from the owner.

c. Whether liking it or not, the architect-engineer may be forced to take control in such situations. If this happens, the actual work often falls upon the clerk of the works. The duty of the clerk of the works is to control the quality of the installation. This is a full-time job. If he is required to divide his time with other duties, the job will suffer. Very often the clerk of the works is not equipped by training or experience to direct field operations. In any event, he can only insist upon the enforcement of the specifications, and unless the specifications give that authority, the clerk of the works cannot force the various contractors to meet schedules. Without this authority, he cannot coordinate the work in the sense of organizing the job activities and planning ahead as could a general contractor.

d. An illustration of one of the many field problems that could be encountered might be the clean-up. Each contractor is required in the specifications to clean up all debris caused by his operation. Where a general contractor is employed on a large project, sometimes a laborer is hired who is responsible for keeping the job site clean, for making the subcontractors conform, and for cleaning up any debris left by them. Subcontractors who do not clean up are often backcharged. Sometimes subcontractors find it cheaper to permit the general contractor to clean up their debris with common labor rather than use paid skilled labor. In return, they perform some extra service for the contractor. The clerk of the works has no such bargaining power. With three (3) or more contractors, each employing numerous subcontractors, control is difficult. No contractor will remove another contractor's debris. The effort to prove who left various lunch papers around or who is responsible for sweeping a floor covered with mud, loose concrete, mortar, brick, boards, pipe, tar, and paper results in absurdities.

D. THE ARCHITECT-ENGINEER AS GENERAL SUPERINTENDENT

1. Pay

There are ways to avoid the pitfalls of partial contracts. One of these is to have the architect-engineer assume the duties of a general superintendent. If this is the intent, it should be known to the architect-engineer at the start of the project. The owners should be told that the difference in cost between a fixed-price and partial contract is not all profit. An architect-engineer who is to assume the duties of a general superintendent should be paid for it, and an additional four percent (4%) added to the fee is not unreasonable.

2. Duties

When the partial contracts are awarded to the various contractors, the architect-engineer should place a qualified person in the field as project director to be in charge of production. He is used in addition to the clerk of the works, who is responsible for quality. The project director should call a meeting of the various contractors and subcontractors, establish schedules, and insist that these schedules be met. To do this, the project director must have authority and the specifications must be so written to give the position this authority, as well as the right to approve contractors' payments. If this is done, most of the pitfalls of partial contracts can be avoided.

3. Risk

Architects or engineers who take upon themselves the duties of general contractors do so at considerable risk to their reputation and professional status. In assuming the responsibility for supervising the work, one is also liable for the results. The directing of men and machinery at a job site is considerably different from running an office, and a person with considerable experience in field construction work is required. The project director must also be backed up by a competent organization to be effective.

E. ASSIGNMENT

1. Definition

An "assignment" is a legal process where the owner of a right may transfer or assign that right to another. The owner of the right is called the "assignor" and the person to whom the right is assigned is called the "assignee." For example, A, the obligor, a person who is bound to another, owes B some money. B, the assignor, may assign the right to collect that money to C, the assignee. C then has the right to collect the money owed to B from A, and B gives up the right to collect from A.

2. Obligor's Rights

a. If the assignor wishes to assign the obligee's rights to an assignee, the assignor may or may not require the obligor's consent. Usually the assignor can make an assignment with the obligor's approval.

b. In general, where the obligor is not hurt by the assignment, the assignor may assign the obligee's rights to the assignee without the consent of the obligor; however, if the obligor could be hurt by an assignment, his approval would be necessary. For example, if A holds B's note for a specific sum of money due at a specific time, B cannot be hurt if the note is sold to C. B's duty is to pay. To whom B pays the money is irrelevant. B cannot be hurt while living up to the obligor's part of the contract. However, B cannot substitute D as debtor without A's consent. D may have poor credit or may live in another state and be difficult to collect from. For this reason, the law protects A from having the obligee's risk increased without A's consent. Likewise, a skilled worker may not assign his contract obligation to another who might have lesser skill without all the other involved parties' consent.

c. The subject of assignment is very broad, and a law student must spend considerable time studying the subject. The foregoing is a brief generalization to cover a specific case. Further information is available in almost any textbook on contracts.

3. Assigning Subcontractors

a. One of the methods used in avoiding the pitfalls of partial contracts is to assign each partial contract to a general contractor.

b. To do this the architect-engineer should include in each of the partial proposals the right of the owner, at his option, to assign the contract to a general contractor. When the contract is assigned, the contractors become subcontractors responsible to one (1) general contractor. The owner pays only the general contractor, and he, in turn, pays the subcontractors.

c. The general contractor, of course, has to be paid for his service. The general contractor does not know the amount of the contract or details and is usually asked to quote on a percentage basis. That is, A will agree to assume the contract of B and charge the owner a specific percentage of B's contract price—usually between one-half of one percent and five percent ($1/2\%$ and 5%)—for supervising the contract. When bids are taken, such a provision is usually provided in the Proposal Form.

4. Advantages of Assignment

Having a general contractor on the project overcomes most of the disadvantages of partial contracts. While the various contractors may not know, at the time of submitting their proposal, who the general contractor will be, most contractors welcome this procedure. While they run the risk of working for an undesirable general contractor, the advantages of having one are many. They know the contractor cannot shop their bid, and they know that a general contractor will organize a job so that friction with other contractors will be at a minimum.

FOURTEEN
Time and Money

14.01 LABOR EFFICIENCY

A. ECONOMIC CREWS

One of the problems of a subcontractor is to determine the most efficient number of workers to work at the job site. For example, a roofing contractor requires a kettleman to work on the ground and operate the tar kettle and pitch pump, a helper to work on the roof and keep the roofers supplied, a worker to mop the tar on the roof, and a worker to roll the felt into the hot tar. Four (4) workers would normally be the crew for a small job. However, on a larger project the contractor could have two (2) workers mopping and two (2) workers rolling felt, theoretically doubling production by using two (2) more workers. Under some conditions, eight (8) workers could produce three (3) times as much work as four (4) workers. Obviously, efficiency does not continue to increase by adding workers. Each worker must be needed. There is an economical number of workers that can be used, and this number will vary from job to job and from contractor to contractor.

B. MAN-HOURS

As the cost of materials is almost the same to the competing subcontractors and the union governs the cost of labor, the contractor's best chance to save money is to reduce the number of man-hours required to complete a project. If it takes a four (4) man crew forty (40) hours to complete a project, the job would take one hundred and sixty (160) man-hours. This does not mean that one (1) worker could complete the job in one hundred and sixty (160) hours or that one hundred and sixty (160) workers could complete the job in one (1) hour.

C. MINIMUM TIME

Obviously, there is a minimum time required to complete a project. This minimum time is defined as the time required to complete a job where there is no limit to cost, material, or manpower.

D. ECONOMIC TIME

The economic time is the time it would take to complete a job in the least number of man-hours, which means the least cost. If the contractor is delayed or required to slow down so that the time on the job becomes greater than the economic time, the costs are increased. Likewise, if the contractor is required to speed up, the costs are increased.

14.02 THE OWNER AND TIME

The time it takes to construct a project also affects the owner. If he is constructing rental space, a month's delay means a month's lost rent and possible other penalties. If the owner is constructing manufacturing space, a delay could mean the loss of a contract. Time is important to the owner. The degree of importance only he can decide.

14.03 THE RELATIONSHIP

A. THE OWNER'S CONTROL

There is a definite relationship between time and money that affects both the owner and the contractor. The architect-engineer should advise his client as to the cost and time required to construct a project. The owner is in control and he determines how the bids are taken.

B. WHERE COST GOVERNS

1. Even if the cost-time relationship is not important to the owner, scheduling the use of the facility usually is. It would be poor business to disregard time, and every contract should state a time of completion. Where cost governs, the economic time should be written into the contract.

2. The architect-engineer has no way of determining the economic time; it is different for each contractor. Therefore, when taking bids, the best procedure is to permit the contractor to establish the time when submitting the bid. The proposal form would then be written to allow space for the contractor to write the number of days required to complete the work.

C. WHERE TIME GOVERNS

1. General

There are occasions when time is more important than money. Failure to complete the project on time could render the project useless. In such cases when a lump-sum contract is desired, time should be stated in the special conditions. This time should be somewhere between the minimum time and the economic time.

2. Dates

When the owner requires a project to be completed by a specific time, that date can be placed in the contract as a requirement. However, a contractor must know the number of days permitted to complete the work in order to make an intelligent estimate. So if a completion date is specified, an award date must also be specified.

3. Days

a. The difficulty in getting both parties to reach an agreement more than a month in advance of a date has led architects and engineers to set a specific number of days after the contract is signed as the contract completion date. It has the same effect and saves changing the date in the event signing of the contract is delayed.

b. If the term "days" is used, it should be defined. There is considerable difference between a working day and a calendar day. "Calendar days" are understood to mean consecutive twenty-four (24)-hour periods, which includes Saturday and Sunday.

c. A "working day" is more difficult to define. Unless the exact meaning is written in the contract, numerous misunderstandings will develop. Most people would agree that Saturdays, Sundays, holidays, and days when workers could not work are not working days. However, is a rainy day a working day? If some workers work under cover on a cold day, does this count against a contractor's time? If it starts raining at noon, is this half a working day?

d. The difficulty in defining a working day has caused the author to avoid the term. By taking the number of working days required to complete a project and adding a percentage to cover week-ends, holidays, and bad weather, a satisfactory number of calendar days can be determined. Most owners will agree to this method when it is explained.

14.04   SPECIFYING TIME IN A FIXED-PRICE CONTRACT

A. REASONABLE TIME

Time has always been a consideration in building construction, and today it is more so than ever. Contracts requiring buildings to be finished within a time limit are about as old as contracts themselves. However, court decisions going back hundreds of years have maintained that work completed within a reasonable time after the date stated in the contract is considered to be in substantial performance of the contract. At that time, two or three years could have been considered a reasonable time. Today the same English law applies.

B. THE ESSENCE OF THE CONTRACT

If an owner wishes to have the exact dates on the contract respected, the contract must specifically state that "time is the essence of the contract" or words to that effect. This wording warns the contractor that time is an important part of the contract. If these words are missing, most courts would presume that time is a minor consideration, and any time limitations would be difficult to enforce.

C. PENALTIES

Another legal point that must be remembered is that courts are extremely reluctant to assess penalties for contracts that have not been completely fulfilled, unless some party suffers a loss. Normally, the court would not uphold a contract requiring a penalty to be paid for nonfulfillment if the other party suffered no loss.

D. BONUS AND PENALTY CLAUSES

1. If an owner needs a building fast, the best method is to include a "bonus and penalty clause" in the contract.

2. The bonus and penalty clause provides that if the contract is completed before a specific date, the contractor will be paid a bonus of \$_____ per day for each day the job was completed in advance of the contract.

3. Likewise, if the contract is not completed until after the due date, the contractor must pay the owner the same amount for each additional day required.

4. Bonus and penalty contracts are highly respected by the courts and are enforceable.

5. To be enforceable, bonus and penalties must be for the same amount. It is doubtful if any court would recognize a small bonus and a large penalty.

E. DAMAGES

1. As stated before, the courts will not recognize a penalty for not completing a contract on time unless the bonus is also included. However, the owner who suffers loss can collect damages, as in the case of an apartment building not being finished on time. If the apartments were rented and the owner had proved an actual loss, the owner could recover.

2. If the specifications state that "time is the essence of the contract" and that a retail store must be completed ninety (90) days before

Christmas of a specific year, the owner might have a difficult time collecting if the contractor was late. It would be difficult, if not impossible, for the retailer to prove a specific loss in sales and profit. Any figures would have to be an estimate of expected sales. This estimate normally would not be considered as proof.

F. LIQUIDATED DAMAGES

1. To prevent the necessity of proving a loss, an assumed loss for each day that an owner is kept from using his building can be established. "Liquidated damages" is an amount set up in advance as an assumed amount that the owner would lose in the event that the contract is not completed on time. This amount could be five hundred dollars ($500) or one hundred dollars ($100) a day. It cannot be in excess of the actual loss. It is up to the contractor to prove that these liquidated damages are excessive. This places the burden of proof on the contractor.

2. In writing a liquidated-damage clause in the specification, it must be made clear that the liquidated damages are not a penalty. A penalty will not be upheld by the court.

G. COVERAGE

The time clause is usually placed in the Special Conditions. Often it is repeated in the contract between the owner and the contractor.

H. SUGGESTED CLAUSE

1. Specifications

a. There are many ways of writing a time clause in the specifications. The following is but one.

"b. Time is the essence of the contract. The contractor shall complete all work specified within three hundred (300) consecutive calendar days after he has been notified to proceed.

"c. The work shall proceed uninterruptedly, diligently, and at such a rate of progress as ensures completion within the time specified."

2. Contract

In the contract, owners are often advised to include a statement that the owner and contractor agree that the time specified is reasonable, taking into consideration the average climatic conditions and all other conditions prevailing at the job site.

14.05 ENFORCEMENT

A. DELAYS

If a contractor fails to complete the project in the time specified, the contract has been breached. The student might assume from the way the specifications are written that the contractor is automatically subject to serious consequences. The specifications are usually quite complete as to the owner's rights and the contractor's duties but say little about the contractor's rights. This does not mean that he has no rights, and he may have had a good reason for not completing the work on time. The contractor does not insure the owner against a loss due to a late completion.

B. REASONS FOR DELAYS

1. Owner's Delays

While it is not usually stated, it is implied in any contract that one (1) party will not act to prevent the other party from completing the other's part of the contract. It is only reasonable that if an owner or architect-engineer delays the contractor by stop-orders, delays in approving shop drawings or samples, or changes or corrections in the drawings, the contractor is not at fault and the time completion should be extended by the amount of time occasioned by such delays.

2. Acts of God

Should completion be delayed by flood, earthquake, or other "acts of God," the contractor would be entitled to an extension of time and probably additional money. This does not mean that a single early snowstorm or an extra day of rain over the average yearly rainfall would necessarily be reason for an extension of time. The contractor is expected to know the normal weather conditions and make reasonable allowances for unfavorable weather. If, however, the number of rainy days were double the expected days, the contractor would be justified in asking for an extension.

3. Strikes

If a steel strike occurred and the industrial plants of the country were closed because of lack of steel, it would be unreasonable to expect a contractor to complete a contract requiring steel. A strike is usually justifiable cause for delay. However, if the owner could prove that the contractor caused a strike on his own project for the purpose of delaying the job, chances are that an extension of time would be denied by the court.

C. DUTIES OF THE ARCHITECT-ENGINEER

When a bonus and penalty clause appears in a contract, or when time is an important element, the administration of this usually becomes a part of the architect-engineer's work. He should be fair to both the owner and the contractor. This is sometimes difficult because conditions arise that are not covered by the contract, and each party feels in the

14.05 C. (Cont.)

right. The architect-engineer should insist that any extension of time be requested by the contractor at the time the delay occurs, not at the end of the project. The architect-engineer should make a practice of consulting with the owner and approving or disapproving such extension. In this way, the owner is kept informed as to the progress of the project. If the specifications are complete and well-written so that both parties understand what is expected, misunderstandings can be held to a minimum.

14.06 PRACTICAL CONSIDERATIONS

A. ENFORCEMENT

1. In actual practice, the enforcement of time clauses is difficult. A construction project that proceeds without changes is the exception rather than the rule. When change orders are issued, the contractor is usually entitled to additional time. The additional time and the price are subjects of the negotiation, but the contractor is in control. The owner has the choice of accepting the contractor's price and additional time or rejecting the entire bulletin.

2. Justifiable delays occur, and others of a more dubious nature will be construed as justifiable by a shrewd contractor who anticipates failure to complete on time. The architect-engineer must be able to distinguish between the real and the pretended delays.

B. OWNER INVOLVEMENT

One might assume that the courts are loaded with cases where the contractor failed to complete on time. Actually such suits are infrequent. Usually the work is nearly complete and the owner is more concerned with completing the building than with taking legal recourse. Should the owner file a breach of contract suit, the work would probably be halted while legal counsel and clarification were obtained. If the contractor has the proper attitude and a good financial condition, the owner's best course may be to press for completion, using court action as a threat. If the contractor is trying very hard, forcing him to defend a lawsuit will only cause further delay.

C. THE BONUS AND PENALTY CLAUSES

The bonus and penalty clauses are seldom used because owners do not like to bind themselves in a contract where the cost is not known. However, when the urgency is great enough to warrant the cost, a substantial bonus is more likely to encourage speedy completion than any other method.

FIFTEEN

Changes

15.01 METHOD

A. Our definition of a "change" is a revision in drawings or specifications after they have been issued to the bidders for quotations. Changes made within the architect or engineer's office are a normal part of the designing process and are not considered changes within this definition.

B. Changes are made in two ways: by addendum and by change order. The two (2) documents can be similar in appearance and in method of writing; however, the contractual relationship differs greatly. An addendum is issued during the bidding period and is, therefore, a change in the bidding documents; a change order is issued after the contract has been awarded and is a change in an existing contract. Do not confuse them.

C. Drawings, specifications, and other documents may be changed by addenda or change order. One addendum or change order can contain changes in both drawings and specifications.

15.02 ADDENDA

A. REASONS FOR CHANGES

1. Errors

There are many reasons for addenda. The most common is the need to correct simple errors in the bidding documents. To make an intelligent estimate, subcontractors are required to carefully study the plans and specifications; errors and omissions which were overlooked by the draftsman become apparent. In fact, one of the best ways for architects or engineers to discover errors and omissions in their drawings is for them to make a complete take-off of quantities. A subcontractor is often reluctant to call the architect or engineer regarding errors discovered, unless it affects the subcontractor's price and designers should not depend upon them to correct their work.

2. Contractor Requests

a. A bidder may discover that some detail in the specifications has excluded his product, that the quality specified is not in keeping with the architectural character of the project, or that the product or method specified is obsolete. In such cases, the bidder may call the architect or engineer.

b. After talking to sales representatives who complain that their products have been omitted from the specifications and those who complain that the specifications are so indefinite that their competitors with less expensive products can submit prices, the specification writer may decide to open up or tighten up the specifications. This would be done by addendum.

3. Owner's Request

For administration efficiency, a large corporation usually limits the number of people allowed to deal with the architect or engineer. When the bidding documents are issued, the owner often submits copies to his employees. These employees, who will actually use the product, may have worthwhile suggestions. If approved, these suggestions are given to the architect or engineer by management and are put into an addendum.

4. Architect-Engineer Changes

There are some architect-engineering firms that, as a matter of policy, check their drawings and specifications during the bidding period and issue an addendum to correct errors that they discover. On rush projects this may be excusable, but issuing incorrect drawings does not improve one's reputation.

B. LATE ADDENDA

1. Definition

A "late addendum" is an addendum issued after bids have been received but before the figures are published.

2. Reasons for Late Addenda

a. Nothing annoys a specification writer more than to have a contractor request a change when there is insufficient time, before bids are due, to issue an addendum. The author has had three (3) contractors call thirty (30) days after they had received the bidding documents and within two (2) hours of the time when bids are due, all requesting the same change. It was the only error discovered in the thirty (30)-day bidding period and was of such a nature that an addendum had to be issued revising the drawings and changing the date that bids would be received.

b. The contractors are not solely responsible for late requests for changes. These often come from subcontractors who give them the information when they turn in their bids. In this case, an equipment supplier discovered that 110-volt wiring was supplied for a 220-volt motor. The supplier gave this information to each general contractor when telephoning the bid, and they all called the architect-engineer.

c. Subcontractors share the blame. Many estimators for subcontractors make a practice of scheduling their work so they do not see the documents until the day before the bids are due. The author has talked to many. They argue that if they figured from drawings as originally issued, they would have to refigure when addenda were issued. It's easier to figure once. What is the answer?

3. Method

On public projects the bids are read aloud. Making changes with an addendum after bids are submitted is not legal. On private work, however, the bids are not published and it is possible to issue a late addendum. Usually the late addendum is given only to the three (3) lowest bidders and they are requested to submit new bids incorporating the late addendum.

C. METHOD OF WRITING

1. Drawing Changes

a. When an addendum involves a change in the drawings, new drawings are usually issued. The drawings should be marked "revised" and dated to avoid confusion with drawings already issued. In addition, the changes should be marked so that they can be easily found.

b. The drawings should accompany the addendum, a sample of which can be found in the Appendix to this book. The addendum should list the new drawings and the drawings which are obsolete.

c. It is not necessary to issue new drawings for a minor change. It is sufficient to describe the change. For example, it would be sufficient to say, "The overall dimension shown on Section B-B on sheet 3 of 6 is changed from 53' 5$^1/_2$" to 35' 3$^1/_2$"."

d. It is not necessary to describe the changes made on drawings when revised drawings are issued. The new drawings show the new requirements and should show the location of the changes. However, some offices require that the changes on each sheet be listed in the addendum. This is helpful to the estimator.

2. Specification Changes

a. *New-sheet addenda*

(1) When changes are required in specifications, new pages may be issued in the same manner as the drawings. The new sheets should be marked "revised" and the addendum should instruct the bidders to remove the obsolete sheets from the book of specifications and to replace them with the revised sheets.

(2) Difficulty is sometimes encountered when added wording or added paragraphs cannot be placed on the same number of pages as the original being replaced. Should the new pages be near the front of the section, it might be necessary to issue additional pages where no changes are required to keep the page numbering in proper sequence. When too many pages are involved, the change in page numbers could be indicated in the body of the addendum.

b. *Descriptive addenda*

(1) Because of the difficulty and cost, changes are often made by placing the change in the body of the addendum. For example, the following could be placed in the addendum.

"(2) Refer to subparagraph 7.21 C. 12. b. The word 'necessary' is replaced by the word 'unnecessary'

"(3) Refer to subparagraph 8.34 B. 6. f. This subparagraph is deleted and the following is substituted in lieu thereof:

"(4) 'All wood framing shall be constructed with number two (#2) shortleaf yellow pine.' "

c. *Question-and-answer addenda*

(1) General

While the above types of addenda are the most common, the question-and-answer type is also used. It consists of questions, asked by contractors during the bidding period, and answers. This type of addendum encourages contractors to ask questions and distributes the answers to all concerned. An example follows:

(2) Example

(a) Query 1

"1. Question: The overall dimension on the plan shown on sheet A 3 is not the sum of the detail dimensions shown on the same plan. Why?

"2. Answer: The 8' 11" dimension shown for the width of room 107 is incorrect. The correct dimension is 11' 8"."

(b) Query 2

"1. Question: Subparagraph 33 C. 1. a. states 'All pumps

shall be model A 2 as manufactured by the Leakey Pump
Company of 22 Lulu, Honolulu, or an approved equal.'
Is the Nogoodnic Pump model U. R. 1. 2. made in Slow-
poke, Russia, an approved equal?
"2. Answer: No."

3. Tense

Addenda are written in the present tense when directing changes.
However, when we are directing the contractor on how to proceed,
the future tense is used. For example, we would say, "Drawing C-13
is deleted from the contract. Drawing C-13 revised January 20, 1975,
and new drawing S-10 dated January 20, 1975, *are* issued with this
addendum. The bidders *shall* destroy drawing C-13 and add revised
drawings C-13 and S-10 to the bidding documents."

15.03 CHANGE ORDERS

A. DEFINITION

1. A "change order" is a change in an existing contract. The authority
of the owner to make such changes would be a part of the General
Conditions.

2. The change order is written after a contract is awarded and usually
after construction has started. Therefore, it is a change in the signed
agreement between the owner and contractor and should not be regarded lightly.

B. REASONS

The reasons for writing change orders are similar to the reasons for
writing addenda: to correct the contract documents. Change orders
occur when errors are discovered, when the owner makes changes, or
when field conditions differ from the conditions assumed.

C. METHODS OF ISSUING CHANGE ORDERS

1. Agreement

All parties to a contract must agree to any changes made in the document. The method of securing agreement varies from office to office.
The most common is by use of the bulletin.

2. The Bulletin

a. *Definition*
A "bulletin" is a request for a price. It is not an offer. It is not
a directive to do work. It does not give the contractor authority
to proceed with any change. It is not a change order.

b. *Procedure*
The bulletin is prepared in the office of the architect or engineer.

It is issued to the contractor and the clerk of the works. A contractor who receives a bulletin stops work on the item involved and figures out what the change is going to cost in both time and money. The contractor is free to discuss the extent of the change with the architect or engineer, and then quote a price in time and money to the architect or engineer. This is an offer. It can be accepted or rejected. When the price is submitted, the architect or engineer and the owner will decide if it is advisable to make the change. If the owner decides not to make the change, a letter is written by the architect or engineer to the contractor telling the contractor to proceed as in the original contract and disregard the bulletin.

c. *Issuing the change order*

If the price and time quoted by the contractor for the changes described in the bulletin are accepted by the owner, a change order (sometimes called a "work order") is issued to the contractor. The change order is the acceptance of the offer made by the contractor to the contract; therefore, it should be signed by the owner. The architect or engineer may sign in lieu of the owner if he has written permission to do so. The change order gives the contractor authority to proceed with the changes described in the bulletin. The bulletin, the contractor's quotation, and the change order become a part of the contract documents.

3. Direct Change Order

a. In some architectural or engineering offices, the change order is issued directly to the contractor without issuing a bulletin. If a bulletin is not issued, some method for the payment of the contractor must be established. This is usually done in the quotation.

b. Whereas the change order can simply state that all or part of the changes described in the bulletin are incorporated into the contract, the direct change order must contain a description of the changes, since there is no bulletin.

4. Method of Writing

The drawings and specification sheets issued with an addendum replace previously issued drawings and specifications and the sheets or drawings replaced may be discarded. This is not true of a change order. The contract still involves the original drawings and specifications and they must be retained until the contract is discharged. The change order is an addition to the contract documents. For this reason, new specification sheets are not issued to replace existing sheets. New sheets may be issued with a change order when they are to be added to the existing book, but changes in existing work are made in the same manner as in a descriptive addendum.

D. TIME

1. As we have previously stated, time may be as important as money. Therefore, time should be considered when any change is made. The bulletin should be so written that the contractor will know, when preparing the estimate, the amount of time the contract will be extended or if no additional time will be granted.

2. If no additional time is allowed, the contractor will quote a price high enough to cover additional costs, which include any overtime pay.

3. If additional time is required, the bulletin and change order should state the number of days that the contract will be extended or require the contractor to quote a time as well as a price for the work involved.

4. The specification writer should realize that when a bulletin is written, the contractor is required to stop work on the item involved until a decision is reached. This would justify an extension of time to the contract even though the contractor's price for the work in the bulletin were not accepted.

15.04   FIELD CHANGES

A. DEFINITION

A "field change" is a change proposed by the contractor at the job site and approved by the clerk of the works or proposed by the clerk of the works. Such changes are usually required when the conditions at the job site differ from those shown on the drawings or assumed by the engineers in their design.

B. FIELD ORDER

1. A bulletin and change order are not required where the drawings are found to be incorrect or where the clerk of the works approves the contractor's method, which may differ from that shown on the drawings provided the change is minor and involves no change in cost. On any construction, particularly on alteration work, various problems will arise as the work progresses. For example, a subcontractor may ask permission to substitute staples in place of nails. This request should be noted in the clerk of the works' daily report; but to require a change order for every minor change would be ridiculous and costly.

2. Minor changes that do not involve cost are called "field orders." As the practices of owners and of architect-engineering offices vary, the clerk of the works must know the limits of his authority in approving variations from the contract documents. The clerk of the works should make a record of all such changes. Some offices require that all field

orders be issued to the contractor in writing; others permit verbal instructions on minor items. The clerk of the works should make a written record of all field changes in the daily report.

C. FIELD CHANGE ORDERS

1. A "field change order" (sometimes called a "field work order") is a change order issued in the field or a field order involving a change in price.

2. The method of issuing field change orders varies considerably between various offices and with various owners. Some owners will permit the clerk of the works to approve changes where the estimated cost does not exceed a specific sum of money. Others insist on approving all changes in price. Others provide an owner's representative in the field to approve all changes.

3. There are many times when changes are required and the time involved in writing a bulletin, estimating the cost, and issuing a change order is not justified, for example, when the excavating for a project has been completed, and it is discovered that the earth under a single footing will not support the design load and additional excavating is required. Or let us assume that an existing sewer line is not in the location shown on the drawing and must be relocated. In such cases, changes must be made if the project is to be successfully constructed. Requiring the contractor to stop work while a price is agreed upon might not be in the best interest of the owner.

4. As with a direct change order, a method of payment must be established in the contract. Various methods will be discussed in later chapters.

D. AUTHORITY

The field order and the field work order give the contractor authority to proceed immediately with a change.

15.05 PAPER

The specification writer will find it advantageous to issue addenda, bulletins, change orders, field orders on paper of various colors. In an office with several projects, the colored paper makes the filing much easier and serves to assist the contractors and subcontractors in separating the contract documents.

SIXTEEN

Bonds

16.01 DEFINITION

A. A "bond" is an agreement whereby the party issuing the bond agrees to pay damages to the harmed party if someone fails to perform in accordance with the contract. For example, if A has an agreement with B to perform a service and A fails to perform, the bonding company will pay B for damages or secure someone else to complete the contract. The bonding company will have to pay only the amount A agreed upon with B.

B. There are three types of bonds that are of particular interest to architects and engineers: Bid Bonds, Performance Bonds, and Manufacturer's Bonds.

16.02 BID BONDS

A. A "bid bond" is purchased from a bonding company by the contractor and is submitted with the bid on a project. The bid bond states simply that, if the contractor after submitting a bid on a contract fails to enter into a contract with the owner, the bonding company will pay the owner a specific sum, usually five percent (5%) of the amount of the bid price.

B. In common law, a party may withdraw an offer any time before acceptance. The purpose of the bid bond is to require the successful bidder to proceed with work and not withdraw the bid. Bidding and then withdrawing a bid can cause an owner to lose valuable time. Bid bonds are nearly always required on public work; they are seldom required on private work.

C. In cases where there is an obvious error in bidding, for example, where a contractor is a million dollars ($1,000,000) below ten (10) other bidders on a three-million-dollar ($3,000,000) project, the bidder would probably be allowed to withdraw the bid without losing the bond. However, a bidder is usually required to enter into a contract or lose the bond.

D. Of course, the bonds are returned to all but the bidder who is awarded the work, and the bond of the latter is discharged as soon as the bidder enters into a contract with the owner.

E. The cost of bid bonds is not high. Often the bonding company will furnish the bid bond free if the contractor agrees to purchase the performance bond from them upon becoming the successful contractor. A copy of the AIA form for a bid bond appears in the Appendix.

16.03 PERFORMANCE BONDS

A. A "performance bond" is purchased by the contractor in favor of the owner. If the contractor goes bankrupt, or for some reason fails to complete the work, the bonding company will take over the contract and complete the work at its own expense.

B. The performance bond has real value to an owner and is insurance that the contract will be completed. However, it must be remembered that the bonding company is a financial institution. It is interested only in doing its legal duty, and many owners have suffered costly delays and many troubles by having their work taken over by bonding companies. Most experienced architects and engineers advise that it is better to select a financially responsible contractor than to risk involvement with a bonding company. As laws usually require that contracts for government work be awarded to low bidders, performance bonds are usually required on government construction contracts.

C. The performance bond is of value to subcontractors. On government contracts, the subcontractors cannot sue the government or place liens on government property. If the contractor doesn't pay the subcontractors, they can recover from the bonding company.

16.04 MANUFACTURER'S BONDS

A. DEFINITION

1. The "manufacturer's bond" is a written agreement by a financial institution whereby it agrees to make an adjustment to the owner if a specific product fails to perform in accordance with the manufacturer's specifications.

2. Manufacturer's bonds differ from a warranty, a guarantee, or insurance. A "warranty" is the manufacturer's written assurance that they will make an adjustment if their material or equipment does not conform to the specifications. It is only as good as the manufacturer. A "guarantee" is a written assurance by someone, other than the manufacturer, who will make an adjustment if the material or equipment does not perform as specified. Insurance protects the policyholder against financial loss in the event of an unforeseen occurrence.

B. ROOFING BONDS

1. The roofing bond is probably the oldest and best-known of manufacturer's bonds.

2. The roofing bond was started at a time when the roofing industry was disorganized. The amount of tar, the number of plies of felt, and the method of application required to make a good roof varied from contractor to contractor. There were few, if any, standards. About the turn of the century, the Barrett Company advertised that if Barrett roofing products were used and applied by Barrett-franchised roofing contractors in accordance with Barrett specifications, it would give the owner a bond guaranteeing that the roof would not leak for a period up to twenty (20) years. The program was an immediate success, and other manufacturers adopted the bonding principle, so that today all large roofing manufacturers offer bonds.

3. Today, companies manufacturing roofing materials publish specifications; they also franchise established roofing contractors in various areas to apply roofs in accordance with these specifications. When contractors receive a contract requiring a roofing bond they notify the roofing manufacturer. The manufacturer has representatives in various sections of the country. It is their job to visit the job site when the roof is being applied to ensure that the company's specifications are being followed. The amount of inspection varies considerably with the various companies; some inspect almost every large job and others do almost no inspection.

4. If a roof leak occurs within two (2) years from the time the roof is applied, and the trouble was not the fault of the owner or a failure of the building structure, the roofing manufacturer usually requires that the roofing company that placed the roof make the repairs. If they do not, the roofing company stands a good chance of losing its franchise. After two (2) years, the roofing manufacturer usually will pay some roofing company to make the repairs.

5. The roofing bond is not insurance. It covers only the cost of making repairs on the roof; it does not cover damage to the building or to goods stored in the building. It only protects the owner by assuring that any leak caused by defective material or workmanship occurring within the time of the bond will be replaced at no cost to the owner. This is reasonable. If a concrete roof deck cracks because of contraction, one can hardly expect the roofing to hold the building together.

6. The roofing manufacturer charges the roofing contractor for the bond, and the contractor passes the cost on to the owner. The cost of the bond depends upon the size of the roof and the length of the bond period. Flashings may be included in the bond if so requested.

7. All roofing bonds are not the same. Some manufacturers limit their liability to very small amounts, others accept liability to the amount required for a single normal repair, and others accept liability for the full cost of all repairs. The cost of the bond is the same.

8. If a bond is desired, the specification writer should state the time the bond is to remain in effect, the penal sum of the bond (for a specific amount or full value), and if flashing is to be included in the bond.

C. OTHER MANUFACTURER'S BONDS

Bonds may be obtained on other manufactured products. However, most manufacturers warrant their products at no additional charge in lieu of charging the owner for a bond.

D. VALUE OF MANUFACTURER'S BONDS

1. Manufacturer's bonds are often a sales gimmick, and the architect or engineer should know the cost of the bond and exactly what it covers. A roofing bond costing four dollars and a half a square ($4.50/sq) is a high price to pay if the penal sum is limited to twenty dollars a square ($20/sq). On a small roof, this type of bond has little value. For example, the value of a bond for a building twenty feet by forty feet (20' 0" × 40' 0") would be one hundred and sixty dollars ($160).

2. "It's bonded by the largest bank in the country" makes a good sales pitch. What the bond covers is more important. The specification writer should investigate the terms of any bond.

SEVENTEEN

The Invoicing Procedure

17.01 DEFINITION

"Invoicing" is a procedure by which the contractor submits a summation of costs for work performed over a specific period of time with a request for a partial or full payment.

17.02 DESCRIPTION

A. In small work the contractor completes the contract, and when the work is accepted, payment is made.

B. On work involving millions of dollars and involving a year or more in time, requiring the contractor to wait for the owner's acceptance before being paid is not reasonable. Few contractors could finance such a project. Others would be required to borrow money, and the interest on such money would have to be a part of the cost to the owner. As a result, contractors are paid as they proceed with the work. This allows them to discount their bills and save money which is reflected in their bids. The procedure is about the same throughout the country. On or about the tenth day of each month, the contractor submits a bill to the owner for work during the preceding month. The contractor usually requires all the subcontractors to submit statements by the fifth of the month to cover their work. Material suppliers usually submit bills by the first of the month or when the material is delivered. Most dealers offer a substantial discount if their bills are paid within ten (10) days, and many subcontractors discount their bills with their own money before they are paid by the contractor.

C. Contractors add up the subcontractors' invoices, their own material costs, their own labor costs, and their equipment rentals. To this, they add a percentage to cover their overhead and profit.

17.02 (Cont.)

D. The owner usually pays only ninety percent (90%) of the value of the finished work. An owner who paid the contractor for all the work done might find, when the job is completed, that some of the work is unsatisfactory or incomplete. By withholding a sizable sum of money, the owner can be sure that no work will be left incomplete. If the contractor refused to complete the work in a satisfactory manner, the ower could hire someone else and subtract the cost from the sum owed the contractor.

E. In addition to the above, the owner pays eighty-percent (80%) of the cost of all materials purchased and suitably stored on the project. For example, on a bridge project, if all the structural steel were delivered to the job site, stored, and sorted ready for erection at the end of the month, the contractor would be entitled to eighty percent (80%) of the price he paid for the structural steel. Of course, the contractor would not be paid for the erection. The same would apply to brick, stone, or other material stored at the job site.

F. It is up to the architect or engineer to check the amount of work that the contractor claims to have done. In other words, it is the engineer's job to visit the job site and estimate the work done. The contractor is in a poor bargaining position. It is up to the engineer to be fair to both the owner and the contractor.

G. In submitting a request for payment, the contractor lists the various trades and an index of the erection. One type of form follows below.

	Percent of Job	Price	Percent of Trades Completed To Date	Percent of Jobs Completed To Date	Payment Due
Excavating	5	$ 5,000	95	4.75	$ 4,750
Concrete	44	44,000	80	35.2	35,200
Drain Tile	.5	500	100	.5	500
Waterproofing	2	2,000	100	2.0	2,000
Structural Steel	35	35,000	10	3.5	3,500
Miscellaneous Iron	3.5	3,500	2	.07	70
Masonry	7	7,000	0	0	0
Painting	3	3,000	5	.15	150
TOTAL	100	$100,000		46.17	$46,170
					90%

	$41,553.00
Less Previous Payments	14,846.00
Amount Due on Completed Work	$26,707.00
7 M Bricks at Site @ 92 = $644 × 80%	515.20
Amount Due for Month	$27,222.20

H. The general contractor usually will not pay the subcontractor until he is paid by the owner. On most projects, the contractor will hold back ten percent (10%) from the subcontractors. No general contractor will pay the subcontractors more than is collected for the contractor's part of the work. The waterproofing subcontractor may have to wait several months for payment. The painting subcontractor is paid shortly after finishing the paint work. It is possible for subcontractors working on the earlier part of the work to have to wait as much as two or three (2 or 3) years for their final ten percent (10%). This often creates a hardship for the subcontractor.

I. When a job is complete and after the invoices are submitted, the final payment is made by the owner—at which time the owner receives the keys to the building, bonds, and guarantees. The owner gives the contractor a certificate of completion. The contract is then complete.

J. The only thing that is now binding between the contractor and the owner is that the contractor guarantees the building for a period of time against defects. If there are any defects, the owner can call the contractor. The owner may have difficulty in getting back certain contractors; others come back willingly.

17.03   OBJECTIONS

A. On large projects where the cost may run to several million dollars and the time of construction lasts over a year, many contractors and subcontractors have protested, with some justification, that holding ten percent (10%) until completion is excessive. The architect-engineer and the owner should consider the risks, and, if justified, the percentage of withholding should be reduced.

B. The procedure often used is to withhold ten percent (10%) until the building is enclosed, is fifty percent (50%) complete, or some other specific time, and then withhold only five percent (5%) until the project is completed.

EIGHTEEN

Liens

18.01 LIENS IN GENERAL

A. A "lien" is a claim against property. For example, a pawnshop has a lien on the pawned article until it is redeemed; a trucking company has a lien on goods being shipped and can refuse to surrender them until paid; and a hotel has a lien on the guest's luggage until the bill is settled. Likewise, an unpaid seller has a lien on the product sold as security for the payment of the price.

B. A "chattel mortgage" is a lien upon personal property. It is like a mortgage on real property in that it places the right of the chattel paramount to that of the debtor's ownership. It is released only when the debt is paid. On real property, a lienholder has the right only to the value of the land, not to possession of it.

18.02 ENFORCEMENT OF LIENS

A. A lien is enforced by compelling public sale of the property; the debt is paid from the proceeds. Any balance is returned to the property owner.

B. The lien is on the property. Should the original owner sell the property, the lienholder can recover his money from the new owner.

18.03 MECHANIC'S LIENS IN GENERAL

A. VARIOUS STATE LAWS

Most liens previously referred to are recognized by common law. Mechanic's liens, however, were created by statute. As there are fifty (50) states, there are fifty (50) different lien laws; while they are similar in general outline, they differ in details. Although the following text is consistent with the laws of most states, the specification writer should refer to the laws of the state where the structure is built. He should not assume conditions which might not be true.

B. DEFINITION

1. A "mechanic's lien" is a right created by law to secure priority of payment for work or materials furnished for the improvement of real property.

2. This means that a worker who worked to improve land or structures on that land, if not paid for his service, can place a lien on the real property.

C. BACKGROUND

The mechanic's lien laws are the result of many builders of the last century, hiring labor (in many cases foreign-born people who could not speak English and were not familiar with American business practices), promising to pay the worker when the building was completed, and absconding with the money received from the owner.

D. WHO IS PROTECTED

1. The mechanic's lien protects the worker. Any laborer who is not paid for services while working on real property may demand payment from the owner of the property even though the owner has already paid for the worker's services through a contractor.

2. A material supplier has the same right. While it could be argued that the owner doesn't have the right to the goods until the supplier is paid, the supplier does not have the right to remove material that has been built into the structure. In most cases, this would be difficult without wrecking the structure, as in the case of plumbing or lumber. It would be impossible for the supplier of cement or gypsum to recover the material supplied.

3. The lien laws also protect the contractor who is not paid by the owner; and the subcontractor is protected when not paid by the contractor. The owner who deals with contractors who do not pay their subcontractors, or who deals with subcontractors who do not pay their laborers or their material suppliers, is apt to find it necessary to pay twice for the same property.

E. WHO IS NOT PROTECTED

1. The manufacturer who supplies raw material to the supplier fabricating material for the subcontractor is not protected by the lien laws in most states. For example, a steel mill producing slag to be crushed

by a supplier and purchased by a concrete subcontractor could not place a lien on a building where the concrete containing the slag was used. See *Hightower v. Bailey,* Supreme Court of Kentucky, 1900.

2. Likewise, the supplier who furnishes goods or material not attached to the property is not protected. For example, a supplier furnishing a loose rug would not be protected, but a supplier furnishing wall-to-wall carpeting usually would be protected. Lien laws cover only real property. See *Rieser v. Commeau,* Supreme Court of New York, 1908.

F. TENANTS

An owner may lease or rent real property. If the tenant, rather than the owner, contracts for an improvement of the property, the owner's property will not be subject to a lien on the cost of improvements unless the owner has consented to the improvement. Mere knowledge is not consent. Only if the owner instigates the improvement or at least approves it will there be the consent necessary to subject the owner's interest to the lien. See *P. Delaney & Company v. Duvoli,* Court of Appeals of New York, 1938.

G. ARCHITECTS AND ENGINEERS

In the statutes of some states, architects and engineers have lien rights specifically spelled out; in other states, their rights are less definite. Interesting cases have arisen where the architect-engineer draws plans but no building is constructed. Can the architect-engineer place a lien on the property where the building was to be built? The answer is no in almost all, if not all, states. In the case where construction was started, however, the architect-engineer may file a lien. See *Fitzgerald v. Walsh,* Supreme Court of Wisconsin, 1900. In the case where the architect-engineer completed plans and specifications to alter an existing building, but no construction was started, lien rights were denied. See *Foster and Libbie v. Tierney,* Supreme Court of Iowa, 1894.

H. MATERIALS COVERED

While it is understood that a supplier may place a lien to recover the price for goods permanently placed in a building, the question is often raised whether the supplier can recover for goods used in the construction of a building but later removed. An interesting case was tried in Wisconsin. In this case, a lumber dealer placed a lien on a structure to recover for lumber used to construct the concrete formwork. The lumber was used several times and seventy-five percent (75%) of the wood was consumed in the course of the work and the remaining twenty-five percent (25%) had decreased in value. The court ruled that formwork was necessary to build the building and a lien could be placed on the building. See *Moritz v. Lewis Construction Company,* Supreme Court of Wisconsin, 1914.

I. WORK DONE OFF THE PREMISES

Work performed off the premises upon articles designed to go into the construction of a building but never so incorporated is not subject to a lien. As there was no improvement, there can be no lien. However, if the owner or contractor wrongfully prevents a subcontractor from installing material in a building, there can be a lien. See *Berger v. Turnblad,* Supreme Court of Minnesota, 1906.

J. GOVERNMENT WORK

Liens cannot be placed on public property. Therefore, the lien laws do not protect contractors doing work for the federal, state, or local governments. In most cases, however, the general contractor is required to purchase a performance bond, and if a contractor is unable to pay a subcontractor or material supplier, the bills can be presented to the bonding company for payment.

18.04 PRIORITIES

A. In nearly all states, mechanic's liens have priority over all mortgages placed on the property after the improvement is started. Mortgages already on property before the owner signs the contract for the improvement give the lien claimant priority as to the value of the improvement over the mortgages, although the latter will have priority in the value of the land.

B. As a general rule, all mechanic's liens on the same property and arising out of the erection of the same building or improvement, irrespective of the date of filing, stand on an equality and share pro rata in the amount realized from the sale of the property where the proceeds of such sale are not enough to pay all in full. See *Soule v. Orelli,* Supreme Court of Connecticut, 1908.

C. An almost universal exception to the foregoing is found in the case of laborers. A claim of a person for wages as a laborer is usually made a preferred lien.

18.05 PROTECTION FOR THE OWNER

A. GENERAL

1. As we have stated, the owner of property can, in some circumstances, be forced to pay double for any construction. However, to protect the owner, legal safeguards have been established.

2. One of the safeguards is the limiting of time in which a lien can be filed. The time varies in various states, sixty (60) days being the most common. This means that when a subcontractor's work is fin-

ished, a lien must be filed within a specific number of days or the right to file a lien is lost. In other words, a subcontractor who was employed during the early part of the construction has only a limited time to file a lien even though the construction is not complete. It is not unusual for contractors who have not yet been paid to send workers back on the job to clean or make adjustments, just to extend the lien time.

3. The owner can secure protection by refusing to make the final payment to the contractor until the time for filing liens has expired.

B. NOTICE OF INTENT

1. Unlike a contractor who needs only to record a lien, subcontractors, material suppliers, and laborers must give notice of their intent to file a lien to the owner prior to actually filing a lien. This notice must be filed within a specific time limit governed by the law of the state. This is called a "Notice of Intent to File a Lien." A subcontractor or laborer who fails to file the notice loses the right to file a lien. This notice tells the owner that if the laborer isn't paid by the contractor, the laborer will file a lien against the property. The owner can refuse to pay the contractor until given assurance that all parties have been paid.

2. It should be obvious that owners are protected only to the amount they withhold from the contractor; if the contractor collects from the owner each month and doesn't pay his subcontractors the amount owed, the subcontractors could claim more than the amount being withheld by the owner. Of course, the architect-engineer should make sure that the previous month's bills submitted by subcontractors are paid before approving additional partial payments to the contractor. The notice of intent serves as an additional warning to the owner.

3. The question often asked is, Why don't all subcontractors file a notice of intent on every project, thus protecting themselves against loss? The answer is goodwill. Subcontractors depend upon the contractor for most of their business. When they send a notice of intent to the owner, many owners become alarmed at the possibility of a lien. It also leads them to believe that the contractor has selected subcontractors with poor financial backing or that the subcontractors don't trust the contractor. Many contractors consider such a notice a reflection upon their credit and honesty. Most subcontractors do not wish to antagonize their customers.

C. WAIVER OF LIEN

1. Before approving a contractor's final payment, the architect or engineer should obtain a Waiver of Lien from the contractor and each

subcontractor who has performed work on the project. A "waiver of lien" simply states that the contractor or subcontractor gives up the right to file a lien against the owner's property.

2. Obviously, a subcontractor will not give the contractor a waiver of lien until paid. The subcontractor would be foolish to do so.

3. Consequently, the owner is protected by being assured that the sub-contractors are not going to file liens. This, however, doesn't protect the owner from the laborer or the material supplier. They still have a right to sue the property owner.

D. THE SWORN STATEMENT

In addition to the waiver of lien the architect or engineer should obtain a Sworn Statement from the contractor and all of his subcontractors to protect the owner. A "sworn statement" is a written statement of fact signed and sworn to as true by the maker in the presence of a notary public. The sworn statement states that the signer (the contractor or subcontractor) has paid all subcontractors, suppliers, and laborers who have performed work on the project in full. A false sworn statement is perjury, and the one perjuring himself is subject to criminal prosecution. This gives the owner considerable protection but does not relieve the owner of the duty to pay laborers who have not been paid by their employer.

18.06 PROCEDURE FOR FILING A LIEN

A. As we have stated previously, all those who wish to file a lien and do not have a contract with the owner must file a notice of intent before they can file a lien. It is important that the notice be sent to all parties who have an interest in the land. This includes the wives of the owners and those holding mortgages or other claims on the property. If one is not notified, that is sufficient reason to prevent enforcement of the lien.

B. The wording of the notice of intent must be exact, and it would be best for one not familiar with the laws and procedure to consult an attorney.

C. The number of days in which a lien can be filed, that is, after the last material was delivered to the job site by the supplier or the last work was performed by the laborer, varies from state to state. After the notice of intent is delivered to the owner, and within the number of days stated by law, the person who wishes to file a lien should appear before the county Registrar of Deeds. He should have proof of the claim and a copy of the notice of intent sent to the owner. The Registrar of Deeds will record the lien upon the deed to the property, thereby giving notice to any prospective buyer of that property of the presence of a lien.

18.07 DISCHARGE OF A LIEN

A. A lien may be discharged by the payment of the obligation and the notification of the Registrar of Deeds in the proper manner.

B. An owner who believes that the lien was filed without justification may bring suit to have it removed.

C. In some states the lienholder must act to foreclose on the lien within a specific number of days.

18.08 PURCHASE OF REAL PROPERTY

Most architects and many engineers become involved in a client's purchase and improvement of real property. In advising a client in the purchase of property, the architect or engineer should make sure that the client is protected. The deed should be checked by a qualified person. If there is a doubt as to the quality of the title, one may buy title insurance. Title insurance guarantees that the title is clear. If someone has a claim against the title, it is up to the insurance company to defend or pay off the claim. Of course, the title insurance company is going to examine the title to see that it is free and clear before issuing the insurance.

NINETEEN

Government Contracts

19.01 RANGE

A large part of all construction projects are financed by government and a sizable part of all civil engineering work consists of designing roads, dams, water supply, sewage disposal, industrial waste disposal, drainage, and other such projects. Water and air pollution are becoming additional problems. As federal, state, and local governments represent a sizable percentage of the clients of architects and engineers, a separate chapter discussing the rules pertaining to government work and the resulting differences in the specifications is included in this book.

19.02 SIMILARITIES AND DIFFERENCES

Most common-law principles of private contracts apply to government contracts. There are, however, several differences between them. These differences result from: the Constitution, the government's historical immunity from suit, the restrictions on federal employees from binding the government, the governmental controls over the expenditure of public funds, laws affecting government procurement, the established procedures for administering contracts, the freedom of public property from liens, the government's need for uniformity in making and enforcing contracts, and special labor laws which affect government work. There follow a few comments on each of these differences.

19.03 THE CONSTITUTION

A. Federal courts cannot try a case against a state government brought by a citizen of another state or foreign nation. The Eleventh Amendment to the Constitution of the United States reads, "The judicial power of the United States shall not be construed to extend to any suit in law or equity, commenced or prosecuted against one of the United States, by citizens of another state, or by citizens or subjects of any foreign state."

B. The Eleventh Amendment was adopted after the Supreme Court, in the case of *Chisholm v. Georgia* (1793), decided that an individual could bring suit against the state of Georgia. The decision created such a shock and surprise that Congress at their next meeting almost unanimously proposed the Eleventh Amendment, which was then adopted by the legislatures of various states. The Eleventh Amendment reversed the decision of the Supreme Court. Chief Justice Jay and Associate Justices Blaw, Wilson, and Cushing were reversed by the people, but time has proven they were far ahead of their day.

*19.04   THE GOVERNMENT'S IMMUNITY FROM SUIT

A. THE KING CAN DO NO WRONG

1. A private citizen cannot sue his government without consent of that government. This concept comes from the belief that kings ruled by divine right and could do no wrong. This theory has legal backing that carries over to the present time. Sir William Blackstone (1723-1780), the noted English jurist, wrote in his commentaries, "No suit or action can be brought against the King, even in civil matters, because no court can have jurisdiction over him." This rule was followed by Chief Justice Marshall in the case of *Cohen v. Virginia* (1821), wherein he sets forth the universal opinion that no suit can be commenced or prosecuted against the United States. "There can be no legal right as against the authority that makes the laws on which the right depends."

2. It is rather interesting to note that while the democracies held to the theory that the king could do no wrong, Frederick the Great of Prussia (1740-1786) said, "Judges ought to know that the poorest peasant is a man, as well as the King himself; all men ought to obtain justice, since, in the estimation of justice, all men are equal, whether the prince complain of the peasant or the peasant complain of a prince."

B. THE COURT OF CLAIMS

1. Before 1855, a person with a claim against the United States government had no recourse other than to request a special appropriation from Congress. The first tort claim granted by a private bill went into

*A part of the historical data in this subchapter was obtained from "The Federal Torts Claim Act" by William B. Wright. Used by permission of the Central Book Company Inc.

effect on April 13, 1792. It was for damages to premises occupied by federal troops. However, no one had the right to any relief for injuries caused by the government; any reimbursement was considered a matter of grace.

2. As time passed, the mass of business growing out of the private claims increased until there was insufficient time for a congressional committee to properly consider each case. This resulted in injustice. In 1855 a Court of Claims was created, primarily to relieve the pressure on Congress caused by the volume of private bills. The court was regarded as an experiment and Congress was reluctant to give it authority to make its judgments final; instead it was authorized to hear claims and report its finding of fact to Congress. The court took testimony, determined the legality of the claim, and made recommendations to Congress.

3. By the end of 1861 it was apparent that the limited powers conferred on the court were insufficient to relieve Congress from the laborious necessity of examining the merits of private bills. President Lincoln in his State of the Union message recommended that the judgments of the Court of Claims be made final. On March 3, 1863, Congress expanded the jurisdiction of the Court of Claims to permit suits against the government founded upon any contract "expressed or implied" with the United States. The law provided appeal to the Supreme Court in some cases. However, Congress did not release control of the money involved. The law provided that no money should be paid out of the Treasury on any claim until an appropriation was made by Congress. In 1866 this provision was removed from the law.

C. THE TUCKER ACT

1. The Tucker Act was passed in 1887. This act not only expanded the jurisdiction of the Court of Claims but, for the first time, gave federal district courts general authority to hear and determine claims against the government. District courts hear cases involving ten thousand dollars ($10,000) or less and have the same authority within their jurisdiction as the Court of Claims.

2. The Tucker Act considerably reduced the number of private bills in Congress, and while the courts placed a very broad interpretation upon the wording "expressed or implied," some just cases were not within the scope of the Tucker Act. Torts and patents were not covered.

D. PATENTS

In 1910, Congress consented to suits in the Court of Claims for patent infringements.

E. ADMIRALTY

In 1920 and 1925, the government consented to suits in the district courts upon admiralty and maritime torts involving government vessels, without limitation as to the amount.

F. THE SMALL TORTS CLAIMS ACT

The Small Torts Claims Act of 1922 provided that heads of departments may "consider, ascertain, adjust, and determine any claim ... on account of damages to or loss of privately owned property where the amount of the claim does not exceed one thousand dollars ($1,000), caused by the negligence of any officer or employee of the Government acting within the scope of his employment."

G. THE FEDERAL TORTS CLAIMS ACT

1. The Federal Torts Claims Act was passed by Congress in 1946, as Title IV of the Legislative Reorganization Act, after nearly thirty (30) years of congressional consideration. This bill made it possible for a person with a tort claim against the government to obtain relief in a similar manner to those with a contract claim. By the time this bill was passed, the number of private bills presented to Congress was excessive and Congress was taking action on a small percentage (see Article I in this subchapter). The private bill procedure is inefficient and the necessity of establishing a procedure for hearing mass claims was imperative. When he signed the bill, President Truman classed it as "one of the most significant advances in the organization of the Congress of the United States since the establishment of that body."

2. The purpose of the Federal Torts Claims Act is to provide civil action for an injured party to recover money damages for personal injury, death, loss of goods, or damage to property due to negligence or wrongful act of an employee of the government while acting within the scope of his employment. The intent of the law is to have the government accept liability under the same circumstances that would bring private liability.

3. The claimant with a claim of less than one thousand dollars ($1,000) may elect to take action in accordance with the Small Claims Act of 1922 or the Federal Torts Claims Act.

H. PROCEDURE

As the Tucker Act and other consent laws are contrary to the common law, the rules, procedures, and requirements must be followed promptly and precisely. The laws are precise, but without them there could be no suit against the government.

I. AMOUNT OF LITIGATION

1. The Federal Torts Claims Act has not completely served its purpose to relieve Congress of private bills. On occasions Congress has

granted relief after it has been denied by the courts. Conspicuous among such bills is the Texas City Relief Act. The need for the Torts Claims Act can be realized after reading the following partial listing of bills presented to Congress prior to the passage of the Act in 1946.

2. In the Sixty-eighth Congress (1924) approximately 2,200 private bills were introduced, of which 250 became law; in the Seventieth Congress (1928), 2,268 private bills were introduced asking more than $100,000,000. Of these 336 were enacted, appropriating about $2,830,000. In the Seventy-sixth Congress (1940) approximately 2,200 bills were introduced, of which 315 were approved for a total of $826,000. In the Seventy-eighth Congress (1946) 1,644 bills were introduced. Of these, 549 were approved for a total of $1,355,767.12.

3. It is interesting to note the increase in government litigation in the hundred (100) years since Lincoln's time. On March 31, 1962, there were 68,000 civil cases pending in the district courts. The federal government was a party in approximately one-quarter of these cases, and, of course, in all of the cases in the Court of Claims.

J. GOVERNMENT ACTION

The government's immunity from suit and the consent laws in no way prevents the government from taking action against a delinquent contractor. The government can enforce the terms of a contract in federal or state courts the same as a private citizen.

K. THE GOVERNMENT AS A SOVEREIGN

1. Because of its size, the government has many departments and can possess more than one character. In fact, there have been several cases where government attorneys have appeared on both sides of a controversy. An example is *Secretary of Agriculture v. United States* (1956).

2. While a contractor has permission to sue the government, the government is not liable for damages under the same conditions as might be expected of a private party. For example, in the case of *Horowitz v. U.S.* (1928) it was ruled that the government cannot be held liable for an obstruction to the performance of a specific contract resulting from its acts as a sovereign. This is illustrated by the case of *B. Shapiro & Company v. U.S.* (1941).

3. B. Shapiro was the highest bidder for approximately fifty thousand pounds (50,000) lb) of miscellaneous metal placed on sale as surplus property at the Norfolk Navy Yard. After Shapiro's bid was received, the government established a ceiling on the price of certain metals. Shapiro sought relief from his bid because the government, as a party to the contract, had changed market conditions to his disadvantage and prevented him from reselling the material at a higher price.

19.04 K. 3. (Cont.)

Shapiro was advised that he must accept delivery and pay for it according to contract or pay damages. The government possesses several characters. In placing a ceiling price on metal, it was acting as a sovereign, and it cannot be held for damages of a sovereign act while acting as a party to a contract.

19.05 GOVERNMENT PERSONNEL

A. THE CONTRACTING OFFICER

No official of the government can bind the government unless authority for him to act is provided by law. The person having authority to sign contracts for the government is called a "contracting officer." This may be a military officer or a civilian. A contracting officer must have expressed authority and can bind the government only when acting within that authority. The government is not liable when the contracting officer acts outside his authority even though he has the apparent authority. This differs from private contracts, where an agent with apparent authority can bind the principal.

B. THE PCO, ACO, AND TCO

1. There are three (3) types of contracting officers: the procuring contracting officer, called the PCO; the administrative contracting officer, called the ACO; and the terminating contracting officer, called the TCO. The PCO receives the bid package from the engineers, requests and receives proposals, and signs contracts. After a contract is awarded, the administration of the contract is assigned to an ACO, who is responsible for seeing that the contract provisions are fulfilled. The TCO deals with contracts that are being terminated by the government.

2. On small government installations where the employment of two (2) contracting officers could not be justified, the duties of the PCO and ACO are performed by the same person.

3. Contracting officers may sign contracts binding the government; however, there is usually a dollar limit on this authority. On contracts over a specific amount of money, the contracting officer is required to obtain approval of a higher authority before signing. On very large amounts, the higher authority is often a committee consisting of various department heads and a qualified attorney.

4. Some contracting officers have subordinates to whom they may delegate authority. The specific agency regulations may limit what power can be delegated. Anyone doing business with the government should insist that any contractual act performed by subordinates be authorized by the contracting officer.

5. As a general rule, contracting officers are neither attorneys, auditors, nor engineers, but they may request technical assistance. They may request recommendations from an established board or request that a board of experts be appointed to advise them upon a special problem. However, in most agencies the contracting officer may accept or disregard recommendations. While most agencies have training courses for contracting officers, there appear to be no educational requirements for the appointment. Most contracting officers receive their training by working for others in the same field.

C. THE GOVERNMENT ENGINEER

1. The government engineer has no authority to make, sign, or change contracts. In many agencies, he has very little authority of any kind. His advice is often sought, however, frequently on an emergency basis, and his recommendations are usually accepted.

2. Many engineers employed by the government are designers. They prepare the drawings, the specifications, and the cost estimates. While most professional engineers working for the government are competent, they are required, at times, to make these designs conform to obsolete or inappropriate regulations that appear to be written by nonengineers; and unfortunately, there are times when an engineering department will be under the direction of a person who lacks basic engineering knowledge.

3. There are not enough government engineers to design all government projects, and the engineers are required, at times, to obtain assistance from professional engineering firms. Government engineers prepare each statement of work and an estimate of the fee the architect or engineer will charge to do the work. The architect or engineer is selected by a board composed of government personnel. The procuring contracting officer then tries to negotiate a contract with that architect or engineer. If he suceeds, money is set aside and a contract is signed. If the procuring contracting officer cannot come to an agreement with the architect or engineer selected, the negotiations are terminated and the board is requested to make another selection. Architects or engineers are professionals and are not required to bid for work as do contractors.

D. PROFESSIONAL ENGINEERING FIRMS

1. The statement of work usually requires the architect-engineering firms to prepare the plans, the technical sections of the specifications, and the cost estimate in the same manner as done by the government engineers. The preparing of the conditions, advertising, and accepting proposals is performed by the government. When the architect-engineer's work is complete, the original tracings, the mats to print the specifications, the exact number of copies of the specifications,

19.05 D. 1. (Cont.)

and the cost estimate are delivered to the procuring contracting officer. The government engineers check the plans and specifications for errors and make sure they conform with the statement of work. If the plans and specifications are approved, the procuring contracting officer is notified and the architect or engineer is paid. This often ends the architect's or engineer's services for that project. If additional work is required, usually it will be performed by government engineers. Professional engineers are sometimes employed to act as clerk of the works; this is usually done under a separate contract and will be discussed later.

2. Many government agencies have no qualms about making changes on the tracings or in using them for projects other than those for which they were designed. Of course, the architect or engineer is not responsible for changes made by others, but his name and seal appear on the drawings. Many architects and engineers object to having their carefully designed work mutilated by others without their knowledge. Some agencies act on the theory that the drawings were purchased by the government and the agency is free to use the plans on any future work in other parts of the country. This is contrary to professional standards, which hold that an architect's or engineer's drawings should be used only on projects for which they were designed.

E. THE INSPECTOR

A clerk of the works (see Article 2.07C) working on a government project is usually called the Government Inspector, although in some agencies he is called the Quality Assurance Representative, or simply QAR. The government inspector has the duty to accept or reject the contractor's work. He has no authority to correct or change any requirement in the specifications, to issue field orders, or to stop work. He may suggest changes to correct errors or to facilitate the work, but he may not authorize the contractor to deviate from the specifications without the approval of the contracting officer.

19.06 CONTROLS OVER EXPENDITURES

A. Another difference between government and private contracts is the means the contractor has to collect for his work. If a corporation enters into a legal contract for the services of a contractor, the fact that the board of directors did not appropriate the money to pay the contractor is irrelevant. It is different with the government. Unless funds have been appropriated for a contract out of the general appropriations available, or out of a special appropriation passed by the proper legislative body, the contractor cannot collect even a reasonable value for the work performed. The reason for this rather harsh ruling is that it prevents government officers from committing funds which have not been authorized. This gives the legislative body control over the budget.

B. The rule applies to state and local governments. In one case, a city engineer contracted for a street improvement without having authority from the city council. When the work was completed, the contractor could not collect for the services performed.

C. The federal government works on a fiscal year ending June 30. Most appropriations are made annually and are made available for commitment only during that year. As a result, government agencies never know until the first of July exactly how much money they will receive for the year. If the money appropriated is not committed during the year, it must be returned to the fund from which it came.

D. Before a contract is signed, the money to pay for the entire project is set aside or obligated. Once money is obligated, usually it remains obligated until the contract is completed.

E. The foregoing policy results in waste. When money is made available in July, contracts are awarded in an orderly manner. However, if all money is not obligated as the year ends, the agency directors demand that the money be spent in some manner. An agency that returns money is apt to have its budget cut the following year. The year-end rush often results in hastily drawn contracts being issued with little study as to the need for them or their sufficiency. Some agencies appear to judge their administrators on how rapidly they can spend money.

19.07 LAWS AFFECTING GOVERNMENT PROCUREMENT

A. FIXED-PRICE CONTRACTS

1. Bidding

In private work, the method of taking bids is determined by the owner. He may award a contract to any bidder at his discretion. The laws govern how federal, state, and local governments make awards. In most cases, public officials are required to advertise publicly, accept only sealed bids, open the bids in public, and read them aloud. The purpose, of course, is to prevent discrimination or preferential treatment of any contractor. Awards are usually given to the lowest responsible bidder, provided that the low bid is within the appropriation. This means that the low bidder is awarded the work unless the government can prove a contractor is not responsible. This is often difficult, and as a result, many government contracts are awarded to substandard contractors.

2. Prequalification of Bidders

Some states have an arrangement where contractors must be prequalified before being allowed to bid on a project for the state government. Contractors wishing to bid on a project submit financial statements, notarized statements as to their existing contracts, and other pertinent information to a board. The state boards have standard methods of determining whether a contractor would be able to complete the project. Those who do not meet the boards' standards are not permitted to bid. States that have tried this system report far fewer terminated contracts.

B. NEGOTIATED CONTRACTS

1. Explanation

Under specific conditions, the federal government may negotiate a contract. A negotiated contract is one where the price is arrived at by negotiation rather than by taking bids. A board of government employees selects the contractor they believe will best perform the work and send the contract documents to this contractor. Government engineers and the contractor make estimates of the cost. At a meeting between the parties, a satisfactory price is determined if possible. If no agreement is made, the relationship is terminated and another contractor is selected.

2. The Truth in Negotiations Act

a. Public Law 87-653, generally known as the Truth in Negotiations Act, was signed into law on September 10, 1962. This bill amends the Armed Services Procurement Act of 1947. The purpose is to require contractors to disclose complete, current, and accurate cost and pricing data to support their proposals and to protect the government against inflated cost estimates in negotiated contracts.

b. This law deals only with noncompetitive negotiated contracts (such as architect-engineer contracts), subcontracts, and modifications to existing contracts in excess of one hundred thousand dollars ($100,000). It provides that before any of those contracts are awarded, the contractor be required to submit cost or pricing data that are accurate, complete, and current. In addition, it requires that each contract contain a clause enabling the government to adjust the price of a negotiated contract if it is determined that it was significantly increased because any of the data were not accurate, complete, and current.

3. Contracts That May Be Negotiated

a. The federal law permits contracts to be awarded without taking bids during a national emergency or when delay cannot be tolerated without great cost. The latter is called "Public Exigency."

b. The law allows contracting officers to make small purchases, those under two thousand five hundred dollars ($2,500), directly from a seller, when the cost of advertising and taking bids would exceed any possible saving.

c. Professional services or services from an educational institution may be purchased directly.

d. Medicine, medical supplies, except artificial limbs, and perishable goods when there is a danger of spoilage may be bought informally.

e. Brand-name items may be bought directly from any manufacturer, provided they are to be resold, such as in commissary stores.

f. Where there is only one source for a product; when patents or copyrights are involved; when the contract is for the purchase of utilities, for transportation or replacement parts, and in other cases where it is impracticable to obtain compensation, formal advertising and bidding may be omitted.

4. Research and Development

The government finances billions of dollars each year in research and development programs, and much of our existing scientific progress started with research financed by the government. As the time it takes to make a new discovery cannot be predetermined, the goverment may enter into a cost-reimbursement type of contract.

C. COST-REIMBURSEMENT CONTRACTS

1. Cost-Plus-Fixed-Fee Contracts

The "cost-plus-a-fixed-fee contract" is the most common type of contract for research and development projects because most contractors would refuse to take the risk required in a fixed-price arrangement. In a cost-plus-a-fixed-fee agreement, the contractors take no risk, promising only to provide their best effort, and the government promises to reimburse them for all allocable, allowable, and reasonable costs which may be incurred during the performance of the contract, plus a fixed fee for their effort. The time the contractor is allowed to complete the work and a limitation of the cost are always specified. If the contractor fails to obtain the desired results within the time or cost specified, the government will review the progress and either terminate the contract, extend the time, or provide additional funds and authorize the contractor to continue performance under the contract.

2. Incentive Contracts

a. *Types*

(1) The purpose of an incentive contract is to motivate the contractor to complete the work at the lowest possible cost. There

are two (2) types of incentive contracts—the "cost-plus-incentive-fee," and the "fixed-price incentive contract." In the cost-plus-incentive-fee contract, a ceiling price, a minimum price, and corresponding fees are negotiated. If the ceiling price is reached without satisfactory results, the contract is completed and the contractor is paid the minimum fee. If results are obtained at or below the minimum price, the contractor receives the maximum fee. When the costs are between the minimum and the ceiling, the fee is proportional.

(2) The fixed-price incentive contract is negotiated for a ceiling price, a target price, and a minimum price. The government pays the contractor's costs. When the costs reach the ceiling price, the contractor is paid the minimum agreed profit but is required to complete the work even if, in doing so, he loses money. The contractor's normal profit is figured upon the target price. If the costs are below the minimum costs, the contractor is reimbursed and paid the maximum agreed profit. When the costs are between the minimum and ceiling, the costs are paid by the government and profit is decreased as the cost rises. This is best shown by an illustration. Let us assume agreement has been reached on the costs and profit in the following example.

b. *Example of a Fixed-Price Incentive Contract*

(1) Problem:

		Cost	Profit	Paid Contractor
(a)	Ceiling Price	$1,200,000	$ 10,000	$1,210,000
(b)	Target Price	$1,000,000	$100,000	$1,100,000
(c)	Minimum Price	$ 900,000	$150,000	$1,050,000

(2) Answers:

(a) If the contract cost was $1,500,000, the cotractor would be paid only $1,210,000 and would suffer a $290,000 loss.

(b) If the contract cost was $800,000, the contractor would receive $800,000 plus $150,000 profit, or $950,000.

(c) If the cost is between $900,000 and $1,200,000, the contractor would be paid the cost plus a profit based upon an agreed-upon formula.

D. TWO-STEP PROCUREMENT

1. "Two-step procurement" is a type of buying adopted by the government for a particular need when the required specifications are not sufficiently definite or complete to permit free competition. This can be best explained by an example.

2. Let us suppose the government wanted to purchase housing for unmanned weather stations to be placed in polar regions throughout the world. In such a case, the government might choose to issue a performance specification to industry for the design, fabrication, and delivery of such housing. Bidders would then submit cost proposals, along with their design, computations showing that their product would conform to the required performance, and reasons why their design should be accepted.

3. The government would evaluate the various proposals and select one. The bidder who submitted the selected design would then enter into a contract to prepare drawings and specifications and possibly to build a prototype to check the performance of the design and the accuracy of the drawings. It is possible on critical and expensive items, or items purchased in large quantities, that the government might award two or more contracts to different bidders for prototypes before making their final selection. When the drawings and specifications are accepted, the first of the two steps in the procurement would be complete.

4. The government would then use these documents to secure bids from other contractors. The list of bidders would be limited to those who submitted proposals on the Step One solicitation. Subsequent purchases would be open to all.

E. GOVERNMENT ASSISTANCE

1. Small Business

a. The government has a definite policy to assist small business, and the Small Business Administration was established in 1953. This administration assists small business to qualify and obtain government work, helps them to obtain loans, helps them to obtain advance or progress payments, and offers other useful services.

b. At one time "small business" was defined as a company employing less than five hundred (500) people. This would include most contractors. However, the policy has been changed. For example, one of the smaller automobile companies was declared a small business even though it is one of America's large corporations. They have been described as a tall man in a field of giants.

c. The Small Business Administration is interested in the size of a business in relation to other businesses in the same industry. A steel mill employing less than five thousand (5,000) people would be a small business; however, a professional engineering firm employing five thousand (5,000) would not be small. A complete definition of a small business is published in the Code of Federal Regulations, Title 13, Part 121. This takes several pages of print and is subject to change at any time. In general, it can be stated that a small business concern is independently owned and operated, is not dominant in its field of operation, produces the bid item in quantities less than five percent (5%) of the total volume of all industries producing that item, or is one that has been designated as a small business by the Small Business Administration.

2. Labor Surplus Areas

Executive Order 10582 issued pursuant to the Buy American Act and Defense Manpower Policy No. 4 of the Office of Emergency Planning requires that the Secretary of Labor of the United States determine geographical areas of concentrated unemployment or underemployment and publish a list of these areas at regular intervals. Firms in or near such classified sections of concentrated unemployment or underemployment, upon request, are required to be certified by the Secretary as eligible for preferred treatment in the placement of federal government contracts, provided that such firms have agreed to employ, in the performance of such contracts, a proportionate number of disadvantaged persons residing within the classified section or referred to the employer by a government employment service.

3. Preferred Treatment

In the event of tie bids or in the evaluation of bids, the bidder's status is taken into consideration in making the award.

4. The Set-Aside Procedure

a. The United States Department of Labor employs people who cooperate with the various government procuring agencies to assure that a proper amount of government procurement is placed with small business concerns. When the contract documents are being prepared, the small business administrator recommends work that could be set aside for small business and labor-surplus-area concerns.

b. The various governmental agencies have very precise regulations in regard to the authority of the small business administrator and the contracting officer, as well as rules governing the set-aside procedure. The best-known of these is the *Armed Services Procurement Regulation,* a book of several hundred loose-leaf pages nicknamed the *ASPR.*

c. In general, proposed procurement for construction, including maintenance and repairs, in excess of twenty-five hundred dollars ($2,500) and under five hundred thousand dollars ($500,000) are considered for a set-aside. Construction contracts over a half-million dollars ($500,000) are not set-aside.

d. A set-aside may be total or partial. In a total set-aside, proposals are accepted only from contractors who can qualify as eligible for preferred treatment. The specifications should be clear as to who can bid, as most contractors cannot be expected to understand the confusing and involved government regulations. Many small contractors refuse to bid because they don't understand how the government is trying to help them.

e. In a partial set-aside, the procuring contracting officer (PCO) may issue two (2) separate proposals for the same item or a single proposal divided into a set-aside and a non-set-aside portion. Big business may bid only on the non-set-aside portion.

f. In evaluating bids, small businesses which are in labor-surplus areas usually are given preference over small businesses which are not. The method by which bids are to be evaluated should be placed in the specifications to protect the government against charges of favoritism. To do this, the specification writer must be familiar with the law and the regulations of the government agency for which he is working.

5. Subcontracts

It is the policy of the government to enable small business concerns to be considered fairly as subcontractors to general contractors performing work under government procurement contracts. Most government contracts require general contractors to accomplish a maximum amount of subcontracting with small business concerns that the contractor finds consistent with the efficient performance of a contract. On most contracts with the government for over a half-million dollars ($500,000), the general contractor is required to establish a Small Business Subcontracting Program and to award a percentage of the subcontract work to small business concerns.

19.08 PROCEDURES FOR ADMINISTERING CONTRACTS

A. RECEIVING PROPOSALS

On private work the architect or engineer prepares the Instructions to Bidders, and the General and Special Conditions and then advertises the project and receives bids. On government work the completed drawings, specifications, and cost estimates are delivered to the procuring contracting officer, who is required to obtain bids. When releasing the documents, the engineer no longer has control. This is true for both the professional architectural or engineering office and the government engineer. If an addendum is required, the engineer can only recommend to the contracting officer that it be issued, but cannot issue it.

B. THE PREAWARD

A PCO who is not sure that a low bidder can perform the contract in a satisfactory manner may request a preaward survey. A "preaward survey" is an investigation of a prospective contractor's financial resources, record of performance, record of integrity, organization, labor relations, experience, operational controls, equipment, and technical ability to perform in accordance with the terms of the contract. It is also necessary to check the contractor's workload to determine if the contract can be completed within the time limit. The prospective contractor must give permission to have the survey made. Those making the survey give the results to the PCO, who decides who should receive the award.

C. THE PRECONSTRUCTION MEETING

1. After the procuring contracting officer awards the contract to the contractor, a meeting is scheduled. This meeting is called the "preconstruction meeting" by some agencies and the "postaward meeting" by others.

2. The meeting is scheduled by the procuring contracting officer in some agencies and by the administrative contracting officer in others. Both contracting officers are usually in attendance. The government engineer, the government inspector, and other government personnel concerned with the construction or the finished product are usually invited. The contractor's invitation usually includes any subcontractor the contractor wishes to bring to the meeting.

3. The purpose of the meeting is to obtain an agreement as to when the contractor should start work, how the contractor intends to proceed, and other details. The contractor may ask questions on procedures or on technical requirements in the specifications that are not understood. Usually, the administrative contracting officer and the government inspector are introduced to the contractor at the meeting and the ACO explains the procedures described in the general and special conditions and makes sure the contractor understands the responsibilities. The contractor is also made aware of local safety requirements, labor rules, traffic regulations on government property, laws regarding equal employment, and how to make application for payments.

D. SHOP DRAWINGS

The administrative contracting officer often needs technical assistance. One example is in approving shop drawings. If shop drawings are required, the contractor must have them approved by the administrative contracting officer. When the drawings are received, the administrative contracting officer gives them to the government engineer, who checks them and recommends that the contracting officer approve or disapprove them. If they are rejected, the reasons for this action must be given to the contracting officer.

E. PAYMENTS

The administrative contracting officer is responsible for making the progress and final payments. The ACO requires assistance from the government inspector, who gives written assurance that the work is performed in accordance with the contract. When work is completed or when a progress payment is due, the contractor requests payment from the administrative contracting officer. The contracting officer approves the request and sends it to the finance officer, who makes payment.

F. DISPUTES

1. With the Contractor

a. Disputes sometimes arise between the contractor and the government inspector. When this happens, the administrative contracting officer will usually try to settle it in an informal way. The ACO may request and receive engineering assistance. If still dissatisfied, the contractor may file a claim with the contracting officer. The contracting officer is required to reply within thirty (30) days.

b. In the Supreme Court case of *U.S. v. Moorman* (1950) it was decided that parties to a government contract could agree to submit questions of law to the contracting officer and to accept the decision as binding. This decision was nullified by Public Law 356, which provides, "No Government contract shall contain a provision making final, on a question of law, the decision of any administrative officer, representative, or board."

c. A contractor who receives a written decision from the administrative contracting officer may send a written notice of appeal to the secretary of the department involved through the contracting officer. The case will be held before the Armed Services Board of Contract Appeals, the General Services Administration Board of Review, the Corps of Engineers Claims, and the Appeals Board or one of five other boards, depending upon the agency financing the project. After exhausting administration remedies, the contractor may file a claim in federal district court if the claim is under ten thousand dollars ($10,000) or in the Court of Claims.

2. With the Subcontractor

A subcontractor may not appeal a decision of a contracting officer or use the administrative disputes machinery unless the subcontractor can show privity existed with the government. The subcontractor is expected to negotiate the dispute with the contractor and, if dissatisfied, to take the dispute to the proper court, usually the local state court. However, the contractor may appeal a contracting officer's decision on behalf of a subcontractor.

19.09 LIENS

A. GENERAL

1. In general, liens cannot be placed on public property. It has been tried. Local governments have tried to place liens on state property, and local and state governments have tried to place liens on federal property. Such liens, even if granted by a local court, are unenforceable.

2. If a contractor refuses to pay a subcontractor, the subcontractor can sue the contractor. If the contractor goes bankrupt, the subcontractor can collect as a general creditor. This means that the subcontractor who takes this course of action might have to settle for as little as one cent on the dollar. On a government contract a subcontractor can take no action against the government unless able to prove some privity of contract between the government and the subcontractor.

B. THE MILLER ACT

The Miller Act requires the contractor to post a performance bond before entering into a construction contract with the government. Thus, if a contractor fails or defaults, an unpaid subcontractor can collect on the bond. According to the latest decisions, a supplier to a subcontractor would be protected but a supplier of raw material to a supplier might not be.

19.10 UNIFORMITY IN LAWS

Federal law, not state or local, governs contract actions in which the national government is a party. The courts recognize the need for uniform design throughout the country. Therefore, the federal government is not bound by local codes or laws.

19.11 LABOR LAWS

A. INTRODUCTION

1. Congress has passed several laws regarding the employment of labor on government projects. Much of this legislation was passed by Congress during the Depression years from 1930 to 1936. Whereas private industry wished to purchase goods at the lowest possible price, the federal government passed laws which raised the government's cost. The purpose was to place buying power in the hands of the workers and to discourage employers who bid low and then hire their labor at starvation wages.

2. Some of the important labor laws that apply to government contracts follow.

B. THE EIGHT-HOUR DAY LAW

The Eight-Hour Day Law was passed in 1912. It requires contractors doing work for the federal government to compensate laborers and mechanics at a rate of not less than one and one-half times the basic hourly rate for all time in excess of eight (8) hours in a single day.

C. THE DAVIS-BACON ACT

1. The Davis-Bacon Act of 1931 requires that mechanics and laborers working on a government contract for a contractor receive not less than the prevailing wage as determined by the Secretary of Labor. Should the workers be paid a lesser wage than provided by the Secretary of Labor, the Comptroller General may withhold money from the contractor and pay the workers directly.

2. When the government sends a bid package to the bidders, the minimum rates of pay for each trained classification are printed in the contract documents. These may or may not agree with the union wage, and once established, they remain in effect for the life of the contract.

D. THE BUY AMERICAN ACT

The Buy American Act was passed in 1933 during the Depression. It requires that only materials or supplies mined, produced, or manufactured in the United States may be used on projects financed by the government. The government may make exceptions when the materials or supplies required are not available in the United States.

E. THE MILLER ACT

1. The Miller Act was passed in 1935. It requires that all construction contracts for federal work of over two thousand dollars ($2,000) in value contain a clause requiring the contractor to process a payment bond with a surety to protect the wages of all workers.

2. The Act also protects suppliers to subcontractors of the contractor (those having direct contractual relationship with the contractor) and suppliers or sub-subcontractors having direct contractual relationship with the subcontractor.

3. The courts have uniformly held that the supplier of a sub-subcontractor, a supplier of a supplier of a subcontractor, or a sub-sub-subcontractor cannot recover, under the contractor's bond, for materials or work because there has been no direct contractual relationship with the contractor or his subcontractors. Thus, they are not protected by the Miller Act. See *Aetna Insurance Company v. Southern, Waldrip & Harvick,* District Court of California (27 September 1961).

4. However, the U.S. Court of Appeals ruled, in the case of *Glens Falls Insurance Company v. Newton Lumber and Manufacturing Company, et al.* (6 September 1967), that the Miller Act protected the supplier of a subcontractor. The ruling in this case was that the contract between the contractor and his subcontractor was merely a sham entered into for the purpose of insulating the contractor from liability from firms supplying materials to the sub-subcontractor for use in performing the prime contract. In this case the subcontractor was ruled to be the contractor's agent or employee. Any other ruling, notes the court, would permit the contractor to defeat the purpose of the Miller Act, which is to protect the suppliers of the actual subcontractors of the contractor. In other words, the substance rather than the form of their relationship must be considered in determining who is the contractor's actual subcontractor.

F. THE WALSH-HEALY ACT

The Walsh-Healy Act was passed in 1936 and requires that all persons employed by contractors manufacturing or supplying goods or materials for any United States government agency, in an amount exceeding ten thousand dollars ($10,000), be paid not less than the prevailing minimum wages as determined by the Secretary of Labor. It also provides that no person can work in excess of eight (8) hours per day or forty (40) hours per week without additional compensation; that no child or convict labor will be employed; and that materials and supplies will not be manufactured under unsanitary conditions.

G. THE COPELAND "ANTI-KICKBACK" ACT

This act, passed in 1948, applies to construction contracts and not only covers federal building projects but applies to all work financed in whole or in part with federal funds, loans, or grants. It prohibits an employer from using threats, intimidations, or other means to induce an employee to give up any part of compensation.

H. THE FEDERAL AID HIGHWAY ACT

The Federal Aid Highway Act was passed in 1956 and applies to the construction of roads financed with federal money. It provides for the application of the Davis-Bacon Act to all laborers and mechanics employed by contractors and subcontractors working on interstate highways.

I. CIVIL RIGHTS

1. The policy of the government is to ensure equal opportunity for all qualified persons, without regard to race, color, religion, sex, or national origin. Executive Order 10925 was issued by President Kennedy on March 6, 1961, establishing this principle. This order was not issued under any congressional directive but pursuant to the executive powers of the President under the Constitution. Basically, the order requires contractors doing work for the government to take positive action to ensure nondiscrimination with respect. not only to hiring but also to the terms and conditions of employment. Some time later Executive Order 11114 was issued, which broadened the scope of the original order to include age. The fore-stated orders were super-seded by Executive Order 11246 effective October 24, 1965. The President's Committee on Equal Employment Opportunity was abolished and its functions vested in the Secretary of Labor. All rules, regulations, orders, and other directives issued by the President's Committee that are not inconsistent with EO 11246 remain in full force. Executive Order 11375 on October 13, 1967 amended EO 11246 to include discrimination against sex.

2. The Civil Rights Act of 1964 that became fully effective July 2, 1968 establishes an Equal Employment Opportunity Commission and contains procedures for the law's enforcement by way of federal court action and criminal penalties resulting from contempt proceedings. However, the law contains no criminal penalties for violations other than contempt proceedings. However, sanctions are covered in EO 11246.

3. The exemptions, complaint procedures, hearing procedures, sanctions, posting of notices, advertising, age nondiscrimination, compliance reports and reviews, segregated facilities, and apprenticeship programs are covered by law and executive orders. The full impact of the legislation is just beginning to be felt, and a good many cases will be in the courts for years to come.

4. The laws now in effect apply to contracts for construction financed with assistance from the federal government, and applies to contractors and subcontractors through the second tier and beyond for construction work at the site of construction. The law applies to many others, including banks rendering services to the government.

5. One phase of the Executive Orders that affects contractors doing federal work is that they must report their degree of compliance each year on the forms provided. When a contractor submits the form, he must agree to permit access to his books, records, and accounts by the contracting agency. The purpose of the investigation is to ascertain whether the degree of compliance is in accordance with the required rules and regulations.

J. DEBARMENT

A contractor may be debarred from doing government contract work who violates the Eight-Hour Day Law, the Davis-Bacon Act, the Buy American Act, the Walsh-Healy Act, or the Copeland "Anti-kickback" Act. A contractor may also be debarred for willful failure to perform a contract or a history of bad performance on government contracts.

K.   REASONS FOR LABOR LAWS

1. The amount of good the labor laws do is doubtful when employment is plentiful. One can only imagine the reply of a union bricklayer when asked to kickback a part of his pay to his employer. While the laws do no good, they are costly for both the employer and the government. Let us take the Davis-Bacon Act as an example. Before a construction project is advertised for bids, the government must determine the prevailing wage rate for each trade in the area where the project is to be constructed. These rates are printed and submitted to each bidder along with the plans and specifications. After award the contractor is required to list every employee on the payroll, their classification, the hours worked each day, their hourly rate, and their total pay for each week. The contractor must require the same from each subcontractor. These are submitted with each invoice. These are checked by the government before the contractor is paid.

2. The author knows of one case where a subcontractor hired an apprentice roofer from the union hall to replace an apprentice who was sick. He worked as an apprentice. At the end of two days the regular employee returned and the other man was paid for his two days' work at the union rate for apprentices which was approximately a dollar an hour below that paid to journeyman roofers. At the end of the month a list of employees was submitted to the general contractor with the invoice. The general contractor submitted the same list along with the lists from other subcontractors and his invoice to the government for payment. The name of the apprentice was not listed in the state apprentice program, and when this was discovered, the contracting officer refused to approve the invoice. The roofer obtained a written statement from the president of the local union that the worker was an apprentice and a statement from the government inspector that the apprentice did only work usually performed by apprentices. At a meeting, the subcontractor explained to the Contracting Officer that it was not his fault that the apprentice had failed to register. The Contracting Officer ruled that the workman was not an apprentice and should receive a journeyman's pay. He stated he was withholding money due the contractor until he had proof that the worker had been paid. The subcontractor tried to locate the apprentice. He had left town and could not be found. The contractor offered to pay the government or the union the sixteen dollars ($16); neither was accepted. Three months after the invoice was submitted, the Contracting Officer authorized payment to the contractor, but only after receiving written proof that the subcontractor had made every possible effort to locate the apprentice.

3. The foregoing transaction cost both the government and the contractor a great deal of money and illustrates why many contractors refuse

to bid upon government contracts and why others bid higher on government contracts than they would on private contracts.

4. One who was not living during the depression years of the Hoover and first Roosevelt administrations has a hard time realizing the need for an anti-kickback law. In 1934, the construction laborer making fifty cents an hour (50¢/hr) was considered lucky. Many were working for thirty-five cents per hour (35¢/hr) and glad to have the work. Bidding was extremely competitive on government projects, with twenty (20) or more contractors bidding on each project. The job went to the low bidder. The Davis-Bacon Act was passed to protect the workers by forcing the contractor to pay a living wage and bid accordingly. With the government checking payrolls, the contractors and subcontractors had no choice but to conform. Many employers made out checks in the proper amount to each employee and then demanded a cash return of a percentage for various reasons. The employee had no choice but to conform or lose the job, and there were plenty of others willing to take it. The Copeland "Anti-kickback" Act was passed to protect the workers.

5. When employment conditions are good, there is no need for labor laws. They are costly. The records and paperwork required from the contractor and the government personnel required to read and enforce the laws are an economic waste. Yet any member of Congress who proposed repeal of any of these laws would be branded as anti-labor.

19.12 WRITING FEDERAL SPECIFICATIONS

A. DIFFERENCES

One might presume that the specifications for government projects would be about the same as for a similar project for a private owner. In general there is little change; however, there are some differences which are required.

B. THE CONDITIONS

1. As the federal government usually furnishes printed forms for the Instructions to Bidders, the Proposal Form, and the Conditions, the specification writer working for the architectural or engineering firms can devote most of the time to writing the technical sections. However, the writer should read and be familiar with government requirements and bidding procedures. If the printed forms do not cover the conditions that the contractor will encounter at the job site, such items should be added to the specifications or called to the attention of the contracting officer.

2. State and local work varies. Some cities and states provide the archi-

tect or engineer with forms the same as the federal government. Others require the architects or engineers to provide complete contract documents. It is essential that specification writers preparing the bidding documents and conditions for a state or local government be informed as to the laws and requirements of that government.

C. CONTRACTING OFFICER

1. On U.S. government work there is but one person to whom the contractor is responsible: the administrative contracting officer. For this reason the administrative contracting officer is the only person mentioned in the specifications as representing the government. The contractor is not expected to know the differences between the administrative and purchasing contracting officer. This is government procedure. The specifications refer simply to the Contracting Officer.

2. On private work a specification reads, "the owner will furnish material and the assembly shall meet the approval of the architect or engineer." On federal work a specification reads, "the Government will furnish the material and the assembly shall meet the approval of the Contracting Officer."

D. RESTRICTIONS IN SPECIFICATIONS

1. Government Policy

a. It is government policy to encourage competition. Therefore, the various agencies discourage the use of brand-name specifications except when there is a single source and the use of that product is in the best interest of the government. For example, it might be better for the government to specify one brand name for the hardware when building an addition to an existing building in order to obtain the proper master-keying and to match the appearance of the two structures. Before writing a closed specification, the specification writer should present the reasons for so doing in writing to the procuring contracting officer in the agency financing the work. If the reasons are rejected, the clever writer can usually write a specification in such a manner that it appears to be open but is actually a closed specification.

b. A performance specification can become a de facto single-product specification when there is only one product on the market that will conform with the performance required. Likewise, a brand-name or equal specification can become a single-product specification if there is no product on the market equal to the standard specified. Such specifications have the appearance of an open specification, and, unless they are challenged by a supplier, will usually be accepted by the Contracting Officer. However, if they are challenged, the entire project can be delayed, and defending the specifications can be costly to all concerned.

c. There appear to be an increasing number of court cases challenging government specifications and it is becoming considerably more difficult for specification writers to obtain the quality of product they want. Most of the state and local courts have held that the government has a right to obtain the product specified. For example, a court in Ohio ruled that a bid for a bituminous concrete road can be rejected when a Portland cement road is specified. Likewise, the New Jersey Supreme Court upheld the specifications as indicated in the following case.

* 2. Kingston Bituminous Products Company v. City of Long Beach and Tar Asphalt Service, Inc. (12A 2d 227)

a. *The facts*

The City of Long Beach issued stringent specifications for the purchase of an asphalt liquid road oil. A sample was required to be submitted with the bid. Five bids were received. All but the low bidder were bidding on the same product. The low bidder's price was $0.185 per gallon lower than the next lowest bidder but did not conform to the specifications. The low bid was rejected and the award was made to the second lowest bidder. The low bidder brought action that eventually reached the Supreme Court of New Jersey.

b. *The plaintiff's case*

The low bidder claimed that the specifications and tests were so arbitrary, stringent, and severe that only one manufacturer's product was procurable, and therefore open competition was impossible. This was in violation of law. It was further argued that the requirements in the specifications and tests which they failed to meet were of no consequence and did not add to the quality, durability, or usability of the material. This showed bad faith on the part of the engineer in barring all but one material.

c. *The defendant's case*

The state claimed that for a number of years they had used the oil specified with excellent results.

d. *The decision*

The Court recognized that there was a sharp difference of opinion among experts, particularly in the allowable percentage of sulphur, and was reluctant to substitute its judgment on the matter. He ruled that limiting the amount of sulphur in the oil was a matter well within the discretion of the engineer and in the absence of

*Reported in *The Construction Specifier,* January 1974.

proof of fraud or bad faith, satisfactory past experience can justify a more restrictive specification than ordinarily might be considered acceptable.

e. *Comment*

From this decision, it would appear that, in the absence of fraud, satisfactory past experience can justify a restrictive specification.

3. The Federal Government

The federal courts and particularly the Armed Services Board of Contract Appeals are more apt to favor the contractor in disputes regarding specifications. This will be discussed in more detail in Chapter XXX.

E. FEDERAL PRISON PRODUCTS

Architects and engineers are encouraged to use the output of federal prisons in government construction. Lists of products to be used in federal work are available. Purchases are made directly by the agency and furnished to the contractor for installation.

F. GUIDE SPECIFICATIONS

Architects and engineers doing work for the federal government can usually obtain copies of the Corps of Engineers Guide Specifications. They are well-written and, if used properly, can be helpful. However, as the name implies, they are only a guide. They should not be copied verbatim.

G. COMPLETE AND CLEAR

1. Private and Government Projects

Specification writers working for professional architectural or engineering firms sometimes have difficulty when writing specifications for governmental agencies. The difficulty arises because a specification that is acceptable to a private owner will be a source of trouble on a government project. Government engineers responsible for checking specifications are often accused of being finicky because they demand long and precise work. Yet, they know the trouble caused by vague specifications.

2. Contractors

a. Government work can be hazardous for a contractor unfamiliar with the terms and procedures required. The contractor doing government work for the first time is sometimes overwhelmed by the extra paperwork and loses considerable time learning how the various forms should be completed.

b. There are many contractors who refuse to bid upon government projects as a matter of policy. There are other contractors who specialize on government work and seldom bid on private projects.

c. The contractor bidding on private work knows it is necessary to please the architect or engineer in order to obtain repeat business. Most architects and engineers will recommend that their clients bypass contractors who continuously cause trouble, and many corporations will refuse to consider contractors who ask for extras repeatedly. A contractor cannot afford to be barred from too many projects. As a result, contractors bidding on private work estimate the job with the intent of doing a complete job even though necessary components are not specified.

d. Contractors specializing in government work know that if they are the low bidder, they will be awarded the contract. As a rule, they know the law, both their rights and their obligations. To them government paperwork is routine. Such contractors appear to have an uncanny ability to find cheap and unsuitable materials that conform to the wording of the specifications. If the specifications are not complete and clear, they bid low on the base bid with the intention of demanding extras as the work progresses. They make their money on the extras. Unfortunately, many honest contractors bid on government work as they would on private work. After considerable bidding and seeing the work go to others, they confine their bidding to private contracts.

e. Of course, there are many honest contractors who build for the government. A complete and clear specification gives no advantage to the undesirable contractor. Many contractors would do good work even with poor specifications, but there are enough of the other type of contractors to make specification writing difficult, and the writer who is not careful is headed for trouble.

3. Writing

a. Government specifications should be exact. In specifying, the writer describes each product used in detail. This includes not only main products but small items such as nails, screws, and similar materials. Installation should be described step by step. Specification writers should review their work and try to find loopholes. If they are careful, they can avoid much trouble.

b. Specifications written to government standards can be used to advantage on private work, and some employers of specification writers prefer those who are familiar with government work. The specification writer trained in exact and precise wording is always in demand.

19.13 SUMMARY

A. Contracting with a government agency is filled with red tape. The general rules differ from common-law contract rules, and any architect, engineer, or contractor contemplating a first major contract with the federal government should consider all of the legal implications.

B. While this chapter emphasizes contracts with the federal government, many of the basic principles apply to state and local contracts. In general, state laws require competitive bidding, do not recognize common-law principles of apparent authority, and have controls to ensure that funds are not committed beyond budget allocations.

TWENTY

The General Conditions of the Contract

20.01 PURPOSE

The purpose of the General Conditions of the Contract is to establish the legal responsibility and relationship of all parties involved in the project. This includes the owner, the architect or engineer, the contractor, the subcontractors, and, indirectly, suppliers and employees of the contractor. It is important that this form be acceptable to the principal parties concerned.

20.02 USE

The General Conditions of the Contract include information of a general nature relative to any construction project. Because these conditions are general and apply to any project, it is not necessary to write a special section for each project, and there are many advantages to using a printed form. Many large corporations have printed forms that have been approved by their engineers and attorneys. These forms have been proofread for mistakes that might be costly. The form used by most architects and engineers is the General Conditions of the Contract for Construction prepared by the American Institute of Architects.

20.03 AIA GENERAL CONDITIONS

A. HISTORY

1. Early Years of the AIA

The American Institute of Architects was founded on February 23, 1857, in New York City by thirteen (13) idealistic architects led by

Richard Upjohn, the first president. Besides promoting state laws for registration of architects, they played a decisive role in establishing the nation's first architectural schools at Massachusetts Institute of Technology and Columbia University. The AIA continues to support matters concerning professional practice and publishes many documents for this purpose. The *General Conditions of the Contract for Construction* has been a standard for the construction industry for more than sixty (60) years and is used by professional engineers as well as architects. An earlier document known as the "Uniform Contract" was developed by the Institute in co-sponsorship with the National Association of Builders in 1888. In 1911, under the heading of "Standard Document," the AIA copyrighted what became the first edition of the *General Conditions of the Contract*. The Second Edition was published in 1915 after a thorough review of contract procedures. This document established the format for subsequent editions. The Third Edition in 1918 incorporated minor refinements. The principal change incorporated in the Fourth Edition in 1925 was the rearrangement of the order of the Articles into a more logical sequence. The Fifth Edition, published in 1937, the Sixth Edition in 1951, and the Seventh Edition in 1958 contained changes resulting from experience obtained in the years following the Great Depression and the Second World War. The Eighth Edition in 1961 and the Ninth Edition in 1963 clarified uncertainties concerning liability of the architect and his status and responsibilities during the construction of a project.

2. The Tenth Edition

Work was started on the Tenth Edition of the *General Conditions of the Contract* in 1964 and continued until the document was published in September 1966. This was not a revision of the previous editions; it was a complete rewriting in which a new format was established. Architects, attorneys, and insurance counselors assisted in the preparation of the new edition.

3. The Eleventh Edition

The Eleventh Edition was published in 1967, just one year after the Tenth Edition. It contained modifications, refinements, and editorial improvements resulting from experience gained in the field and deliberations with construction industry representatives and legal and insurance counsel.

4. The Twelfth Edition

a. In using the Eleventh Edition, the need for certain improvements became apparent as the result of legal interpretations, and in April of 1970 the Twelfth Edition was published. Article 2.2.1.2 of the Eleventh Edition gave the architect authority to stop work when he considered it necessary or advisable to ensure the proper implementation of the contract documents. The purpose of this clause was to permit the architect to stop construction if the contractor refused to correct defective work. Unfortunately, the courts have used this clause to hold the architect liable for injuries to workers because the architect failed to notice defects in construction and to stop work before the injury occurred. The *General Conditions* still permit the architect to reject defective work.

b. Other modifications were made as a result of joint deliberations by the Documents Boards of the American Institute of Architects and The Associated General Contractors of America. As a result, both organizations have approved and endorsed the use of the Twelfth Edition.

5. The Federal Edition

The American Institute of Architects publishes a Federal Edition of the *General Conditions* which is a supplement to the basic *General Conditions.* It modifies the wording of the documents to cover the procedures of the federal government and adds additional conditions required by law.

B. REASONS FOR REVISIONS

1. Through the past sixty (60) years, almost every article in the AIA *General Conditions* has been tested in the courts. To understand that statement, we must realize that legal decisions are based on past interpretations of the law. Our whole system of common law is formulated upon a series of court decisions going back hundreds of years to the courts of England. To say that a document is tested in the courts means people have in past lawsuits asked the courts to interpret the meaning of certain paragraphs in regard to special problems. Those decisions were made. If the same problem arose again, it would be decided in the same way. As a result, the former editions of the AIA *General Conditions* established a court history.

2. In publishing the *General Conditions,* the American Institute of Architects has always tried to select language that could be subject to only one interpretation. In some cases, the courts have not interpreted the wording as the AIA intended, and it was necessary to reword the document in order to express the desired intent. One might expect after sixty (60) years that the *General Conditions* would have reached a state of perfection that would require no additional changes. However, in our modern society, our laws, our standards, and our way of life have changed, and these changes are reflected in the decisions of our courts. Legal decisions regarding the payment of damages to workers injured on a construction site have been responsible for some of the recent changes in the *General Conditions.*

20.03 (Cont.)

C. LIABILITY FOR INJURY

1. Liability without fault is a legal concept that is finding support in the courts. It is sustained by the principle that someone should compensate those persons injured regardless of who or what is at fault. The architect or engineer is sometimes named in a suit when he is without fault. Even when others are required to pay the damages, the architect or engineer is required to bear the expense of defending himself.

2. The amount that an injured worker can collect under workmen's compensation is limited, and some of these amounts were established when the wage scale was less than it is today. As a result, the injured worker looks for someone to blame in order to collect just compensation for the injury. The architect or engineer is fair game, and several suits have been started to recover from him. The theory is that the architect or engineer has authority, and if there is the authority, there is a corresponding duty to act. The failure to act may constitute negligence.

D. TORT LIABILITY

1. Several lawsuits have been started because the clerk of the works failed to notice a dangerous condition in time to prevent a worker from being injured. The American Institute of Architects and the National Society of Professional Engineers have taken the stand that the contractor is responsible for safety at the job site. However, if the cause of an accident can be even remotely traced to negligence of the architect or his clerk of the works, they may be involved in a lawsuit with the possibility of being charged for the full amount of the damage.

2. The AIA in their *Information Bulletin Number One* gives an excellent example of tort liability. An architect designed an apartment building with a marquee at the front. Two years after construction the marquee fell on a man while he was boarding a taxicab. It fell because only eleven supports were specified, where twelve should have been specified, and the contractor installed only ten. The architect had the duty to design a safe structure. A person who breaches that duty may be held liable for injury of any person or property if the injury results directly from the breach of duty and if the person or property is within the scope of foreseeable danger. The fact that the contractor was also negligent is not important.

3. Several people may be responsible for one injury; the owner, the architect, the engineer, and the contractor may all be liable to the person injured by the fall of the marquee. Each of these may have been liable because of their own negligence. The concurrent negligence of others is not an excuse if one has been negligent oneself. The fact that one is more negligent than another is not an excuse.

The courts will not decide which of several defendants is the more negligent. If the hotel guest boarding the taxi in front of the hotel was hurt when the marquee fell, he might be able to sue successfully (a) the owner for maintaining an unsafe marquee, (b) the engineer for not specifying proper support, (c) the contractor for not following the requirements of the specifications, and (d) the architect for not observing that the contractor did not follow the specifications. The pedestrian might sue any one of them and recover in full, or might sue all of them and each would have to share equally in the verdict. The courts are not inclined to decide between those who are jointly negligent. This is important to remember when considering the matter of indemnification.

E. ADDITIONAL READING

For the reader who wishes to study the legal decisions involving the AIA *General Conditions,* the author recommends the purchase of the *Legal Citator* from any office of the American Institute of Architects. This loose-leaf book lists each article in the *General Conditions* and references the court decisions made on that article. Those decisions can be found in most legal libraries. The specification writer should be familiar with these decisions and should follow all new decisions as they are published.

20.04 ENGINEERS GENERAL CONDITIONS

The National Society of Professional Engineers publishes the *Standard General Conditions of the Construction Contract* to be used in place of the AIA document on engineering projects. This specification is not as well-known as the AIA *General Conditions* and does not have the same historical background of court decisions. However, it is a well-written document and is preferred by many engineers. It should be noted that nowhere in the specification is the statement regarding time being the essence of the contract. The specification writer should remember to place such a statement in the Special Conditions when he specifies time.

20.05 REASONS FOR USING AIA OR NSPE *GENERAL CONDITIONS*

A. There are several good reasons for using the AIA or NSPE *General Conditions.* One advantage is saving typing time. Typing is costly.

B. Another reason is avoiding the possibility of errors. Mistakes in copying are not unusual, and there are cases where a typist omitted the word "not," completely changing the meaning.

C. Both the AIA and the NSPE *General Conditions* carry a copyright. Any other general conditions would have to be composed. This takes time.

There are few companies that can afford to spend the time required to research and write as complete a document.

D. The historical precedent established by the AIA in more than half a century of continuous use of their document permits precedents to be established in the courts. The engineers, working with their attorneys, have considered these precedents in preparing the wording of their General Conditions.

E. The wording is familiar to most contractors and is readily understood. There is little room for argument.

F. Both documents are fair and equitable.

20.06 COPIES

Copies of both the Twelfth Edition of the AIA *General Conditions of the Contract for Construction* and the 1974 edition of the NSPE *Standard General Conditions of the Construction Contract* appear in the Appendix. They are subject to revision. Users should always assure themselves that they are using the latest edition.

20.07 USE AS A REFERENCE SPECIFICATION

A. As the AIA *General Conditions* is well-known to most contractors, the author has used it as a reference specification by placing a simple statement in the section entitled "General Conditions." A suggested wording would be: "The Twelfth Edition of the *General Conditions of the Contract for Construction* as published by the American Institute of Architects is a part of this specification to the same extent as if bound herein. Copies may be obtained from the Architect (or Engineer) upon request."

B. The author has used the above statement for many years without ever being asked for a copy of the *General Conditions.* The purpose of the statement about furnishing copies is to overcome any possible legal objection.

C. The American Institute of Architects does not approve of this method. They recommend that a copy of their *General Conditions* be bound into each set of specifications.

20.08 SUPPLEMENTARY CONDITIONS

Some architectural and engineering offices that use published *General Conditions* also issue a section entitled "Supplementary General Conditions," or simply, "Supplementary Conditions." This section is used where the architect or engineer wishes to make changes in, or additions to, the printed form. The American Institute of Architects publishes a *Guide to Supplementary Conditions* for a reference. However, many writers prefer to place any addition required to the General Conditions in the Special Conditions.

TWENTY-ONE

Special Conditions

21.01 SCOPE

The Special Conditions are sometimes called "Supplementary General Conditions of the Contract." The name is not too important, but it is necessary to note the difference between the Special Conditions and the General Conditions. Special Conditions are concerned with items that do not appear in the General Conditions. General Conditions apply to all construction jobs designed in an architectural or engineering office. Special Conditions are written to apply only to one particular project. The specification writer should remember that the entire book of specifications is not read from cover to cover by anybody but himself and possibly the owner. The subcontractors usually read only the technical sections with which they are involved and the Special Conditions. They are familiar with the General Conditions and, except for the due date, they are not usually interested in the Bid Form or the Instructions to Bidders. The general contractors are interested in the Instructions to Bidders, the Bid Form, and the Special Conditions. Their interest in the technical sections is mainly to be assured that all items are covered. All bidders should read the Special Conditions; it is the section in the book most read.

21.02 PRIORITIES

Should there be a discrepancy between the drawings and the specifications, the specifications will govern. If there is a discrepancy between any section and the Special Conditions within the book of specifications, the Special Conditions will govern. This is generally understood, but for legal reasons it should be stated in the specifications.

21.03 OUTLINE

The following outline is to assist the student in preparing this section of a specification. Under each heading are notes explaining the items of work that should be included.

21.04 SCOPE OF THE PROJECT

"Scope of the project" includes an outline of the project involved in the construction. If there is an alteration in the work or an addition to an old building, the scope of the project becomes involved. Its purpose is to give a general, overall word picture of the project. The details are specified in the technical sections of the specification.

21.05 WORK BY OTHERS

Often the owners intend to do certain work with their own forces when building a structure. If the owners expect to install all the machinery themselves and want all the electrical work to be performed by others, the specifications should so state. It is very important when more than one contractor is doing work on a project that the limits of each contract be completely defined. When one piece of work ties into another, it is important to state who is responsible for the connection.

21.06 THE SITE

A. LOCATION

Each subcontractor and the contractor must know where the work is located. The street address, city, county, and state appear in the specifications.

B. RAILROAD FACILITIES

The cost of the work will depend on the cost of delivering materials to the site. If materials have to be transferred from railroad car to truck, the cost will change. It should be stated whether or not there are railroad facilities. If there are none available, it should be so stated.

C. VISITING THE SITE

It should be the responsibility of the contractor and all subcontractors to visit the site. The specifications should so state. However, the owners might object to having unidentified persons around on their property. Usually in such cases, the owners provide for people to escort the contractors and subcontractors around the site of the proposed work. If contractors can visit the site at any time, it should be so stated in the Special Conditions. If there is any time limit or formality required, it should be so stated.

D. PARKING

Today most employees drive to work. Is the owner going to provide parking space for the employees of the contractor or must they pay for their own? It might make a difference. If the owner doesn't want to have the contractor's employees in his parking lot, it is up to the architect-engineer to so state in the specifications.

E. STORAGE SPACE

In construction, certain items must be on hand. Normally these items are shipped to the job site and stored there. If storage space is available, it should be stated; or if no storage space is available, as in the building of a downtown skyscraper, that situation should be noted. If the owner will provide no storage space for the contractor, it could be a costly item to the contractor.

21.07 DRAWINGS AND SPECIFICATIONS

A. SETS FURNISHED

The printing of drawings and specifications is rather expensive. The architect-engineer's fee is somewhat limited. The architect-engineer should state how many sets of plans and specifications he will furnish the contractor without charge. If additional sets are required, the contractor should be permitted to have additional sets at the cost of the printing. In no case should the architect-engineer furnish less than six (6) sets free; in many cases twelve (12) or thirteen (13) sets are needed.

B. CONFLICTS

It is generally assumed that the specifications govern over the drawings and that the Special Conditions govern over sections in the specifications. Very often these things are stated in print to prevent any litigation.

C. SHOP DRAWINGS

1. Detailed drawings are often needed by subcontractors to fabricate or erect their work. A good example is structural steel. The architect-engineer designs the sizes of beams and columns. The type of connections wanted is usually specified. It is up to the detailer to examine each individual beam and determine the length and the number of rivets in each connection. In sizable structures, shop drawings can amount to hundreds of drawings. Extreme accuracy is needed; consequently, drawings are checked and rechecked to prevent errors from occurring.

2. Shop drawings are mentioned in both the AIA and NSPE *General Conditions.* If either of these forms is used, the statements in the Special

Conditions should be coordinated to ensure that there is no discrepancy.

3. Under this heading, the method of submitting shop drawings should be described for both contractors and subcontractors. This includes the number of copies of drawings required, how they should be submitted, whether or not they should be checked by the contractor before submittal, when the approved drawings will be returned, how the approved drawings will be stamped and distributed, and how the drawings which are not approved will be handled.

21.08 NOISE

Around a hospital or sometimes around office buildings, the least possible noise is desirable. However, there are certain noises, such as rivet guns, which can cause serious disturbance. Sometimes it is specified that noise should be limited to certain times of the day. If this is a requirement, it must be stated in the specifications.

21.09 TIME

A. GENERAL

Article 8 of the AIA *General Conditions* defines time, establishes that time is of the essence of the contract, and covers delays and extensions of time. The Special Conditions should cover the time of completion and any bonuses or penalties. Refer to Chapter XIV in this book. It should be remembered that, if the AIA *General Conditions* are not used, the fact that time is of the essence of the contract must be established someplace in the specifications to make completion dates effective.

B. SPECIFIED TIME

1. When construction must be completed by a specific date, that date must be specified. As the completion date depends upon the time construction starts, the latest date that the notice to proceed may be issued must also be given.

2. Where the completion time is established as a specific number of days, the number of days must be specified along with a definition of a day. Refer to paragraph 14.03 C. 3. in this book.

C. UNSPECIFIED TIME

Where the contractor establishes the time, the time is written into the contract. The specifications should cover the penalties in the event that the contractor is delinquent.

21.09 (Cont.)

D. BONUSES, PENALTIES, AND LIQUIDATED DAMAGES

1. Any bonus and penalty clause must be described in detail. In writing such a clause, it must be realized the wording might be subject to legal interpretation.

2. If liquidated damages are established, they must be spelled out. It also must be clear that the liquidated damages are predetermined damages that the owner will suffer if the work is not completed on time and are not a penalty.

21.10 OVERTIME

Sometimes contracts are written stating that work must be completed within a certain time, and the contractor is required to work Saturdays in order to keep the work up to schedule. The specification should state who pays for overtime.

21.11 SUNDAYS, HOLIDAYS, AND HOLY DAYS

Having a contractor using rivet guns or pouring concrete on a church addition during religious services could be distracting to the congregation. Work on church work is usually forbidden on Sundays and holy days. As various denominations do not recognize the same holy days, the dates work is forbidden should be in the specifications. On recreational facilities, hotels, or restaurants the owner may wish to prohibit construction on holidays. The dates work is forbidden should be specified.

21.12 CHANGES IN THE WORK

A. An owner may wish to make a change in the construction after the contract is signed. Provisions should be made in the specifications for such possibility.

B. The method of making changes should be described in detail in the Special Conditions. The authority of the clerk of the works to make or sign field orders should be stated.

C. As the exact method of handling bulletins, change orders, or work orders and field orders varies from office to office, a full description is required. Changes are one of the areas of contention between the owner and the contractor. Every effort should be made to cover all areas where disputes could arise. See Chapter XV.

21.13 INVOICING

Contractors are primarily interested in how they will be paid. While the method of partial payments is well established, various offices and various owners have procedures that differ. Contractors should be told exactly how they should submit their bills, when these should be submitted, and to whom. The percentage of withholding should be stated. If they are required to fill out specific forms, it should be stated who furnishes the forms and how they are to be completed.

21.14   PARTIAL ACCEPTANCE

A. Most owners want to move into their building before completion. Normally, the contractor has the right to his work without interference from the owner. This can lead to arguments. The author worked on a project that caused such a disagreement. A new factory building was nearing completion and the painting subcontractor was ready to paint the underside of the steel roof deck over the crane bay and sixty feet (60) above the floor. The work was delayed because the painting foreman wanted to use the overhead crane, and it was necessary to wait until it was connected electrically. This traveling crane extended over a railroad track and a storage area and it was the subcontractors intention to build a platform on the crane from which the painters would work, the crane moving from bay to bay as the painters proceeded with the painting. About the time the subcontractor was ready to proceed with the painting, carloads of the owner's machinery began arriving at the plant, and the owner wanted to use the crane to unload the railroad cars and spot his equipment. He was willing to accept the crane, the crane rails and the electrical equipment required to operate the crane and make a final payment to the contractor for this equipment. The owner wanted to continue using the crane and expected the contractor to build a scaffold for the painters. The specifications did not cover this situation. The author decided in favor of the contractor, thus earning the owner's ill will. As a result, a change order was issued deleting the painting of the roof deck from the contract.

B. If the owner intends to occupy the building before the completion date, specific terms should be stated in the specifications. The owner should pay in full for the parts of the building accepted and the contractor should furnish the owner all of the warrants and guarantees required dated the date of the partial acceptance. The specification writer should try to visualize problems that might arise and provide the answers ahead of time.

21.15   FINAL PAYMENT

As the final payment is usually a sizable sum of money, the date the payment is due is important to the contractor. Contractors should know when to expect their money and what must be done to be entitled to final payment.

TWENTY-TWO

The General Contractor's Work

22.01 SEPARATE SECTION

Some specification writers combine the section on the General Contractor's Work with the Special Conditions. Others write separate sections for each. Either method is acceptable.

22.02 SCOPE

As the architects or engineers do not know, when they write the specifications, what trades the contractor will perform with the contractor's own forces and what trades will be subcontracted, they assume that all trades will be sublet and write their specifications in that manner. However, the contractor does have some work to do even if every trade is sublet. It is about this work that the chapter is written.

22.03 HEADINGS

The following is a list of items that should appear under the heading of General Contractor's Work, whether written in a separate section or combined in the Special Conditions.

22.04 PERFORMANCE BOND

A Performance Bond is a bond sold by a bonding company guaranteeing that the project will be completed. The contractor buys the bond from a bonding company, and in the event he is unable to finish the project, the bonding company is obligated to complete the contract. They do this by awarding the work to another contractor. Performance Bonds are not necessary; but if one is required, it should be so stated in the specifications.

22.05 APPROVALS

A. SUBCONTRACTORS

1. About eighty-five percent (85%) of building construction is done by subcontractors. Therefore, the architect or engineer should require the general contractor to submit a list of the subcontractors he intends to employ on the job. This list should be approved before the contract is signed. In examining the list, the architect or engineer may ask the general contractor to substitute different subcontractors for the ones listed. It must be remembered that the contractor has used the price quoted by the listed subcontractor in consolidating a bid. If the architect or engineer asks that the general contractor change subcontractors, the cost to the general contractor would probably increase and he would have to be reimbursed by the owner. However, it is possible that the cost would be small compared with the superior service. A change might be worthwhile.

2. Approval of subcontractors is covered in the AIA *General Conditions.* If the AIA *General Conditions* are used and no additional conditions are required on the project being considered, this article could be omitted from the general contractor's work.

B. OPTIONS

Optional materials and methods are often specified. If options are specified, it is assumed that any one of the options specified is acceptable and there should be no need for approvals. However, where the use of an "or equal" material is proposed by the contractor, the method to obtain approval from the architect or engineer should be specified. The specifications should also make the party using an "or equal" material responsible for the correct installation. The importance of this was brought to the author's attention some time ago. A mechanical contractor proposed and received approval to use an air compressor that was represented to be equal to the one specified. When it was placed in the pit, the grating specified to cover the pit couldn't be placed because the compressor was slightly taller than the one specified. Fortunately, the specifications required the mechanical subcontractor to reimburse the general contractor for deepening the pit.

C. SUBSTITUTIONS

Sometimes, when a method is specified, a contractor knows a less expensive way of obtaining the same results. Some architects welcome suggestions, others do not. If suggestions are desired, the method of submitting them should be described under this heading. If the architect or engineer wishes no changes, the same should be stated under this heading.

22.06 PERMITS AND INSPECTIONS

Usually the architect or the engineer obtains the general building permit. However, all other approvals or permits, such as for the use of public fire hydrants, and inspections of plumbing, electrical, and other work are usually arranged and paid for by the general contractor or his subcontractors. Who arranges for permits and who pays for them should be stated under this heading.

22.07 INSURANCE

Article eleven in the AIA *General Conditions* specifies insurance in general terms. The amount of protection required in each type of insurance should be specified under this heading. Purchasing insurance is a part of the general contractor's work. The owners must decide how much protection they are willing to pay for. As the owners of the property, they can be held liable for damages to an injured party resulting from construction. If the owners wish subcontractors to carry insurance, it should be specified.

22.08 FIRE PROTECTION

A. GENERAL

The owner should be protected against fire, and the specifications should specify procedures that would limit or prevent fires.

B. OPEN FIRES

It is quite handy on a job to build an open fire to burn rubbish, but this may be objectionable in certain places. If a permit is needed, it should be so stated. If open fires are forbidden, this should be stated.

C. TAR KETTLES

Tar kettles are required for most roofing and waterproofing. Almost all tar kettles are heated with an open flame. This could be a fire hazard. If tar kettles are required on a project, specific conditions should be specified for their use, such as the distance they must be kept from buildings or other structures.

D. WELDING

There are some places where welding could be dangerous. In such cases welding should be forbidden in the specifications. There are other places where welding may be required. If the contractor is required to take any precautions, such precautions should be specified.

E. SMOKING

If for any reason smoking is forbidden, the same should be specified.

22.08 (Cont.)

F. OWNER'S FIRE EQUIPMENT

To say anything in the specifications that would lead the contractor to believe the owner's fire-fighting equipment could be depended upon in the event of a fire could involve the owner in a lawsuit. Where tar kettles are required, where welding is specified, or where the danger of fire exists, it is better to require the contractor or his subcontractor to furnish fire extinguishers or fire hoses. Normally, the subcontractor would furnish fire extinguishers with his equipment; however, some specification writers prefer to make the contractor responsible for fire protection. The specifications should be clear as to what is required from the contractor and from the various subcontractors.

22.09 WORK SCHEDULE

Establishing schedules is a part of the contractor's work. The purpose of a schedule is to determine the economic time in cases where the time is established by the contractor, and the labor requirements where the time of completion is established. An equally important function of a schedule is to establish when the various subcontractors will be at the job site. Many contractors prefer the "critical path" type of schedule. By requiring the contractor to submit a schedule for approval, the architect or engineer forces the contractor to plan his job within the time limit specified. From the schedule it is possible to determine whether the progress of the work in the field is adequate to meet the completion date. The type of schedule required should be specified.

22.10 SUPERVISION OF THE WORK

A. SUPERINTENDENT

The contractor should employ a general superintendent to supervise the project. The superintendent should have authority to act in the absence of others. If the job is such that it requires the services of a full-time superintendent, it should be stated. Otherwise, the contractor could provide part-time supervision.

B. PROFESSIONAL ENGINEER

A professional engineer or a professional surveyor should be on the job to lay out the work to make sure the project is properly located. Owners have found themselves in trouble when the contractor, by mistake, extended the work beyond the property line. Levels should be maintained. Large jobs or work of a complex nature should have the services of a capable engineer to design formwork and shoring, to protect adjacent property, and to prevent accidents. Requiring the contractor to employ a professional engineer may save the owner many troubles.

It should be noted that hiring a professional engineer does not relieve the general contractor of the responsibility for doing the work right. It does give the owner some protection against delays due to mistakes.

C. SUBCONTRACTOR'S SUPERVISION

1. Supervisors

It is up to the general contractor to coordinate the work of the subcontractors.

2. Storage of Material and Equipment

If the owner has space available for the storage of equipment, the responsibility for assigning the space to the various subcontractors belongs with the general contractor. The specifications should give him that authority and also the responsibility for keeping the area clean and materials neatly piled.

3. Cooperation with Owner and Architect-Engineer

It is up to the contractor and all subcontractors to cooperate with the owner and the architect or engineer as far as possible and assist them in making their inspections.

4. Fitting and Drillings

a. If a general contractor has a contract to furnish a complete structure, it is understood that he must furnish and install with his own forces all work required by the contract documents that is not performed by subcontractors. At times, a subcontractor will ask the specification writer to interpret the specifications regarding who should do what. That the question is asked reveals a weakness in the specifications and is the type of question the specification writer should avoid answering. The specification writer has no business being involved in an argument between a contractor and subcontractor, even when it appears that the contractor is imposing upon the subcontractor. If a concrete wall is poured before pipe sleeves are in place, someone must drill the holes through the concrete. Who does the work does not involve the architect or engineer.

b. If the owner has contracts with several contractors to do various phases of the work and then assigns the contracts to a general contractor, the situation is different because the general contractor has no control of the wording of the contract. An assigned contractor is not the same as a subcontractor.

c. Where separate contracts are awarded and assignment is contemplated, it is advisable that the specifications contain a paragraph on fitting and drilling. This paragraph would require the general contractor to coordinate the work, and to perform with his own forces any drilling and fitting that was required to join the work of the various assigned contractors. The general contractor would include the cost of such work in the proposal.

5. Finishes

With various subcontractors doing work on various phases of a project, it is possible to obtain finishes meeting the specifications that do not match exactly. To get a structure that is complete and to the owner's satisfaction, somebody has to coordinate the work. The one person who can do this is the general contractor. If the exact matching of finishes is a part of the job requirements, it should be so stated in the specifications and the responsibility for obtaining matching items should be given to the general contractor.

22.11 TEMPORARY WORK

A. DEFINITION

"Temporary work" is work that has to be built to complete a project and that is torn down or removed after the project is completed.

B. BUILDINGS

1. Office

The clerk of the works needs an office with a desk, a place to work, and possibly space to hold meetings. In addition, the general contractor needs an office on the project. In one of those two offices, space should be provided for meetings with subcontractors. The architect or engineer has to be specific about what he wants in his own office. If he wants a good floor, or wants heat and light, he must say so. Usually the specifications also require the general contractor to provide janitor service.

2. Sheds and Trailers

a. Certain materials must be protected from the weather and sheds are built to protect them. Sheds are also required to protect small items from being lost or stolen. They should be inexpensive but so constructed to present a reasonably tidy appearance. The specifications should so state.

b. Many contractors have found it advantageous to use trailers that can be moved to the various job sites in lieu of building temporary offices and sheds. If the trailers are of the proper size and appearance, there should be no objection. Giving the contractor an option could save the owner money.

3. Sanitary Facilities

a. Sanitary facilities must be furnished for all workers. The type of sanitary conveniences should be stated in the specifications.

b. The owner may have other buildings on the site and might prefer to use them rather than pay for temporary facilities. If so, the specifications should specify the location, the conduct of the contractor's employees while going to, coming from, and using the owner's facilities. Provision should be made for the maintenance of these facilities either by the owner or by the contractor. The specifications should be explicit as to the responsibility of each party.

c. The owner may not want the contractor's employees in his buildings, or the project may be on a new site where there are no facilities. If this is the case, the contractor should be required to construct temporary sanitary facilities for the employees and his subcontractor's employees.

4. Maintenance

The method and requirements for maintaining all temporary buildings should be specified.

C. UTILITIES

1. Water

Water is one of the main materials needed to construct a building. Where is water obtainable? It is necessary for the general contractor to know. If water must be transported, the general contractor should be informed of it because it is a costly item. Sometimes it is necessary to dig a well. This should be so stated in the specifications.

2. Temporary Heat

a. *Temporary buildings*

Certain temporary buildings, such as the architect-engineer's office, should be heated. Who will pay the cost of heating should be specified.

b. *New Construction*

(1) Until the building is enclosed it is desirable to have the general contractor supply the heat; but after the heating system is in, who is going to supply the heat? This is a question that has been debated many times. There has been no completely satisfactory method.

(2) The owner could supply heat using the newly installed heating system. This has objections because it requires the heating system to be turned over to the owner before the work is complete. The contractor couldn't be responsible for the system after it has been used and possibly abused by the owner.

(3) The general contractor could be required to heat the building using the newly installed heating system. This can lead to trouble because the general contractor can abuse the system. The heating subcontractor cannot be responsible for the misuse of the equipment. Requiring the general contractor to replace damaged parts is not a completely satisfactory method.

(4) The specifications can require the heating subcontractor to supply the temporary heat. This has the advantage of having the subcontractor who furnished the system responsible for its operation. However, the heating subcontractor has a difficult time establishing costs. He is not responsible for the length of the contract and cannot control heat being wasted by others.

(5) If the owner wants a heating system delivered in a new and unused condition, the contractor would be required to set up a temporary heating system. This could be expensive.

(6) In areas where temporary heat could be a problem, the specifications should be explicit. Temporary heat can be expensive, and the specification should cover all phases of the problem.

3. Electric Power

With modern tools, most trades use electric power during the construction period. For each subcontractor to install individual temporary power would be costly. Usually the general contractor provides temporary power throughout the project which can be used by all subcontractors. If that is the intention, it should be so stated in the specifications. Voltage and current should be stated so that the general contractor knows what must be supplied and subcontractors know the character of the current to be furnished.

4. Telephone

It would be unreasonable to expect the general contractor to pay for all long-distance calls made by the clerk of the works. As a rule, the general contractor pays for the installation of a telephone for the clerk of the works and pays for the local calls; the architect or engineer pays for his own long-distance calls. In addition, telephones should be installed for the use of subcontractors. The contractor should have the option of installing a pay station for subcontractors. Telephones should be specified if they are needed.

D. CONSTRUCTION AIDS

1. Ladders and Hoists

If the general contractor is required to provide ladders, it should be stated in the specifications. On large, multistory construction jobs, it is usually cheaper to have the general contractor supply the hoists for all trades than have each subcontractor erect and disassemble his own.

2. Pumping

If rain water accumulates on the job, somebody should be responsible for seeing that this water is pumped to the sewer or ditches. The contractor responsible should be stated in the specifications.

3. Temporary Roadways

It is costly if subcontractors are unable to proceed because somebody neglected to install temporary roads. It is not economical to have high-price mechanics spending hours getting their trucks out of the mud. If temporary roadways are required, the specifications should state who will build and maintain them.

E. PROTECION

1. Public and Adjacent Property

If a building is adjacent to the owner's property, it should be the general contractor's duty to protect that building and keep it from being damaged.

2. Present Structures

If there are present structures, protection of these structures should be specified.

3. Trees and Shrubs

If it is the owner's wish to protect trees, a method of protection should be specified.

4. Protection for the Owners, Employees, and General Public

The general contractor should be required to protect the public with barricades, etc. If this is not done, the owner could be held for damages.

5. Guards

A structure way out in the country might not need a guard. At other times it may be desirable to have a guard to prevent children from playing on the site. If somebody is hurt when there is no guard, the owner doesn't have much legal protection. A guard can also guard against theft.

F. PHOTOGRAPHS

Very often the owner wants photographs showing the progress of the job. If photographs are desired by the owner, they should be specified. The number, the size, and the binding should appear under this heading.

G. CLEANING UP

Keeping the job site clean and cleaning up the building during construction introduces many problems. Each subcontractor creates debris. In addition, employees' lunch papers and other debris can soon cause a messy-looking area. The architect or engineer can save a lot of trouble by making the general contractor responsible for seeing that the property is maintained in a clean condition at all times.

TWENTY-THREE

Workmen's Compensation

23.01 DEFINITION

Workmen's compensation laws are state statutes under which an employer is bound to pay a predetermined amount of compensation for any injury suffered by an employee.

23.02 THE COMMON LAW

A. Under the common law an employer had no duty to compensate an employee injured at work, while the employee was disabled, unless the injury resulted from negligence on the part of the employer. However, the employer would not be considered negligent if a safe place to work, safe equipment, and properly shielded machines were provided, and if the employer warned the employees of hidden dangers and used care in not employing careless workers.

B. In order to collect damages, an injured employee would have to show that the employer was negligent. However, the employer who was proved negligent in every possible way could still defeat the action in any one of three ways. If the employee was negligent in the least degree, that contributory negligence was a complete defense for the employer. If the employee knew of the danger and continued working, he assumed the risk as a part of the employment for which payment was being made; this was also a defense for the employer. The third defense was the "fellow servant rule" making the employer not liable if the injury was caused by the negligence of a fellow employee.

C. The employer also had another aid: hunger. If by chance the employee was able to win a judgment, the employer could appeal and delay. In time, the injured man with no income would be forced to drop the case. The one rule that favored the employee was that, if he could collect, the common law put no limit on the amount of money it was possible to receive.

23.03   THE WORKMEN'S COMPENSATION STATUTES

A. The introduction of power machinery caused the number of industrial accidents to increase manyfold and created a demand for laws for the protection of workers. The Employers' Liability Act was adopted in England in 1880. In 1908 the Federal Employment Compensation Act was passed to protect federal employees. In 1911, ten (10) states passed workmen's compensation acts. The state of Washington and the state of Kansas were the first states to pass such a bill on March 14, 1911. Today all of the states have such an act.

B. The laws of the various states differ in detail. In general, under workmen's compensation, the employer is liable for all accidental injuries to employees that occur in the employer's employment, without regard to fault or negligence as a cause. The three (3) defenses of the employer, contributory negligence, assumption of risk, and fellow servant rule, are abolished. The employee may appear before a commission without an attorney to state a case. Hearings conducted by the commission to determine the facts are informal. However, there is a fixed scale of payment for each type of injury. This is usually a percentage of the employee's pay; it is paid for a specific number of weeks with an established maximum amount of money an injured worker can receive.

C. The amount of money an employee can collect for a specific type of accident varies considerably from state to state. However, the maximum amount of money one may receive was established many years ago, and while this amount may have been liberal when established, it is considered inadequate today.

23.04   THIRD-PARTY LIABILITY

An employer who has taken out proper insurance in compliance with the workmen's compensation law is free from further liability to the employee. The money the employee receives from the insurance company is a complete settlement with the employer. The employee does not, however, lose his rights against third persons who, by their negligent or willful conduct, may have been responsible for the injury. There is no statutory limit on the amount the injured party may collect from a third party.

23.05   RESULTS OF WORKMEN'S COMPENSATION

A. With the passage of workmen's compensation laws, insurance companies began selling protection to the various industries. To determine the cost of the policy, the risk had to be established. Thus, the safety engineer came into being. It soon became apparent to industry that insurance was expensive when risks were high and considerable effort was expended in developing safe machinery. Today many plants are proud of their safety record and publish their accident record.

B. Another result of workmen's compensation is caused by dissatisfaction with the law. The courts today are more liberal with the amount paid for injuries than they were years ago. With the amount an employee can receive from the employer established by law, the injured person is looking for other parties from whom to collect additional money. The architects and engineers are often considered possible parties to sue for injuries on construction jobs. This will be discussed in the following chapter.

23.06 OTHER BOOKS

An entire book could be written on the various phases of the Workmen's Compensation Act in the various states. The records contain hundreds of cases regarding the administration of the act, who is covered, the type of injury covered, when the employer is responsible, the amount of compensation payable, and similar matters. Such cases are well-written in other books and beyond the scope of this text. There are a few cases, however, that apply directly to specifications; these follow.

23.07 CASES

A. MILLER & ROSE v. INDUSTRIAL COMMISSION OF WISCONSIN & RICH (1928)

1. Facts

a. Mrs. Fern Rich was the widow of Harry Rich, who was accidentally killed while performing at the State Fair Amusement Park in Milwaukee, Wisconsin. The commission had awarded compensation to Mrs. Fern Rich against Miller and Rose, who had engaged Rich to give his exhibition. Miller and Rose applied to the court for a review of the Commission's award.

b. Harry Rich was a professional entertainer going from place to place. He paid his own expenses, furnished his own apparatus, and was not subject to control by Miller and Rose. He secured contracts in advance. His contract called for a lump-sum payment.

2. The Law

If a person is injured while working for an independent contractor, that person's primary claim is against the contractor and not against the owner of the property on which the person was hurt. The whole basis of the Workmen's Compensation Act presupposes the relation of master and servant or employer and employee. If the relationship between the injured party and the employer is one of independent contractor and owner, there is no liability to pay compensation. However, if the contractor is not an independent contractor and legally has the status of being an employee of the owner, then the claim is against the owner, because technically the owner is the employer, not only of the contractor, but also of the contractor's workmen.

3. Decision

The court held for Miller and Rose and set aside the award to Mrs. Rich. It was ruled that Rich was an independent contractor, as he was his own master and subject to no one; he was an independent performer in business for himself and could no more be an employee than would be Paderewski, Chaliapin, or Madame Schumann-Heink.

B. BUTLER ST. FOUNDRY & IRON CO. v. INDUSTRIAL BOARD OF ILLINOIS (1917)

1. Facts

a. Frank Willman, Jr., was an employee of John Martin, a subcontractor doing work for the Butler Street Foundry and Iron Company, a contractor for the erection of structural ironwork on a building in Chicago. On October 14, 1915, Willman sustained an injury in the course of his employment which resulted in his death. At the time of the injury, Martin carried no Workmen's Compensation Insurance. The widow, who was also the administratrix of the estate, was awarded three thousand five hundred dollars ($3,500) plus fifty dollars ($50) expended in first aid and one hundred eighty-three dollars and thirty-three cents ($183.33) for medical, surgical, and hospital services to be recovered against Martin and the Butler Street Foundry and Iron Company jointly or severally. The Butler Street Foundry and Iron Company petitioned the circuit court of Cook County to review the case on the grounds that they did require the subcontractors to take out insurance—even lent them money to do so; therefore, only the subcontractor should be held liable. The circuit court did review the case and supported the decision of the Industrial Board. Then the contractor appealed the case to the Supreme Court of Illinois.

b. The Butler Street Foundry and Iron Company was able to prove that on several occasions they had directed Martin to take out insurance for the protection of his employees, and Martin had said he would take out such insurance. On the day before Willman was injured, the contractor advanced Martin two hundred dollars ($200) to pay for the insurance. This money was used by Martin to pay off his men, and no part of the sum was used to buy insurance. The contractor insisted that, by demanding that Martin take out insurance and advancing him money to do so, he had done all that was required.

2. The Law

a. *Joint and Several Judgements*

(1) A "joint judgment" means that the debt is owed by two or more parties. The entire amount can be collected from any one of the parties.

(2) A "several judgment" collection can be made for a specific part of the judgment. If not otherwise stated, it would be assumed that the parts would be equal. If a several judgment was made against three parties, each would be responsible for one-third, unless otherwise stated.

(3) In a "joint or several judgment," collection can be made either way. In a case where one party is financially strong and the other weak, it might be easier to assume a joint judgment and collect the entire amount from the financially strong party, and let him collect what he can from the other party.

b. *Responsibility*

Any subcontractor is responsible for employees injured in the course of their employment. Likewise, a contractor is responsible for employees on his payroll who are injured. The law in the state of Illinois states that if a contractor does not "require" the subcontractor to insure the subcontractor's liability to pay the compensation provided in the act, the contractor and subcontractor are jointly and severally liable to pay the compensation.

c. *Amount*

The Illinois law, at that time, in paragraph a., section 8, limited the liability of an employer for necessary first aid, medical, surgical, and hospital services to two hundred dollars ($200.00)

3. Decision

a. The Court reversed the lower court on the grounds the "total amount which can be awarded for first aid, medical, surgical, and hospital services is the sum of two hundred dollars ($200). The award of two hundred thirty-three dollars and thirty-three cents ($233.33) for such services was in excess of the limitation prescribed in the statute, and should have been approved and confirmed only in the sum of two hundred dollars."

b. The Court did support the circuit court in that the contractor was responsible and was rightfully named jointly with the subcontractor as liable. "By making it a part of his contract with the subcontractor, the contractor can require him to take out this insurance as easily and effectively as he can require him to perform any other provision of the contract between them."

C. DAVIS v. INDUSTRIAL COMMISSION (1921)

1. Davis was in the hardware business. He also owned an apartment house. He contracted with Greenough Company to clean the outside walls of the apartment. Two employees of Greenough, while cleaning the walls, fell from a scaffold. Greenough was insolvent and had no liability insurance. The employees obtained an award for compensation against Davis. Upon appeal by Davis, the Circuit Court affirmed this decision. Davis then appealed to the Supreme Court of Illinois.

2. Davis contended that he was in the hardware business and not engaged in the business of maintaining buildings. In no respect was he a general contractor.

3. The Supreme Court held that it was not necessary for him to be exclusively engaged in a hazardous occupation to make him liable to compensation. The business the owner was engaged in at the time was in maintaining his buildings. The lower-court judgment was affirmed.

23.08 SUMMARY

From the foregoing cases, it should be apparent that the owner can be held liable by failure of a contractor to pay compensation. The architect or engineer should specify that the contractor carry insurance, and require the contractor to protect the owner from claims resulting from the contractor's oprerations, the subcontractor's operations, or those of anyone directly or indirectly employed by either of them. Before being allowed to work on the project, a contractor should be required to submit insurance certificates or other proof of insurance, along with assurance that the insurance cannot be canceled during the construction of the project.

TWENTY-FOUR

Safety

24.01 SAFETY IS GOOD BUSINESS

Everybody is in favor of safety —but everyone is not willing to pay for safety. It is expensive. With the passage of workmen's compensation laws, employees were required to buy insurance, and it was the insurance companies that became the prime source of safety control. A business with a high accident rate was required to pay an exorbitant price for its insurance, and it was just good business to maintain safe working conditions to reduce the insurance rate. As a result, a completely new profession of safety engineer came into existence. The safety engineer's job was to reduce the accident rate to the level of the least expensive insurance.

24.02 ACCIDENT RATES

A. REDUCTIONS

Workmen's compensation laws were responsible for reduced accident rates over the years. Unions and other state laws also had an effect, but accident rates are still too high.

B. MANUFACTURING

In 1946, the United States injury frequency rate (the number of disabling injuries per million employee-hours worked) for manufacturing, according to the Bureau of Labor Statistics, was almost twenty (20). By 1958, this had been reduced to less than eleven (11). However, the rate rose in 1959, and by 1969 it was almost fifteen (15).

C. CONSTRUCTION

By the very nature of the work, accident rates for construction have always been above those of industry. However, until 1967 they were dropping by a sizable percentage. From 1960 until 1967, they dropped from thirty-two to twenty six (32 to 26). By 1969, they had risen to twenty-eight (28).

24.03 COST

A. It is just good business for a factory to place railings around an open stairway and to build safety cages around high ladders. The cost measured against the life of the structure is small. However, the cost of building a railing around the perimeter of every floor slab and every opening in the floor in a multistory building during construction would be excessive, considering the time they would be in place. Most building contractors realize that they must maintain reasonably safe working conditions to keep their insurance costs from going higher. For example, it used to be common to see iron workers riding structural steel beams as they were hoisted from the ground. A contractor permitting this today would probably have his insurance canceled, if it was discovered. Cost-conscious contractors, guided by insurance safety engineers, should evaluate the cost of correcting any potentially dangerous conditions against the risk involved and the possible resulting increase in insurance rates.

B. All corporations are not mercenary. Some spend sizable sums of money promoting safety as a matter of service to their employees and keep a low accident rate a public policy. The duPont de Nemours Company is one of these. The making of gunpowder is a hazardous business, yet this company has a remarkable safety record. This record is maintained by making a detailed investigation of every lost-time accident followed by studies to prevent the same type of accident from happening in the future. The company has a policy of requiring their construction contractors to take safety precautions beyond those normally taken by the building industry. This is expensive for the owner because the contractor's added cost is added to the price of the building. However, duPont de Nemours is willing to pay for safety.

24.04 OSHA

A. The Occupational Safety and Health Act was signed into law on December 29, 1970. Some claim the act was necessary because the individual states were unable to enforce rigid safety laws for fear that the industry might leave the state; others claim it was another grab of power from the states by the federal government. Who is right is not important. The fact is that OSHA has established building standards that no architect or engineer can afford to ignore.

B. The detail contained in the regulations is difficult to imagine. Part 1926

24.04 B. (Cont.)

of Chapter Twenty-seven of the rules and regulations is divided into twenty-four (24) subparts, some of which are divided into ten (10) or more sub-subparts, which in turn may be divided into as many as twelve (12) sub-subsubparts. For example, sub-subsubpart 9 of sub-subpart b, of subpart L of part 1926 of Chapter Twenty-seven, reads, "Two-inch by four-inch lumber shall be used for side and middle rails of double-cleat ladders up to twelve feet in length; two-inch by six-inch lumber for double-cleated ladders from twelve to twenty-four feet in length."

C. The law is so complex that private companies have been organized to provide their clients with technical assistance in complying with the law. Over sixteen hundred (1,600) changes were made in the law between 1971 and 1974, and it appears that few know where or how to start in complying with the law.

D. As some businesses will be required to make extensive changes in their equipment and methods of operation in order to comply with OSHA's standards, the law authorizes the Small Business Administration to make loans to assist contractors in making the required alterations.

24.05 OSHA AND ARCHITECTURAL AND ENGINEERING DESIGN

No architect or engineer can afford to ignore the requirements of OSHA in their design. It is the law. Those doing design work should have a copy of the requirements and follow them to the letter. The specification writer must make sure that the finished building will comply with OSHA standards.

24.06 SAFETY IN CONSTRUCTION

A. The American Institute of Architects and the National Society of Professional Engineers take the position that safety at the job site is the sole responsibility of the contractor. The statements in the General Conditions requiring the contractor to comply with all laws, ordinances, rules, and regulations applicable to the work (see AIA *General Conditions,* Article 4.72, or NSPE *General Conditions* Article 6.15) and requirements for safety (see AIA G. C., Article 10, or NSPEGC, Article 6.20) are all that is required in the specifications. They recommend nothing be added. To add a safety program or OSHA requirements in the Special Conditions or elsewhere may expose the architect or engineer to the responsibility for enforcing safety requirements. This could lead to legal involvement if the contractor fails to perform.

B. Where the client insists, and if the client is the government they may insist, that OSHA standards be made a part of the contract, the architect can only hope to have insurance that will give proper protection if a court case develops.

TWENTY-FIVE

The Proposal Form

25.01 THE OFFER

The Proposal Form is the document upon which the bidder submits a price for doing work. The legal term is "an offer." The form is filled out by the various contractors bidding on the project. It is submitted to the architect, engineer, or owner at the time and place required. The architect or engineer compares the various proposals and recommends acceptance of one proposal, or, in some cases, rejection of all bids. When the contract between the owner and the contractor is signed, the proposal of that contractor is made a part of the contract documents.

25.02 METHOD OF WRITING

A. It would be possible to have each bidder submit a proposal on a form or a letter composed by the individual bidder. However, this would make it difficult to compare prices, as no two bidders would be wording their bid exactly the same.

B. In order to secure bids in a uniform manner, the Proposal Form is made out by the architect or engineer. Blanks are left to be filled in by the bidder. As the bidder is only allowed to fill in the blank spaces, the bids will be uniform and easily compared.

C. While the Proposal Form is composed by the architect or engineer, it is prepared to read as though it were written by the bidder. For example, a sentence might read, "We, the undersigned, agree to complete the work within ninety-five (95) calendar days after being awarded the contract."

25.03 ITEMS INCLUDED IN THE PROPOSAL FORM

A. NAME

Usually the first things that appear on the form are the contractor's name and address.

B. PRICE

1. The second and most important item on the Proposal Form is the space where the bidder writes the proposed price. A full description of the work should appear to make the document complete. For example:

2. "We, the undersigned agree to build and complete a swimming pool, bath house, and filter shed as shown on drawings 0-00 dated February 28, 1974, and designed by Doolittle and Crowe, Professional Engineers, for the sum of _____ dollars ($_____)."

3. It is usually advisable to allow space for the bidder to write out the contract amount of the bid as well as indicating it by figures. A simple error could be made by a typist in copying a figure. The possibility of an error in the written amount is less likely. As the amounts involved in construction contracts are usually large sums of money, a mistake could be very costly.

4. As a matter of interest, if there is a difference between the written amount and the amount appearing in figures, the courts have ruled that the written amount will govern.

C. BREAKDOWN

There will be many more spaces for the bidder to fill in. The owner may, for accounting reasons, or for personal interest, want a breakdown of the contractor's costs. It is quite common for architects and engineers to ask that the bidder break down costs between the architectural, the mechanical, and the electrical work. If this is desired, space should be provided in the Proposal Form.

D. ALTERNATES

1. When bids on alternates are desired, a separate section entitled "Alternates" should appear in the specifications. In this section the various alternates should be listed by number.

2. Space must be provided in the Proposal Form to permit the bidders to submit their price on each of the alternates. It is not necessary to describe the alternates other than by number, since they are described in the specifications, but each alternate must be listed separately. An example appears in the Appendix.

E. FEES FOR ASSUMING CONTRACTS

As previously described, it may be advantageous to the owner to take separate bids on parts of a project. In this case, there are partial contracts. The owner may wish to assign the several contracts to one general contractor. The general contractor must be paid for the supervision of the work and a fee must be determined. The general contractor does not usually know the work involved in the separate contracts, as those bids and his are usually due at the same time. For that reason, the general contractor is asked to quote a fee based upon a percentage of the various contracts he is expected to assume. Space is left on the Proposal Form for inserting the percentage figure. Of course, if the other contracts have been awarded before the general contract, the amount that the general contractor could charge would be included in the bid price.

F. FEES FOR ADDITIONAL WORK

1. Extra work has been previously discussed. When extra work is ordered in the form of an addendum, the additional price for that work should be included in the contract price. When work is authorized by a change order, the payment for that work is agreed upon when the owner accepts the price quoted by the contractor on the bulletin. The manner of payment for a field change order is established in the Special Conditions, and provision for the payment should be made in the proposal form. The contractor will charge for the work plus a fee for overhead and profit. The explanation of overhead should be given in the Special Conditions or in the Instructions to Bidders.

2. The contractor can perform extra work with his own forces, by subcontracts, or by a combination of both. Work awarded to a subcontractor usually does not require the same overhead as work done by the contractor's forces. For that reason, two percentage prices should be requested: one for work with the contractor's forces and one for work with a subcontractor's forces. See the Proposal Form in the Appendix.

G. UNIT PRICES

In a unit price contract, the award is made on the unit price quoted. In a lump sum contract, there may be items of cost where the quantity is unknown. An example might be rock excavation. In such a case, the contractor is requested to bid on these unknown quantities at a price per cubic yard, per cubic foot, per square yard, per square foot, or per lineal foot, as the case may be. In the event of rock excavation, if no rock is encountered, there is no change in the cost to the owner. If rock is encountered, the amount of rock removed must be measured, and the contractor will be paid for the amount removed at the price quoted in the Proposal Form. For this reason, it is important to establish a unit that can be easily measured in the field.

H. TIME

If the time allowed to complete the contract is specified, there is no need to mention it in the bid form. If, however, the time of completion is to be established by the contractor, time is a very important part of the bid. A method of having the contractor establish a time of completion is shown in the Proposal Form in the Appendix.

I. SUBSTITUTIONS

1. The contractor may wish to substitute a material or method for the one specified. It is often to the owner's advantage to take advantage of the offer. One contractor may have just wrecked an old structure and may have salvaged a lot of fine marble or rare wood, or a contractor may have secured a new piece of equipment which might better accomplish the desired results, though the method would not conform to the method specified. It is to the owner's advantage to give the contractor an opportunity to suggest methods of saving money. If the contractors limit their suggestions to changes that will not lower the quality of the final product, there is no harm in accepting the suggestion; but often suggestions may be made which are not acceptable to the designer and may result in the owner, who does not understand the difference in quality, insisting that less expensive items be used. For this reason, some architects and engineers do not allow substitutions.

2. If the "Substitutions" heading is used, the price submitted should be a deduction from the lump-sum bid. For example, the Proposal Form might have the following paragraph under the heading of "Substitutions":

3. "If we are permitted to use _____
   _____ material or method in lieu of
   the material or method specified, _____
   dollars ($_____) shall be deducted from our proposed
   price."

4. Stating the proposal in this manner gives the owner the right to accept or reject any suggestions.

J. ADDENDA

During the bidding period, addenda may be issued. As these addenda may affect the bid price, it is necessary to know that each bidder is quoting on all of the addenda that may be issued. A space is left in the Proposal Form for the bidder to list each addendum that is received. It is at once apparent if the bidder has not received all addenda.

K. SUBCONTRACTORS

Because subcontractors usually wait until the last minute to submit their bids to the general contractors, it is not practical to require the bidder to list all subcontractors in the Proposal Form. It may be desirable to ask the bidder to list the principal subcontractors. If this is required, space should be provided in the Proposal Form for a contractor to list the principal subcontractors.

L. LEGAL STATUS

It is helpful for the one writing the contract between the owner and the contractor to know if the contractor is an individual, a partnership, or a corporation; and, if the contractor is a corporation, the state where it is incorporated. This information can be easily obtained from the contractor by asking that contractors indicate their legal status on the Proposal Form.

M. SIGNATURE

The proposal is a legal document called an "offer." That is, the bidder is offering to build a specific project for a specific amount of money. Unless this document is signed by a person who can bind the bidder to the agreement, it is of little value. Space should be provided for the name of the bidder, the signature of the party signing for the bidder, his title, and the date the offer was signed.

TWENTY-SIX

The Instructions to Bidders

26.01 PURPOSE

The Instructions to Bidders has three main purposes: to inform the bidder of when bids are due, to instruct the bidder how to prepare the Proposal Form, and to inform the bidder of what to do with it after it is prepared. Any other information regarding the bidding should also appear in this section. A proposal form with the instructions appears in the Appendix to this book.

26.02 DATE

Except when the Invitation To Bid is bound into the specifications, the Instructions to Bidders is the first section to appear. The date that the bids are due is a most important item to the bidders, and this time and date should appear in the first paragraph.

26.03 INSTRUCTIONS

The instructions for filling out the bid form should follow. It is usually best to go through the bid form and give detailed instructions on how to fill in each item.

26.04 FEES FOR ADDITIONAL WORK

Such items as fees for additional work and unit prices often are trouble-makers if not carefully explained. A contractor, when adding a percentage for overhead and profit, must know exactly what items to include in overhead. For example, if additional work is required, there is no question that the owner should pay for all material and labor used at the job site. However,

26.04 (Cont.)

should the owner pay for the time spent by an office employee at the contractor's home office ordering material, or is this overhead? Should the owner pay for the rental of a power back-hoe if such is required? If so, should the owner pay for the use of the workers' hammers and saws? Are taxes overhead?

26.05 UNIT PRICE

Unit prices can also cause trouble if the method of measurement is not clear. For example, it is easy to request a contractor to quote on painting a square foot of wall. However, the question immediately arises as to how projections, such as window stools, the returns at sash, and other trim, are paid for. If all surfaces painted are to be paid for on a square-foot basis, the job of measuring accurately every projection and recess could be endless. The point being stressed is that care must be used when requesting unit prices.

26.06 OTHER ITEMS

Any other item that is of interest to the bidders regarding the filling out of the bid form, the delivery of the bid form, or the method of awarding contracts should be stated in the Instructions to Bidders.

TWENTY-SEVEN

The Invitation to Bid

27.01 DEFINITION

The "Invitation To Bid," sometimes called the "Advertisement," is, as the name implies, a request for contractors to bid on a project. On private work this is often done by telephone, or more formally by letter. Telephoning or writing letters is usually done by the contract administrator and does not affect the specification writer. However, on public work, advertisements in two or more public newspapers are often required by law. This is to prevent favoritism and to obtain as many bidders as possible. However, there are few contractors who depend upon newspaper notices for bidding material.

27.02 PLACING

If an advertisement is to be published, the wording is usually determined by the specification writer. A copy of the newspaper advertisement is often bound in the book of specifications before the Table of Contents and entitled "Invitation To Bid." As it is not a part of the specification, it carries no section number. The purpose of placing the Invitation To Bid in the specifications is to give bidders who have not seen the published invitation the same information as those who did. The invitation in the book of specifications is also helpful in giving basic information to the contractor who must decide whether or not to submit a proposal.

27.03 WRITING AN INVITATION

A. GENERAL

The advertisement need not be long, but it should contain enough basic information so that a contractor can decide if he wishes to submit a proposal. There are six (6) basic items that an invitation should contain.

B. ITEMS

1. Type of Project

The type of project should be stated. A building project, a road-paving project, or a street-lighting project would each attract a different type of contractor.

2. Size

The approximate size of the project is also important to the bidder. A ten-million-dollar ($10,000,000) project would not attract the same type of contractor as a ten-thousand-dollar ($10,000) project. Size can be expressed in money, in area, or in volume. A million-gallon (1,000,000-gal) water tank, two (2) miles of asphaltic concrete resurfacing, a pedestrian bridge spanning one hundred feet (100'), or a building costing two million dollars ($2,000,000) all express size sufficient for a contractor to determine whether to look at the contract documents.

3. Location

Contractors usually bid in limited areas. Therefore, the approximate location of a project is important to those considering making a proposal.

4. Time

The time that bids are due is of interest to anyone making a proposal. Keeping an even flow of work for the estimator is a problem for all contractors.

5. Bonds

Some contractors, particularly those figuring small work, may not be able to furnish a bond. If a bond is required, it should be so stated. The same is true if a deposit is required for the plans and specifications.

6. Obtaining Documents

Of course, anyone desiring to bid would have to know where the plans and specifications can be obtained.

27.04   CONCLUSION

A. It is not in the best interest of the engineer to have people request plans if they do not submit proposals. The cost of reproducing plans, proposal forms, and specifications, the cost of mailing, and the cost of handling are considerable. When many people request contract docu-

27.04 A.   (Cont.)

ments and do not submit bids, it represents a dead loss to the engineer.

B. The advertisement, to be helpful, should be short, but it should contain enough information to permit potential bidders to determine whether they wish to submit a proposal.

TWENTY-EIGHT

Checking

28.01 PROCEDURE

A. As each section of the specifications is written, that section should be checked before it is given to the typist. The typist is usually made responsible for the correct spelling and correct copying. Offices with more than one typist often check each other's work, one typist checking the typing and the other reading the original text. When the typed copy is checked and ready for reproduction, it is returned to the specification writer.

B. In order to better distribute the typing, the specification writer writes the sections least likely to be changed first. When the typing is returned, the specification writer keeps the copy on the desk for reference while preparing other sections. Since the drawings are being made at the same time that the specifications are being written, the specification writer can only hope that new developments will not affect the sections that have already been typed. When they do, new typing is required. As the due date approaches, the specification writer is under increasing pressure; and when the typing is complete, there is little time for checking. The checking must be as efficient as possible.

28.02 CHECKING SPECIFICATIONS

A. When the last section of the specifications is written and given to the typist, the specifications writer should get a complete set of the latest, up-to-date drawings, and also should leave word with the various draftsmen and their chief that any changes made while copying the sketches on the finished drawings should be reported to him at once.

B. The drawings should be examined in detail to ensure that every item shown on the drawings is specified. Failure to specify what is shown is the most common and often the most disastrous type of error.

C. When the drawings have been checked, the specification writer should read the "Scope of the Work" and the "Work Not Included In This Section" subsections in each of the technical sections and should make sure that all work is covered. One of the chief advantages of having a "Work Not Included" subsection is to make the checking easier. Wherever reference is made to another section, it is easy to refer to that section to make sure such work is covered. Not properly covering all work is the type of error that is very costly.

D. If time permits, the Special Conditions should be checked. Disputes are often involved with this section.

28.03 CHECKING DRAWINGS

A. In some offices, which do not have separate checking departments, the specification writer is required to coordinate and check the drawings. This does not mean checking the technical aspects of the engineering. The electrical, mechanical, and structural departments are responsible for their designs; besides, most specification writers would be incompetent to do all phases of the work. The checker's duty is to make sure that the project can be built from the drawings. He should make sure the dimensions check on the various drawings, that sufficient space is shown on the architectural drawings to permit the mechanical and electrical equipment to be installed, and that the equipment shown on the mechanical drawings is properly located on the electrical and architectural drawings.

B. To be a good checker requires a high degree of technical skill. It also requires the ability to get along with people—one must be a diplomat. The checker should confine work to finding errors; making basic changes is not part of the work. There may be other methods of producing a result that the checker believes superior to the one shown. The checker must remember that the designer may have a good reason for a selection, and unless it is definitely faulty, it should not be changed. This does not mean that a checker should keep quiet on finding the library placed next to the music room in the design of a school.

C. The checker who goes to the chief draftsman with a drawing all marked up and says, "Look at all the mistakes I found," may give the chief evidence that he is a hard worker but he will earn the ill will of the entire drafting room. It would be better to show the errors to the parties who made them, have them corrected and report to the chief draftsman that some minor mistakes were found that have been corrected.

D. No one likes to be told that he made a mistake. "I can't make these dimensions add up" is better than "Your dimensions are wrong." "Show me how you intend to place a light over the door" is better than "There's no room for a light over the door."

28.04 CHECKING DEPARTMENTS

A. Some of the larger and better offices have a separate checking department responsible for the correctness of the drawings and specifications. In such offices the specification writer is relieved of the duty of coordinating the civil, architectural, structural, mechanical, and electrical drawings.

B. There are several advantages to having someone who is unfamiliar with the project check the contract documents. One who is unfamiliar with the details, the changes, the conferences, and the hard work will view the project in the same manner as would a bidder. Therefore, such a person is able to find, in a short time, the items that are not clear, places where additional details are required, incomplete details, inconsistencies and obvious errors which were overlooked.

C. Many of those selected to be checkers are former specification writers because of their training.

D. The checking department also checks specifications. The experienced writer welcomes the chance to correct errors. However, if the checker is inexperienced with the method of writing specifications, he may have ideas that differ from good specification writing. In such cases the specification writer should hold to principles and appeal to higher authority. If trouble develops, no one will thank him if he makes an incorrect change requested by a checker.

28.05 THE TABLE OF CONTENTS

A. When the typing is complete, the typist types the table of contents. In addition to the section number and title, the number of pages in each section should be indicated. Legally this would protect the architect or engineer in the event a page is removed from the specification. If the number of pages in the specification differs from the number indicated in the table of contents, it should be a warning that a page is missing.

B. Some offices require the subsections in each section to be listed in the table of contents. Whether the results justify the additional work is a question each writer must decide.

28.06 PRINTING AND COLLATING

A. The typewritten pages would be placed in order before being sent to the printer. The printer is usually responsible for printing, collating, and binding the specifications.

B. When the printed copies are returned, the specification writer should check the printing and collating. A page out of order can be confusing to the reader, and if the missing page is in another section, it could be missed by the reader. As collating is often done by machine, a single mistake could be repeated in all of the books.

28.07   MASTER COPY

The specification writer should keep one master copy of the specifications in the office to mark up any corrections and to use as a ready reference when salesmen or bidders call. This copy should never be taken from the office until the project is completed and the contractor paid. It should contain all addenda, bulletins, and change orders and be up to date at all times. As a result, the saving in time for the specification writer, who must have this important information ready for immediate use, is many times over the time it takes to keep the specification writer's copy up to date.

TWENTY-NINE

Industrial Specifications

29.01 DEFINITION

This book would not be complete without a discussion of industrial specifications. By "industrial specifications" we mean specifications for the purchase of industrial products or services as opposed to construction specifications.

29.02 WHO WRITES INDUSTRIAL SPECIFICATIONS

A. The ultimate consumer is usually the general public, and they select from what is offered for sale. Those who sell to the public sell what they purchase from wholesalers or manufacturers. With a few exceptions the sellers do not write specifications. The quality of a product is usually determined by the manufacturer. It is true that to stay in business the manufacturer must produce a quality that will be accepted by the consumer. However, the manufacturer is the one who decides what product is to be made and how.

B. The government is the major exception to the foregoing. The government does write specifications for manufacturers to follow. For economic reasons, most government specifications are written for products already in production, but specifications for a quality above that normally produced or for items not in production is not unusual.

C. Manufacturers, their subcontractors, and their sub-subcontractors usually write specifications for the assemblies, subassembly parts, and raw materials they buy. This is the type of specification that we are discussing.

29.03 TYPES OF INDUSTRIAL PURCHASES

A. GENERAL

There are three (3) basic types of purchases made by a manufacturer. They are for service, tooling, and production materials.

B. SERVICE CONTRACTS

Service contracts are agreements between a manufacturer and an outside firm to supply janitorial service, food service, or other type of maintenance services at the manufacturer's plant.

C. TOOLING CONTRACTS

By "tooling contracts" we mean contracts for the purchase of machines, conveyors, equipment, apparatus, dies, jigs, fixtures, and other tools of production. Maintenance materials such as fuel for heating, cleaning materials, paint, and other materials consumed, as well as light bulbs, ladders, fans, and other materials used to maintain production, are purchased in the same way and for the purpose of this text will be classed as tooling contracts.

D. PRODUCTION MATERIALS

By "production materials" we mean materials actually used in the manufacture of the product being sold. These could be raw materials such as iron ore, limestone, or coal; finished materials such as sheet steel or copper wire; fabricated materials, such as screws, pipe, structural steel, or subassemblies and assemblies used in the final product.

29.04 DIFFERENCES BETWEEN CONSTRUCTION AND INDUSTRIAL SPECIFICATIONS

A. CONSTRUCTION SPECIFICATIONS

A construction contract is usually written for the purchase of a single structure consisting of a field assembly of many parts by many subcontractors on the owner's property. For this reason, fixed-price contracts are usually written for construction projects. Likewise, a sizable number of provisions are required in the General and Special Conditions to protect the owner from liability from acts by the contractor or his subcontractors.

B. INDUSTRIAL SPECIFICATIONS

1. Service Specifications

Service-type specifications are similar to construction specifications in that they involve labor on the buyer's property. Therefore, it is necessary to have clauses in the specifications to protect the owner.

If the type and length of service are specified, a fixed-price contract can be issued. However, many people prefer unit-price contracts giving a specific price per day or per week and allowing either party to terminate work after giving the other party proper notice.

**2. Specifications for Tools
and Production Materials**

a. With the exception of the service-type contracts, almost all specifications issued by industry are for products produced in the contractor's plant and delivered to the buyer in accordance with a specific schedule. Usually the contractor owns the raw material or parts he is fabricating or assembling and responsible for the safety of the plant employees and the general public. Normally the buyer is not liable for injuries in a contractor's plant. As a result, most of the provisions in the General and Special Conditions of a construction contract do not apply to this type of specification.

b. There are differences between specifications for tools required to produce a product and the material used in its production. With the former, the quantity and the time and place of delivery are known when the specifications are being written. With the latter, delivery may depend upon the rate of production. Production depends upon sales, and future sales can only be estimated. For this reason, tools of production can be purchased on a fixed-price contract with a specific delivery date. Materials of production are usually purchased on a unit-price contract with the delivery of parts scheduled in varying amounts for the life of the contract.

C. SAMPLES

1. General

In lieu of the shop drawings normally required in construction work, a manufacturer usually prefers to receive samples. There are several types of samples of industrial products.

2. Types

a. *Pre-contract samples*

Pre-contract samples are parts shown to the buyer in an effort to obtain a contract. They may or may not be the parts the buyer wishes to buy.

b. *Post-contract samples*

Post-contract samples are parts made by hand tools before the contractor has purchased or made the production machinery. The purpose of the samples is to assure the buyer that the contractor understands and properly interprets the drawings. They are used by the buyer to fit with parts produced by others and to ensure that all parts will fit the assembly once production starts.

c. *Pre-Production Samples*

Pre-production samples are parts made by the contractor from the machines to be used in the actual production. The post-contract and the pre-production sample should be the same. They may not be. Dies in power presses might tear metal that could be stretched if made by hand and minor changes might be required in the design of the part to make it suitable for mass production. The purpose of the pre-production is to insure the manufacturer that all parts will fit once production starts.

d. *Production Samples*

Production samples are parts taken from the production line after production has started. Tools wear and minor variations in materials can cause dimensional changes. Production samples are taken to assure the manufacturer that the parts being produced will come within the tolerance specified.

e. *Inspection Samples*

Inspection samples are parts or assemblies taken, usually by the buyer, from a lot or specified number of pieces which have been completed and stored awaiting acceptance by the buyer.

3. Differences

a. Samples submitted to an architect or engineer are submitted for general approval only. The architect or engineer takes no responsibility for dimensions. If the pieces don't fit in the space provided, the contractor is responsible.

b. Samples are of great importance to the manufacturer of industrial products because they represent possibly thousands and perhaps millions of parts to be produced. A minor mistake in the drawings furnished by the buyer, a mistake in interpreting these drawings by the contractor or a mistake in the actual production of the samples might result in many thousands of parts being scrapped at a loss of both money and time.

D. TIME

1. Time Is the Essence

Industrial contracts are relatively new when compared with construction contracts and do not have a long legal history. The courts presume that a subcontractor bidding on industrial materials knows the requirements of the trade and a buyer can usually enforce the exact time requirements even though the specification does not include the "time is the essence of the contract" clause.

2. Production Schedules

a. Time is often important on construction projects. Schedules are established and a statement as to the importance of time should be placed in the specifications. However, many construction projects are weeks and sometimes months behind schedule with little impact. Scheduling of production is of major importance to a manufacturer. Plans are made months in advance to start production on a specific day, and should one part be delayed, considerable money could be lost. To prevent such delays, most manufacturers employ people to schedule the progress of the work in the planning stages and others to expedite and make sure the schedule is followed. Time is one of the most important parts of industrial specifications.

b. The schedules must be set to give each subcontractor time to obtain tools and buy the material. Schedules may not be uniform. When production starts on a new product, the demand will be small at first and gradually increase as the workers learn their jobs. Products with a seasonal demand may have a very irregular schedule.

3. Quantity of Materials Scheduled

a. It is difficult to accurately estimate sales for a production year because it must be done so far in advance. An overestimate can result in the buying of excessive tools and equipment. An underestimate can result in excessive overtime for employees, inefficient production, and poor delivery schedules.

b. Scheduling deliveries of machines and tools of production is not difficult once the number required and date to start manufacturing have been established. Finding equipment manufacturers that can produce the type of machine on time can be more difficult.

c. Where materials of production are not changed from year to year, the quantity purchased at any one time may not be too important. In such a case, a fixed-price contract is in order. However, a manufacturer ordering material that will become obsolete after a year's production must use care, and an open-end contract may be the best.

4. Open-End Contracts

a. An open-end contract is one where a unit price is established but the number of items and the schedule of deliveries are not specified. This means that the buyer may set the quantity of parts he wants (usually within limits) for any specific time during the life of the contract. For example, a manufacturer may notify suppliers during each month the number of parts to be delivered during the following month. This is the most common type of contract for production materials.

b. In order to submit an intelligent proposal, the contractor should know the maximum and minimum quantities expected to be produced each week, month, or other specific period. If there is a large difference between the maximum and the minimum, the subcontractor should base the price upon the most unfavorable conditions. Students often assume that the higher the production, the lower the cost per item. This is often true. However, if a contractor is required to purchase additional machinery in order to maintain a schedule above the normal production or is required to pay a premium price for overtime labor, the cost per unit could be increased.

E. INSPECTION PROCEDURES

1. General

By their very nature there is very little resemblance between the inspection procedures required in construction and those used in industry. Construction contracts are usually for the building of a single final product. Variations in dimensions that cannot be seen by the human eye are usually accepted as being within an acceptable tolerance. Industrial specifications are usually written for numerous identical parts where a variation of a thousandth of an inch might make some parts unacceptable.

2. Purpose

The purpose of inspection is to assure the buyer that the product being bought conforms with the specifications. Any additional inspection is a waste of money; any less subjects the buyer to possibility of receiving defective parts. If a satisfactory part can be produced outside the tolerance specified, the specifications are too restrictive and a change should be considered with an adjustment in price.

3. Definitions

a. *Receiving inspection*

The receiving inspecting is the examining by the buyer of raw materials, parts, assemblies, or other purchased items after delivery to the plant.

b. *In-process inspection*

In-process inspection is any inspection during the process of the work prior to final inspection.

c. *Final inspection*

Final inspection is the last inspection prior to acceptance.

29.04 (Cont.)

F. WHO DOES THE INSPECTION?

1. In the construction work, the clerk of the works is paid by the architect or engineer who is performing a service for the owner. The contractor hires no inspectors and it would not be in the best interest of the owner to have the contractor do so. The inspector would be in an intolerable position. One could hardly expect the inspector to protect the interest of the owner against the interest of the man who was paying for the inspection.

2. Production work is different. Contractors making industrial assemblies employ inspectors for their own protection. They cannot afford to have a shipment of assemblies rejected by the buyer because the raw stock was not as specified. If a machine making defective parts is not stopped, both time and money are lost, and the loss would be increased if additional operations were made on the faulty pieces. Stopping defective parts from going into assemblies is a constant problem. The number of inspectors employed is determined strictly by economics, except when the number required is specified.

3. There are times when a receiving inspector cannot test the subassemblies in an assembly without destroying the part. In this case, an in-process inspection may be desirable. However, having the buyer's inspectors working beside the contractor's inspectors, and sometimes doing similar work, could lead to difficulties. To overcome this problem, the government and many private industries have established a process whereby the contractor does the inspection for the buyer. To do this, the specifications would require the vendor to purchase specific gauges and fixtures to test all, or specific percentages of, parts at specific points in the production line. The system, not the inspectors, is supervised by the buyer. He controls the system in taking samples from each lot of material and reinspecting it in detail. If the samples do not pass, he can reject the entire lot. Having a manufacturer inspect his own product may seem risky to some, but sampling procedures are well established and the reliability of such systems can be established mathematically.

29.05 COST

A. The type of inspection required depends upon the part being inspected, the tolerances permitted, and the reliability required.

B. The cost of inspecting depends upon the type of inspection specified. Destructive testing, consisting of checking all dimensions and making a chemical and physical analysis of the material, could be many times the cost of the part. A visual inspection of each part would be relatively inexpensive. Obviously, every piece should not be tested to destruction, and the limitations of the human eye make a visual inspection valueless in many cases.

C. Cost is always a factor in establishing inspection procedures. Usually it would be foolish to spend a dollar to inspect a ten-cent (10¢) part. However, if the entire operation of the finished assembly depended upon that part being held within tolerance, a dollar's worth of testing might not be excessive.

29.06 INSPECTION AND TESTING PROCEDURES

A. DEFINITION

"Inspection" usually consists of checking the physical dimensions and appearance of an item. It usually involves examining a product to determine whether it conforms to a descriptive specification. "Testing" usually involves examining a product to determine whether it conforms to a performance specification. Some testing will result in the destruction of the part being tested.

B. PROCEDURE

1. The first thing to be done in establishing an inspection procedure is to make a list of the characteristics required in the finished product. This list should be coordinated with the requirements of the drawings and specifications.

2. From the list, the type of testing required to assure compliance should be determined. In many cases simple visual inspection should be satisfactory. In other cases, gauges or machines, such as are needed for ultrasonic testing, may be required.

C. SUPERVISION

Supervision of the inspection should be retained by the buyer. Normally the supervision of the employees remains with the vendor, and the buyer establishes the procedures and the method of work. The amount of supervision would depend upon the product, the method of inspection, and the faith the buyer had in the integrity of the vendor.

29.07 RELIABILITY

A. Reliability is expressed in percentages and is determined by one hundred (100) times the number of defective parts divided by the number of units inspected, all subtracted from one hundred (100).

$$\text{Reliability} = 100 - \frac{\text{Number of Defective Units}}{\text{Number of Units Tested}} \times 100$$

B. Reliability is not the same as tolerance. "Tolerance" is the difference between the allowable maximum and the allowable minimum for any given characteristic.

C. The reliability required by a manufacturer may not be the same for all characteristics. For example, a variation from the specified finish on a piece may cause excessive wear in the final product. If the same piece were oversized, it might not fit and could never be assembled in the final product. In such a case, the buyer might be willing to accept a limited number of oversized parts if the cost of inspection were excessive but require complete inspection on the finish.

D. One hundred percent (100%) reliability requires complete inspection of all parts, which is expensive and many times is not justified. The reliability for each characteristic should be determined prior to the writing of the specifications.

E. Inspection for less than one hundred percent (100%) reliability is done by sampling.

29.08 SAMPLING

A. Proper sampling requires the vendor to separate completed pieces into lots. A lot is a specific number of pieces; a carload or a truckload is a convenient number. From each lot a specific percentage of pieces is taken to be inspected. The purpose of establishing lots is to permit a specific number of parts to be rejected if the samples are unsatisfactory. One might presume that the same percentage of defective parts would occur in the lot as would occur in the samples. On the average this is true, but one must realize that, even if no samples are found defective, there may be defective pieces in the lot. For example, there is one (1) chance in three (3) that ten (10) acceptable samples could be taken at random from one hundred (100) or more parts containing ten percent (10%) rejects. The only way to have one hundred percent (100%) reliability is to require inspection of every part.

B. Where the buyer is willing to accept some defective parts, it is necessary to establish a minimum of reliability that the buyer will accept. From this, the proper sampling procedure can be established.

C. It is not the intent of this book to discuss the theories of probability and the concepts of reliability. Those who are interested can obtain Military Standards 104 and 414, which establish excellent sampling procedures. What we wish to emphasize is the necessity of establishing a procedure.

29.09 VALUE ENGINEERING

A. HISTORY

1. The concept of "Value Engineering" was started during the Second World War, when many critical materials were difficult or impossible to obtain. As a result, engineers were employed to find substitute

materials and designs for standard parts that had been used for years. In most cases, the substitutes were inferior; but in some cases, the new designs with the substitute materials were not only less expensive but actually better than the original product. With this start, one of the executives in the General Electric Company advocated starting a program for the improvement of product efficiency by developing substitute materials to replace the more costly standard materials. This task was assigned to a staff engineer who developed cost-saving ideas far beyond what was believed possible.

2. In 1954, the Navy, borrowing ideas from General Electric, started a cost-saving program in one of their shipyards. The program, named "Value Engineering," was so successful that in the next five years it was expanded to the eleven (11) naval shipyards. By 1967 all military services had established a full-time Value Engineering program. From the time the program started on July 1, 1963, until June 30, 1967, the program saved the government over one billion, one hundred million dollars ($1,100,000,000).

B. WHAT IS VALUE ENGINEERING?

The purpose of Value Engineering is not to make something cheaper. There is too much cheap junk in the market place already. Its purpose is to obtain more value for each dollar. This could mean spending more money to obtain a better product. When the life of a product is doubled by a twenty percent (20%) increase in cost, its value is increased. However, most Value Engineering effort is spent in reducing the cost without lowering the quality of the product.

C. HOW VALUE ENGINEERING WORKS

While a designer must consider cost, his primary job is to design a product that works. The Value Engineer is a specialist in manufacturing costs. In some organizations, he serves as a consultant for the design engineer during the designing process. When the design is completed and prototypes are made and tested, the product goes to the Value Engineering staff, who propose possible methods of reducing the cost without lowering the quality of the product. Obviously, all new ideas must be tested to prove that the value has been increased.

D. THE GOVERNMENT'S VALUE ENGINEERING PROGRAM

1. Most government contracts with industry contain a Value Engineering clause which permits contractors to propose cost-saving ideas. If the change is accepted, the contractor shares in the saving.

2. Normally, contractors are expected to produce a specific product for a given price. Their profit is the difference between their price and their cost. If, by their proficiency, they are able to reduce the cost,

they will increase their profit. All the profit is theirs, and they need not share it. However, if they propose a change in the design of the product, and this change is accepted, they will share in the savings to the government, usually on a fifty-fifty basis. The contractors share not only on the existing contract, but on future contracts using the improved design. They will be paid the saving even if another contractor receives the award. Value Engineering is profitable to both the contractors and the government. One Value Engineering proposal saved thirty-four million dollars ($34,000,000), which the government shared with the contractor. Another saved twenty-one million dollars ($21,000,000). These cases, of course, are unusual. However, one company has made profit on Value Engineering proposals of over two million dollars ($2,000,000) a year, every year between 1964 and 1974.

E. SPECIFICATIONS

In view of the possible savings, industrial specification writers should consider a Value Engineering program, but they should always keep control in their own office.

29.10 WRITING INDUSTRIAL SPECIFICATIONS

A. DIVISIONS

1. Bidding procedures established by industry are less formal than those used by architects and engineers. There is little uniformity between companies and sometimes within various divisions of the same company. While price is important, ability to meet production schedules may be more important, and awarding contracts on a basis other than price is not uncommon. It is considered good business, by some, to buy each purchased item from at least two sources. This prevents a shutdown due to a strike in a supplier's plant.

2. The informal bidding procedures lead to less formal specifications. The bidding documents are seldom bound in book form as are construction specifications. The instructions to bidders can be a cover letter requesting bids by a specific date; the bid form can be a single page, or the forms can be omitted, allowing the contractors to submit bids on their own stationery. As previously stated, if the work is done in the contractor's plant, there is no need for most of the provisions found in General and Special Conditions in a construction specification. These sections are often omitted, the necessary provisions being placed in the contract form.

3. Industrial specifications are usually written for a single product, with the assumption that the entire article will be produced in the contractor's plant. The contractor may delegate work to subcontractors, but the specifications are not written to assist the contractor in taking

bids from subcontractors. In most cases, specifications consist of a single section, although liberal use is made of reference specifications.

B. THE TECHNICAL DIVISION

1. General

When a specification consists of a single section, there is no need for cross-referencing, and subsections entitled "General Note" and "Work Not Included in This Section" can be eliminated. Likewise, there seldom is a need for a subsection entitled "Installation." However, there are other subsections that should appear in an industrial specification. These follow:

2. Scope of the Work

The "scope of the work" paragraph is often considered unnecessary. On fixed-quantity specifications the quantity required is sometimes stated under this heading. On others, it is a general statement such as appears under the heading of "Scope of the Project" in the Special Conditions in a construction specification.

3. Materials

Materials are specified the same as in construction specifications.

4. Samples

a. If post-contract samples are required, they should be so specified. The date for submittal should be specified to allow the manufacturer to try out the sample and make any changes prior to the contractor's tooling.

b. The date for submitting pre-production samples should also be specified. This should be reasonably near the start of production to give the contractor time to obtain tools but with an allowance so that corrections in tools can be made if necessary.

c. The number of samples required and how, where, and to whom they should be delivered should always be specified.

5. Manufacturing Process

a. The buyer may require the contractor to use a specific process while manufacturing the part. Specifying the process may be desirable in some cases. For example, the buyer may desire metal to be rust-proofed in a specific manner to match parts produced by others. A satisfactory process may have been developed in the past and the buyer may not be interested in cheaper methods that might not be as good. As a general rule, however, it is better for the buyer to specify what is wanted in the finished product. Usually the buyer is not interested in the process used to produce the part.

b. When the process specified is used correctly, and the results differ from what the buyer intended, the fault will usually be placed upon the buyer rather than the vendor. This is the same as in construction, where the process and results are specified (see Articles E and F in Subsection 5.08).

6. Tolerances

The tolerances permitted in a manufactured part have a major effect upon the cost. This is often overlooked by specification writers. In many manufactured products extremely low tolerances may be required for some dimensions. This is understandable. The tendency is to require dimensions which are not critical to be held to the same tolerances as the critical dimensions. It is easy to say, "All dimensions shall be held to within plus or minus two-thousandth of an inch ($\pm$.002") of the dimension shown on the drawing," but this could be expensive.

7. Finishes

The type of finish required on the part should be specified. This means plating, painting, or processing. It also means specifying the surface texture. Roughness is not the same as waviness, and the allowable tolerance for each should be specified.

8. Inspection and Testing

a. If the buyer does the inspection when the material is received, no mention need be made in the specifications regarding the method the buyer uses to assure himself that the specifications have been followed. If the vendor is required to inspect the product, the type of inspection and type of tests should be described in detail in the specifications, and the authority for the buyer to supervise the inspecting and testing should be established. If the buyer needs space, telephone, or stenographic service, or the use of the vendor's tools to perform this supervision, those needs should be specified.

b. In some cases a visual inspection or inspection with the help of a few gauges of every part may be desirable; in others a complete-destruction test of various samples selected at random may give the buyer a greater assurance that the specifications are being followed. If destructive testing is required, it should be established whether the pieces tested apply to the quantity purchased or if they are furnished without charge as a part of the contract. In either case, the tests selected should be such that failure to pass would indicate nonconformance with the specifications.

c. If in-process inspection is desirable, the points where inspection is required should be given. Sometimes this is difficult, as the one writing specifications usually does not know the steps or the process the vendor will use in manufacturing.

9. Packaging

a. The method of packaging may be important. Palleting may be desirable if the buyer intends to handle the product with forklifts; moisture proofing may be desirable for material to be stored for a long period. Packaging should be specified if required.

b. On bulk items packaging may not be required, but the maximum- or minimum-size load that the buyer wishes to receive at one time should be considered. Such an item should be specified in lieu of packaging.

10. Delivery

a. *Method*

The buyer has the right to specify the method used to transfer the material to his plant. The specification writer can determine whether the buyer prefers to receive shipments by car or truck but does not know the facilities or locations of the contractor to be selected. To obtain the lowest quotation, some specification writers request separate prices for delivery by railroad car and delivery by truck. This allows the buyer to make the decision after establishing the difference in cost.

b. *Point of acceptance*

(1) General

The specification writer has the choice of specifying where goods may be received by the buyer. This can be at the contractor's plant or at the buyer's plant. There are advantages and disadvantages for each method.

(2) At Contractor's Plant

(a) If the goods are accepted at the contractor's plant, the price is less, as the contractor doesn't include the cost of freight plus overhead in the price.

(b) The buyer can select the least expensive or the most reliable method of shipment after the award has been made. In addition, the buyer can change the method of shipping at any time, if the contract does not state otherwise, without making a change in the provisions in the contract.

(c) A buyer with several plants can change the receiving point without having to make a change in the contract.

(d) The buyer must make shipping arrangements and employ the shipper. Damage during shipping is not the responsibility of the vendor, and any action against the shipper is taken by the buyer.

(3) At the Buyer's Plant

The price will usually be higher if the acceptance is at the buyer's plant, because the vendor usually adds overhead to the cost of shipping. However, when the acceptance point is at the buyer's plant, the responsibility for having the goods arrive in satisfactory condition remains with the contractor. He is responsible for damage in shipment and for prompt arrival.

c. *F.O.B.*

(1) Usually acceptance is made F.O.B. vendor's plant, which means the vendor will load the car or truck and send it to the buyer's plant. The buyer will do the unloading. This is done because both are better equipped with labor and equipment at their own plant. In writing specifications, the writer should be specific as to when title changes hands. Sometimes a buyer's inspector will accept material after it is inspected but before it has been loaded. Trouble could develop for the buyer if "by act of God" or from other causes the material is damaged before the shipper is trusted with its safekeeping.

(2) If not specified, there may be a question as to when title passes on material accepted at the owner's plant. Does the property become the buyer's when the truck arrives, when it is unloaded, or when inspection is complete? The specifications should be clear on this point.

d. *Loading and Blocking*

The method of loading and blocking cars or trucks for shipping should be specified. This is particularly true where acceptance is made at the contractor's plant. The specification writer should be sure that the description of loading meets the approval of the shipper.

e. *Notification*

When the acceptance is at the buyer's plant, the buyer should be informed of each shipment in order to schedule labor to unload the carriers. The specifications should contain a requirement that a specific office in the buyer's plant be notified by the vendor when a shipment is made.

f. *Schedule*

(1) The schedule is one of the most important parts of the specification and the part most subject to litigation. The number of post-contract and pre-production samples required, as well as the date and place of delivery, should be specified in an

exact way that allows no room for disagreement. The same is true of the daily, weekly, or monthly delivery schedule.

(2) Fixed schedules are difficult to establish and many are changed during the life of the contract. Sales may increase or decrease, or one supplier may fail to meet a commitment, requiring increased production from other suppliers of the same product. As reasons for changing a schedule can be almost endless, the experienced writer usually includes methods for such changes and requests prices for percentage increases and decreases in the scheduled amounts. Having an agreement in advance saves hours of time and money in negotiating a new schedule.

(3) Where open-end contracts are involved, the specifications should describe the method by which the contractor will be notified of a change in schedule. The advance notice that a contractor will require to make a change will depend upon the product, and the specifications should include the time allowed.

THIRTY

Performance versus Brand-Name Specifications

30.01 INTRODUCTION

For years the federal government has had trouble from suppliers whose names did not appear in brand-name specifications. Most people realize that there are times when a single-product brand-name specification is in the best interest of the government in order to match existing equipment or reduce maintenance. However, Open Brand-Name Specifications favor products listed in the specifications and place the supplier of equal products at a disadvantage. To be fair and to avoid litigation, the federal government has been instrumental in replacing "brand-name specifications" with "performance specifications," and state and local governments have followed, so that performance specifications are being seen more often.

30.02 HISTORY

Performance specifications are not new. They have been used for many years, usually in combination with descriptive specifications, concrete being specified to a minimum ultimate strength and waterproofing being specified not to leak are typical examples (see Article 5.08 E). With the introduction of more mechanical equipment, performance specifications have come to be more in use. If an open specification is a requirement and an engineer needs a pump with an explicit capacity a descriptive specification is often desirable. This is feasible because various manufacturers and trade organizations have assisted the engineer by adopting standards and publishing uniform data.

30.03 ADVANTAGES OF PERFORMANCE SPECIFICATIONS

In theory, a performance specification or a performance specification combined with a descriptive specification is ideal for mechanical equipment. The specification states the minimum requirements that will be acceptable, and anybody who can meet those requirements can bid, thus assuring the owner of the lowest-priced equipment. The performance specification allows the small, unknown supplier of a quality product to bid as an equal to a well-advertised brand. As he has a small overhead, he can afford to bid at a much lower cost and save the owner considerable money because his lower price will be reflected in the reduced fees for the subcontractor and contractor.

30.04 ADVANTAGES OF BRAND-NAME SPECIFICATIONS

A. Most architects, engineers, and contractors and many owners prefer brand-name specifications. Architects and engineers prefer them because they are easier to write. It is much easier to select a product by name and add an "or equal" than to describe the same product in a manner that would exclude inferior equipment.

B. Most contractors prefer brand-name specifications because they know exactly what is wanted and they know from experience or guides where to obtain it. This is important to a bidder, who is always working against time.

30.05 DISADVANTAGES OF PERFORMANCE SPECIFICATIONS

A. THE OWNER'S PROBLEMS

Most owners have at least one experienced maintenance employee on their staff who is consulted when specifications are being prepared. While such persons often lack formal education, they are usually well-informed as to equipment. The author has found these men to be almost unanimously opposed to using unknown brands. They want equipment that can be serviced and that has dealers with an ample supply of spare parts. Most such maintenance people have had experience with equipment made by manufacturers that are no longer in the business. Most of them hate performance specifications, and if they could have their own way, they would use a closed specification.

B. THE ARCHITECT'S OR ENGINEER'S PROBLEMS

The architect or engineer has a duty to protect the best interest of the client. When this requires a performance specification, there is no choice. Performance specifications are longer, more exacting, and difficult to write. The architect must make sure that every requirement is specified in a manner that excludes undesirable products without limiting competition from acceptable bidders. This takes a lot of research.

C. THE BIDDER'S PROBLEMS

A bidder who decides to spend the money necessary to compile a quotation must make sure that bids will be received from at least one manufacturer of each product specified. When a long performance specification is received, the bidder may be at a loss to discover who makes the product specified. At times this involves considerable research. However, the bidder cannot sit idly by, hoping some supplier will know he is bidding and send a quotation.

30.06 DISADVANTAGES OF BRAND-NAME SPECIFICATIONS

Many manufacturers spend large sums of money to bring their names to the attention of the specification writer. By having salesmen make visits, by advertising in technical journals, and by technical literature they expect to have their names used in brand-name specifications. The cost of this service is added to the price of the product. It is surprising how many millions of dollars have been made by manufacturers who have taken a simple building product, given it a name, packaged it, and sold it in the marketplace as a superior product. The well-advertised brand may be most expensive and yet perform no better than less expensive makes. The specification writer should know costs and not use brand names indiscriminately.

30.07 WRITING PERFORMANCE SPECIFICATIONS

A. There are many ways to prepare a specification. The author starts his performance specifications by listing all of the essential requirements. It is important that none be missed, as one omission can ruin a specification. Included in this list are descriptive items, such as voltage requirements. A second list is then made to include desirable requirements, such as light weight or long life; another list is made of undesirable features, such as noise.

B. Research is then started to determine whether it is possible to meet the essential requirements with a standard product or whether special equipment would have to be obtained. One should then compare the value of each of the desirable requirements. Is the desirable feature worth the cost? A performance specification should be open as possible, listing the minimum acceptable performance on the essential requirements and including all of the desirable features possible within the budget.

C. It does little good to write a performance specification without some assurance that the item furnished will conform to that specification. Therefore, some form of testing should be provided in any performance specification. It must be remembered that testing costs money. Very often, where mechanical equipment is specified, it is less costly to have the manufacturer test the equipment in the plant where it was manufactured and pay the clerk of the works traveling expenses than to set up a testing procedure at the job site. However, the specifications must clearly indicate that plant acceptance of various components does not relieve the contractor of installing a satisfactory system.

30.08 INDUSTRIAL SPECIFICATIONS

Performance specifications are used more often in industry than in construction. Aesthetics, proportions, and space considerations are often more important than performance to the architect specifying materials. The engineer specifying a product is usually concerned with the performance. This is particularly true in specifying machinery.

30.09 "DESIGN AND BUILD" SPECIFICATIONS

The government has found that performance specifications are most useful for "design and build" contracts which are sometimes used for government procurement. Close tolerances and warped surfaces make it difficult to obtain accurate drawings, and it is extrememly expensive to settle claims by contractors who have been misled by errors. The specification for a design and build product is, in some respects, similar to a statement of work. It specifies what is wanted and what performance is required. The contractor is required to produce working drawings of all parts and assemblies. The contractor is then required to make parts from the drawing and assemble the parts into one or two working models which can be tested for performance. If the performance conforms to the specifications, the drawings and models are delivered to the government. The government may then proceed to make quantity purchases with reasonable assurance that the drawings are correct.

30.10 MILITARY SPECIFICATIONS

A. BRAND NAME OR EQUAL

In private work, the courts will support the decision of the engineer when he rejects a product as not being equal to the brand name specified. In government work, when a brand name "or equal" is specified, it is the engineer who must prove that any product submitted by a contractor is not equal to the brand name. The Armed Services Board of Contract Appeals has repeatedly ruled that "equal" does not mean "identical." Although the submitted product does not have the same features as the brand name, and even when the engineer can prove it does not perform as well, the armed services may still be required to accept the product if it performs its function. The following case is an example.

* B. ROBERT E. KRUEGER—CASE 8495, SEPTEMBER 18, 1970

1. The Facts

a. The specification read: ". . . Shall have capacity to cut 1", $7/8$", and $1/2$" wire rope. . . . Cutting force shall be supplied by an explosive charge only. The explosive charge shall be detonated by the force applied through a 12 ft. (Plus 1", Minus 0") pole handle only; not by a lanyard, electric firing cable or any other device. . . . Required for emergency cutting of wire rope lines between ships. Equal to MODEL EAP-500-1000. (Part Number B-96727) as manufactured by Mine Safety Appliance."

b. In answer to a request for bids, the contractor submitted a proposal for furnishing the contractor's own article. The product was accepted as equal on the condition that it functioned satisfactorily, and a contract resulted.

c. The Navy constructed a test rig to hold the cable with minimal tension. When the cutter was tested, it cut all except two (2) of the two hundred fifty-nine (259) wires comprising the one (1)-inch cable, and it nicked the remaining two wires. As a result, the contract was terminated.

2. The Contractor's Claim

The contractor claimed that the test was not representative of the actual conditions under which the cutter was to be used. The cable was to be used between boats generally about one hundred seventy (170) feet apart. Even when slack, the tension due to the weight of the cables would be at least four hundred eighteen (418) pounds. Had the test rig placed that tension on the wires, the cable would have parted.

3. The Navy's Claim

The Navy insisted that the device should cut cables when slack, and "slack" means no tension. Similar tests were made with the brand-name product specified and all wires were severed.

4. Decision

In the decision, the board wrote: "Brand name or equal procurements are troublesome at the very least. They are doubly so when the government does not detail those characteristics of the brand name item which are considered to be significant. . . . Bids cannot be rejected because of minor differences in design, construction, or features which do not affect the suitability of the products for their intended use. It follows that performance cannot be rejected solely because the contractor's item does not perform identically as the brand name item, so long as it is suitable for the intended use. . . . The termination for default is converted to a termination for convenience. . . ."*

C. SALIENT FEATURES

1. The military allow the use of "brand-name or equal" specifications. However, when such specifications are used, they require the specification writer to list the "salient features" in the brand-name product that are required in any product furnished as an equal.

2. "Salient features" means the important characteristics in the brand-name product that would be required in an "or equal" product to make it conform to the minimum needs of the government for that product. The capacity of a storage tank, the material for a bearing, or the time it takes for a machine to make a cycle could be a salient feature. Should the specification writer fail to list the salient features, the court may rule that they are not necessary, as in the following case.

† D. BRUNSWICK, INC.—CASE B-169662, JANUARY 4, 1971

1. The Facts

A pinsetter for a bowling alley was specified as American Machinery and Foundry Model 82-45 or equal. The contractor submitted a Brunswick Model A-1 to the government for approval. The contracting officer, upon recommendation of the engineer, ruled it was not equal, and the contractor appealed to the Armed Services Board of Contract Appeals.

2. The Contractor's Claim

The contractor claimed that the Brunswick was a satisfactory machine and conformed to all the needs of the government.

3. The Government Engineer's Claim

The government engineer showed that the equipment specified returned the ball two seconds faster than the contractor's product. The

---

*"Termination by default" means the contractor has breached his contract and is subject to damages. "Termination for convenience" means the government has terminated the contract and the contractor is entitled to the benefits stated in the contract.

†Reported in the "Federal Contracts Report" published by the Bureau of National Affairs, Inc., Washington, D. C.

engineer proved that the product named had an automatic foul cycle device and an arrangement to permit practice bowling without pins, both of which were lacking in the product submitted.

4. Decision

The board ruled that as the advantages claimed were not listed as salient features in the specifications, they were not necessary to meet the minimum needs of the government.

E. PERFORMANCE SPECIFICATIONS

When an open specification is written, the drawing must also be made so that more than one manufacturer's product can be used. When the drawings locate specific pieces of equipment of one manufacturer, a performance specification does not meet the needs of the government. In the following case, the architect did too much work and must have spent hundreds of dollars paying draftsmen to make drawings that were much less than useless. Had the architect not shown the equipment and allowed the specification writer to write a proper specification, he would have better served his client.

* F. KLEFSTAD ENGINEERING COMPANY—CASE 7146, JULY 27, 1968

1. The Facts

The contractor was awarded a contract for $2,369,800 for air-conditioning a twelve (12)-story hospital by means of a chilled-water system employing a steam turbine-driven centrifugal package chiller of five hundred (500) tons and an absorption-type package chiller of one thousand (1,000) tons. The architectural firm doing the engineering work wrote a performance specification and made drawings showing the location of various pieces of equipment.

2. The Contractor's Claim

The contractor made seven claims for extra money, most of which resulted from extra piping because his equipment would not fit in the space provided and had to be moved to a new location.

3. The Government's Claim

The government maintained that the drawings were diagrammatic and showed only the general arrangement and that notes on the drawings indicated this.

4. Decision

The Court of Claims overruled the contracting officer. Their decision

---

in part read, "The contract required the furnishing and installation of a complete and functioning system, including equipment to be chosen by the contractor. In those respects, the specifications were of the performance type, which, without further detail, would have imposed on the contractor the responsibility for layout and location of the equipment within the space provided in the layout drawings. However, the layout drawings depicted the location of equipment and piping systems in great detail. Those drawings were positive requirements not subject to change at the contractor's discretion. It was, thus, the responsibility of the designers to correlate the space provided for the new equipment with the locations specified in the layout drawings."

30.11   OTHER AGENCIES

A. SPECIFICATIONS

After reading the previous cases, one should realize the difficulty in writing specifications for military establishments and obtaining what is wanted. It is hard. To the specification writer it always appears that someone with a cheaper product is ready to force a less than desirable product on the goverment. To the contractor, the military waste money on specifying products beyond their actual needs. Other agencies also have similar problems; sometimes the results are more favorable, as in the following case.

* B. JOHN McSHAIN INC.—CASE 8475, SEPTEMBER 18, 1970

1. The Facts

A contract was awarded to the appellant contractor for $22,295,500 for the construction of an office building for the Department of Housing and Urban Development. The specification for the metal partitions was a combinantion of a descriptive and a performance specification. The specification was written with three alternates for various types of partitions. One alternate, the one accepted, was written around the Hauserman partition and described features only available in Hauserman panels, although the specifications were drafted without reference to that product and were designed to permit the broadest range of competition. The Hauserman Company submitted a bid to the contractor, and the contractor submitted a bid based upon the Hauserman proposal. After the contract was awarded to the appellant, Hauserman informed the contractor that they could not supply the hardware for the partition, and a subcontract was awarded to another

*Reproduced by permission from "Board of Contracts Appeals Decisions," vol. 70-2, published and copyrighted by Commerce Clearing House, Inc. of Chicago, Ill. 60646.

partition supplier.* The government refused to approve the panel for several reasons, one being the failure to submit certain acoustical test data, and because there was no steel backing as required by the specifications. The appellant contractor was required to laminate a steel backing for the partition before it was approved for use. The appellant sought compensation for the cost incurred by adding the steel backing. The contracting officer refused payment, and the contractor appealed.

2. Contractor's Claim

The contractor claimed that the specification is unduly restrictive in that it describes a feature that is produced by only one manufacturer; therefore, it is proprietary. Since it is a proprietary item, the government was obligated to consider and accept as equal or equivalent the panel as submitted without the backing because it met the performance requirements of the specification.

3. Government's Claim

The government claimed that the backing is an essential part of the specification which was retained, as it is a desirable feature from the standpoint of durability.

4. Decision

a. The board ruled that, except in unusual circumstances, the contractor's remedy against unduly restrictive specifications is a protest prior to award of the contract and not an appeal to the board of appeals.

b. They also wrote, "The Board has consistently held that where a contractor has agreed to perform in accordance with design specifications, the government is entitled to get what it bargained for and it is justified in rejecting a substitute product even though such product may be equal, or superior in performance, than that specified in the contract."

---

*Without knowing all the facts, one should not be critical of the Hauserman Company. It could be that there was a sound reason for their refusal.

THIRTY-ONE

Interpretation of Specifications

31.01 PURPOSE

The architect or engineer is sometimes asked to interpret another's specifications either as an arbitrator or as an expert witness. A few words in this regard seem appropriate.

31.02 DIFFERENT MEANINGS

A. It should be obvious that the way one interprets a specification affects the very heart of the transaction. Serious repercussions can result if there is a misunderstanding, and this reflects indirectly on the architect or engineer. The meaning of a specification cannot always be determined by a simple reading, and the same words may have different meanings to the owner, architect, and contractor. This results from various factors, ranging from simple errors in expression to the fact that some requirements can be so complex that it is difficult to write a specification to cover every possible contractual condition and virtually impossible to anticipate every problem that might arise during the duration of the contract. The general rule of contracts must be remembered: when the meaning is in dispute, the decision will usually be against the one who prepared the contract.

B. When disputes arise as to the meaning of a contract, a judge usually tries to find the intent of the parties at the time the contract was signed. For example, in a contract involving the purchase of apples; one party would not receive a favorable judgment by claiming impossibility of performance because there was no such product as "aplpes." A mistake in spelling would not serve to void a contract when both parties knew the intent when signing. Specifications differ in that they are written by one party and the other party, the bidder, has no say in determining the wording. The bidder must accept what is written or not bid.

31.03   DISPUTES

A. TYPES

Disputes usually fall into three categories: those where the contractor wants to furnish less than what is specified, those where the owner wants something not paid for, and honest disputes where the owner and the contractor interpret the same words in a different manner. Of course, the greedy owner and the shady contractor will insist that their dispute falls in the third category, and it takes an experienced person to determine the truth.

B. THE SHADY CONTRACTOR

Most contractors want to construct a finished product built to the owner's satisfaction; they value their reputation. Others make money by shady methods. After the contract is awarded, these contractors examine the specifications and drawings to find a loophole. Unfortunately, they are usually successful in the courts. They know from experience how far they can go, and they press their claims to the limit.

C. THE GREEDY OWNER

The greedy owner is in the same class as the shady contractor and can be as troublesome to the architect or engineer. Such owners regard all contractors as crooks. As victims of high construction costs, they feel justified in insisting that items not specified be furnished and that general statements regarding workmanship be enforced beyond general trade practice or the intent of the specifications. In an effort to keep the goodwill of the owner, the contractor may comply with unreasonable requests. Threats of no future business for the contractor, and other intimidations by the owner, are deplorable.

D. HONEST DISPUTES

There are a certain number of honest disputes. An example might be where the specifications required one (1) coat of a paint for an existing wall. The specifications also called for superior workmanship and results that could not be met with one (1) coat of paint. The painting subcontractor figured the costs on the basis of one (1) coat of paint; the owner expected the wall to appear as specified. Should the contractor be required to apply additional paint?

31.04   PRELIMINARY STEPS

A. THE FIRST STEP

The first step for an arbitrator is to determine whether the owner is justified in asking the contractor to perform the service in question. The specifications must be studied and trade practices must be known.

B. THE SECOND STEP

The next step is to determine whether the contractor's estimate included the service in question. This is not easy, because a contractor would not present an estimate showing costs he could not justify. If the contractor can prove the item in dispute was omitted, it means the owner received, or will receive, something free. The arbitrator must determine whether the estimator was negligent.

C. THE THIRD STEP

It is not enough to suspect that the contractor understood what the owner wanted and is raising the dispute in order to get extra money. The arbitrator must study the specifications and determine if a reasonable estimator could interpret the specifications the way the contractor reportedly did. If the contractor can honestly justify such reasoning, the question becomes one of interpretation.

31.05 INTERPRETATION

A. An honest dispute is a failure in communication. The arbitrator should realize that it is possible for people, in all sincerity, to disagree on the exact meaning of the same words, and should listen to both sides. If one party's reasoning is circuitous, inconsistent, or difficult to follow and produces an impractical or unjust result and the other party presents a normal, logical, and fair interpretation, the dispute can be resolved without difficulty. The polestay, in arriving at a proper decision, is to render the most reasonable interpretation of the specifications and to be fair in the judgment of the facts. It is, of course, possible to have two equally reasonable interpretations as to the meaning of a single set of contract documents. When the arbitrator is confronted with such a situation, the question should be construed against the party who drafted it. Legally this is known as the doctrine of "contra proferentem." It should be remembered that this doctrine applies to the contractor as well as the architect or engineer. A contractor who prepares a technical proposal, shop drawings, or specifications should be held liable for any ambiguity which results therefrom.

B. If both parties participate in the drafting of a contractual document or fully negotiate and bargain for the terms contained therein, the doctrine of "contra proferentem" does not apply.

31.06 WORDS

A. Disputes often arise regarding the meaning of words. In arbitration, it is best to give words their common and normal meaning unless it can be established that the words in question have a different meaning accorded them by trade usage. Trade usage should be clear, regularly observed, and known (or should have been known) by both parties to be acceptable.

B. The meaning of the word "complete" is often in question. For example, a fan is specified to be installed "complete and ready for operation," yet, by oversight, the motor is not specified. As the installation cannot be complete unless a motor is furnished and connected, most courts would hold against the contractor who omitted the motor, unless the contractor could establish that there was reason to believe the omitted work would be installed by another contractor or by the owner.

31.07   DEFICIENT SPECIFICATIONS

A. DEFINITION

Where, through ignorance, error, or unfamiliarity with existing conditions, specifications are produced that are contrary to sound engineering principles or impossible to perform, they are said to be "deficient."

B. SUPERIOR KNOWLEDGE

Architects or engineers are expected to have superior knowledge of the products and methods they specify, and the contractor has the right to rely on them. However, where the contractor has had previous experience with the product or method and knows, or should have known, that the specifications are deficient, the contractor is precluded from relying upon the superior knowledge of the architect or engineer. Contractors should not blindly follow a specification they know is incorrect; they are expected to question the writer. Where contractors either knowingly assume a risk or negligently enter into a contract they cannot perform, they should not be allowed to claim the inadequacy of the specifications as an excuse for the failure to perform.

C. PRINTED MATERIAL

Where a supplier or manufacturer furnishes printed material to architects or engineers containing hidden, ambiguous provisions and this material is used in the specifications, the architects or engineers are usually found at fault. The architects or engineers are expected to seek clarification. They have the duty to investigate products or methods they use. They should not blindly follow specifications furnished to them. However, where a supplier publishes specifications as to the application of a product and the specifications are followed, the supplier warrants, by implication, that the results will be as published.

D. WHERE THE CONTRACTOR'S KNOWLEDGE IS LIMITED

1. Where descriptive specifications are furnished on a product or in an area where the contractor's knowledge is limited, the contractor has the right to rely upon the superior knowledge of the architect or engineer. A contractor who follows the specifications exactly as written has the right to assume that the end product will be satisfactory. A contractor who is issued specifications that are impossible to perform is entitled to recover the costs in attempting to perform under them. Where faulty specifications result in delays in performance, the contractor is entitled to an equitable adjustment as compensation for any reasonable additional expenses suffered as a direct result of the delays.

2. Where the architect or engineer refuses to recognize an impossibility in a specification after it has been pointed out and insists upon performance as specified, the continued attempts to perform should be considered extra work and the contractor should be paid for such efforts.

E. PERFORMANCE SPECIFICATIONS

Where a performance specification is issued, the design is a part of the responsibility of the contractor. Extra expense encountered to solve design problems should not be chargeable to the owner.

31.08 PERSONAL PREJUDICES

It is important that the arbitrator be impartial. This is often difficult. By training and experience many engineers have fixed opinions, and they are apt to be overly critical of the failure of other professionals. Large amounts of money may be involved and an arbitrator cannot afford to permit personal prejudice to influence judgment.

THIRTY-TWO

Trouble

32.01 GENERAL

A. The only specification writer who has not experienced trouble during or after the completion of a structure is the one who has not written much. Trouble is a way of life for the beginner and is always waiting to pounce upon the overconfident and careless specification writer.

B. When trouble develops, it is usually too late to do much about it except to resolve not to make the same mistake again.

32.02 TYPES OF TROUBLE

A. TYPES

There are three (3) types of trouble: trouble which occurs before the bids are received, trouble which occurs during construction, and trouble which occurs after the building is completed.

B. TROUBLE BEFORE RECEIPT OF BIDS

1. Trouble occurring before bids are received is always minor. Except for the ego of the specification writer and the cost in time, little is lost. An addendum can be easily written.

2. During the bidding period minor questions sometimes arise. At the time, the question may appear so unimportant that an addendum is considered unnecessary. Beware! More times than not the specification writer is later sorry to have failed to issue an addendum to cover some minor point. Items which seem minor during the bidding often become major items of contention after the contract has been awarded.

C. CONSTRUCTION TROUBLE

Very few large construction jobs are built without some disagreement regarding the contract documents. When trouble does develop, a change order may be required. Change orders usually entail an increase in price, which the owner may be reluctant to pay if the fault lies with the architect or engineer. Each request for a change order should be analyzed, using the methods described in the previous chapter. Being fair is important.

D. TROUBLE AFTER OCCUPANCY

1. As a part of their contract, contractors usually warrant their work and guarantee the work of their subcontractors. If trouble develops, they can be required to make the necessary adjustments, but if they have been fully paid, the owner has no financial control over them. Most contractors value their reputation, however, and will comply with reasonable requests to make corrections.

2. The real test of the specifications and the design comes after the owner has operated the facility. No owner will be happy if the roof leaks, if the basement fills with water after every storm, or if it is impossible to properly heat the structure. Air conditioning can be a major source of trouble as can condensation or expansion and contraction.

3. If trouble develops on a project after it is completed, the owner usually calls the architect or engineer. The contract administrator often handles the problem by calling the contractor and the specification writer isn't involved. If a major problem regarding materials does arise, or if the general contractor requires technical assistance to solve the problem, the specification writer may be asked to assist.

32.03 WHO IS RESPONSIBLE

A. NOT ME

1. When trouble develops, the owner usually blames the architect or engineer. The architect or engineer in turn blames the contractor, who blames the subcontractor. The subcontractor can only blame the material, and the material supplier will blame the application. Someone else is always at fault.

2. The reason for this tendency is obvious. But who is actually to blame?

B. THE OWNER

1. No one wants to blame his boss, at least not publicly. Only the architect or engineer knows what instructions the owner has given. Many times the architect or engineer is blamed for the mistakes of the client and takes the blame to protect the client from criticism.

32.03 B.   (Cont.)

2. It should be remembered that the owner, not the architect or engineer, makes the final decisions. The architect or engineer, as well as the contractor, works for the owner. It is his money, and therefore he can state exactly what is wanted. There are times when he demands more space or quality than he is willing to pay for at the going rate. He may insist upon economies against the advice of his architect or engineer. These economies are apt to fall short of expectations. Let us take an example.

* 3. While the plans and specifications for a school were under way, the architect pleaded with the board to be allowed to place a ventilating system in the classrooms. "Let the teachers open the windows if they need fresh air" was the dictum of the school board. The plans and specifications were ready on time, but the approval of the bond issue delayed awarding the contract until autumn. The building was completed in June and immediately shut up for the summer. By July the interior was like a steam bath as the result of moisture from the concrete floors, the poured roof deck, and the plaster work that had never been allowed to dry out. When the school was opened, water dripped from mildewed ceilings and the woodwork had swollen and warped. The only rooms that were dry were the shops where the architect was permitted to place two (2) roof ventilators to exhaust dust and fumes. These rooms, in perfect condition, proved beyond a doubt that the water troubles could be blamed directly on the lack of ventilation. The school board had unwittingly created its own difficulties.

C. THE ARCHITECT OR ENGINEER

1. The architect or engineer holds a position of eminence as the master builder and is expected to have all-embracing skill in design and to prepare flawless contract documents. However, good structures are the product of architects or engineers working in harmony with good clients. When the client disregards or modifies advice, the architect or engineer is placed in a difficult position. One of the profession's greatest tasks is to cultivate a client's trust while satisfying his needs.

2. However, nobody but the architect or engineer is responsible for building inadequacies if he assures his client that he can meet the stated requirements for space and quality within the client's stated limited cost. The design of the civil, architectural, structural, mechanical, and electrical facilities regarding safety, workability, and compatibility are the responsibility of the architect or engineer.

3. If the wrong caulking material is specified or if necessary expansion joints are omitted, the responsibility rests with the architect or engineer, and trying to place the blame on the contractor with "he should

*Reported in *The Construction Specifier.*

have known it was wrong" is cheap and unprofessional.

4. The difficulty of the subcontractor in dealing with some architects or engineers cannot be overstated. On a project a subcontractor bidding on a cellular concrete roof fill approached the architect before the bids were due because the corrugated steel roof deck over which the lightweight concrete was to be placed was specified to be painted. Concrete will not adhere to paint. The subcontractor was told to bid as specified. If necessary, an adjustment would be made after the contract was awarded. After obtaining the contract, the subcontractor again approached the architect with a plea to use a galvanized deck. The architect answered that they didn't deal with subcontractors; the subcontractor should see the contractor. The contractor refused to do a thing. The order had been placed; galvanized metal would be more expensive and would delay the contractor's work. "The architect specified a painted deck; that's what he wants." After the deck was placed, the clerk of the works realized trouble was developing and stopped work on the project. After a considerable loss of time, steel anchors were welded over the entire area of the deck to form a mechanical bond for the lightweight concrete. At first the architect tried to place the blame upon the subcontractor, but when the facts became known, a change order was issued. Even so, the owner received a less than satisfactory installation at an additional cost.

D. THE CONTRACTOR

1. The general contractor's responsibilities are clear. They are written into the contract documents. If the contractor builds as the drawings and specifications require, he cannot be held at fault if the results are not satisfactory.

2. As the general contractors do only a small amount of work with their own forces, they can usually place the blame for a failure on one of their subcontractors. Yet, are the contractors still to blame?

3. The contractors' job is to complete a project for the price quoted, usually within a specific time period. It is also their job to see that the subcontractors perform in accordance with the contract. This latter duty is often neglected. Anything the subcontractor can slip past the clerk of the works is fine with some contractors.

4. If for some reason a job falls behind schedule, the contractor tries to hurry the subcontractors to make up for lost time. The subcontractors who perform their work near the end of the project are the most affected. Many contractors will insist that painters apply paint to surfaces before they have dried out in order to meet the schedule. However, if the paint peels, the contractors are the first to blame the subcontractor.

E. THE SUBCONTRACTOR

1. There are two types of subcontractors. One type manufactures the materials they install and the other buys the material. The first are primarily manufacturers and the installation is a small part of their investment. The field operation is a service to sell the manufactured product. The other type buys its material and sells only the installation service. They are often small, and because of the limited investment required to start such a business, there is usually a great deal of competition. They bid against other subcontractors to get the job and are subject to shopping, backcharging, and other imposition by the contractors. In addition they have to fight the weather, road conditions at the site, and the schedules imposed by the contractors. To stay in business, they still must make a profit.

2. The subcontractor who cheats on materials and workmanship is a scourge to the construction business. The owner wants a specific quality and is willing to pay for it. The subcontractor who furnishes less not only deprives the owner of what is wanted but also keeps an honest subcontractor from getting the work. The subcontractor who cuts the price knowing it will be necessary to cheat to make a profit hurts the entire construction industry.

F. THE SUPPLIER

1. Some architects and engineers contend that all building inadequacies are due to faulty material. This is not entirely true. Some failures are due to improper design. Many others are due to improper application of the materials.

2. There are two types of suppliers: one who produces stock items, such as cement, bricks, boilers, pipes, flooring, and electric fixtures; the other produces custom-built products or products fabricated for a specific building. The former can be held responsible for providing material conforming to the specifications. They are too far removed from the job to control the use of their products.

3. The custom-built product producers are able to distribute and install their product through franchised subcontractors. In such cases, the manufacturer should be held responsible for material failures when due to improper installation.

4. The producers of stock items cannot be responsible for their improper use. Paint manufacturers should not be responsible for a failure if a paint manufactured for interior use is used on the exterior. However, suppliers who have to fabricate their product for a specific building should know if their material is being misused and they should at least be held partly responsible for an improper installation.

5. The official spokesman of all producers of material is the literature

they publish. However, such literature often lacks the necessary information for an architect or engineer to make a proper selection. A producer of material should state the limitations as well as the qualities of a particular product. For example, manufacturers of flooring material should state in their literature the type of subfloor not recommended for their material. If it cannot be used on a slab placed on the ground, the literature should so state. If they fail to do so and install it knowing the installation is risky, they should be held at fault. The trouble is that materials are placed on the market and described in glowing terms without adequate details. The material is sold to some subcontractor who knows less than the manufacturer about the product. When failure occurs, who is to blame?

G. RESPONSIBILITY

The responsibility for a failure can fall on the owner, the supplier, or anyone in between. Specification writers who are given a bad building performance to investigate should realize the buckpassing they will be faced with.

32.04 FINDING THE CAUSE

A. The specification writer will seldom be involved in simple problems. If the client says the roof leaks during a rainstorm, the contractor will be called by others; however, if the roof is reported to be leaking when it isn't raining, an investigation may be required. Leaky pipes or condensation could be the cause.

B. Field investigation can be time-consuming. If the owner complains that a parapet wall is moving out of line, it isn't enough to determine that the expansion of the poured roof deck is the cause. Why is it expanding? Were expansion joints properly placed? Is this deck expanding more than other decks of the same size? If so, why? Consultations with the contractor, the subcontractor, and the material supplier will be required. If there is a technical representative of the manufacturer's association in the area, he should be consulted. Only one thing is sure, and that is that the other fellow will be named at fault.

32.05 RESOLVING THE TROUBLE

With all the facts at hand, the specification writer should return to the office and determine who is at fault. If the fault lies with the owner or the architect, the specification writer should admit it. If the fault lies partly with the owner or architect and partly with the contractor, a reasonable adjustment can usually be reached. If the fault lies in the construction, the contractor should be told how to make corrections. The owner has a contract with the contractor only. The architect or engineer shouldn't become involved with the contractor's relations with the subcontractors or the material suppliers.

THIRTY-THREE

Computerized Specifications

33.01 HISTORY

A. The abacus, probably the oldest mechanical computing aid, is known to have been used in China as early as the sixth century before Christ. The slide rule was invented by William Oughtred, an English mathematician, in 1620, but it was not until the final years of the nineteenth century that it came into use. Blaise Pascal invented the first mechanical adding machine in 1642; by the turn of the twentieth century the machines were being mass-produced. The punch card machines for calculating data were introduced by Herman Hollerith in 1886; in 1944 the IBM Corporation built the first large-scale digital computer. This machine, consisting of three-quarters of a million (750,000) parts, was conceived by Howard Aiken of Harvard University and used punch cards as the input medium for computing data. The field expanded in the next several years, and when the vacuum tube was replaced with a solid-state transistor, making smaller units possible, the field exploded. Today, the word "computer," which was originally a machine to compute, has been expanded to mean any business machine with a memory.

B. A large part of any specification section is the same for every project. For example, the "General Note" is the same for each section. The materials used to make mortar, or the specification for concrete block backup, could be identical for many projects. There are, however, enough differences between the two projects to require separate specifications. Most work done by experienced specification writers is the compiling of previously written work in a new combination with relatively little new writing. As a result, many large offices tried to standardize specifications, the purpose being to make the work more uniform between various specification writers within the office and to ease the burden of training new men. Harold Reeve Sleeper, AIA, in 1939 wrote an eight hundred (800)-page book of standard specifications, leaving blanks to be filled for the special features required in each project. Although this book was popular, going through six (6) printings in the following eight (8) years, the use of standard specifications was very limited. The reason is that standardized specifications help only one phase of the writing process. The specification still has to be copied complete by a typist, checked for errors, corrected, and then reproduced.

C. Computerized specifications require standardized sections. They must be carefully written, but once written, they can be used repeatedly. The savings results from the faster mechanical typing and the reduced amount of checking and correcting.

33.02 COMPUTER HARDWARE

A. THE PUNCH CARD SYSTEM

1. Equipment

a. *The card-punching typewriter*

(1) The existing card-punching machines operate similarly to a typewriter. When the keys are depressed, characters are printed at the top of the card and holes are punched below, lining up with the type. The vertical location of the hole or holes is determined by character punch by the operator. One card is required for each line of type.

(2) Each card should be numbered. With one card for each line of type, the number of cards required for any major specification would run into thousands. A numbering system for the cards is required so that they can be kept in order.

b. *The card finder*

The card finder is used to remove one or more cards from the set of cards. A finder card or cards, each punched with the number of the card to be removed, are placed in the card finder. When a set of cards is placed in the machine, each card with a number matching the number punched on the finder card is separated from the set.

c. *The collator*

If the cards are not in the proper numerical sequence, the collator can be used to properly arrange them.

d. *The printer*

(1) The printer takes each card from a pile, scans it electrically, and types the information on paper.

(2) The printer can type single pages or, using carbon paper, multiple pages. It can also type on mats or vellum that can be used to reproduce copies by another method.

2. Using the computer

a. By typing an entire specification on cards and placing the cards in the printer, a printed specification can be obtained. New specifications are obtained by revising the information on the existing cards.

b. The number of the card should appear at the extreme right at the end of the line of type. When the writer wishes a line of type deleted from the specification, he can have the number of that line typed on a finder card. When the finder card is placed in a card finder, all cards with numbers matching the numbers on the finder cards will be removed.

c. Information can be added to the specification by typing the new information on new cards. Each card would be numbered to place it in the proper location. A letter would follow the number, indicating a revision. If more than one card was to be inserted, the alphabetical order would determine the location. When placed in a collator, any number of cards can be inserted between any two cards in the set.

3. Possible Advantages of the Card System

Once a section of any specification is placed on cards, it can be reprinted automatically at high speed. The work required to type the same section for a future project would be limited to typing the changes and placing them in the machine. The printer can type much faster than a person can and will not make errors, thus saving considerable time in the typing and proofreading of specifications.

4. Disadvantages of the Card System

a. One disadvantage of the card system is the large number of cards required to make a complete specification. Assuming that fifty (50) lines can be typed on each page, ten thousand (10,000) cards would be required for a two hundred (200)-page specification.

b. When the above system is used, a line of numbers would appear at the right of each sheet. These numbers would not necessarily run in sequence, as the order would be broken when lines of type were deleted from the original specification. This could be confusing to the reader.

B. THE MAGNETIC CARD SYSTEM

1. General

The magnetic card system is similar to the punch card system but has many advantages, the chief one being in the reduction of cards. The punch card requires one card for each line of type; the magnetic card requires one card for each fifty (50) lines of type. In other words, we would need one card for each page.

2. Hardware

The magnetic card system consists of a special typewriter which is connected electrically to a console which is set adjacent to the typewriter. The typewriter has a standard keyboard and works like a standard typewriter. The typist inserts paper and types. That which is typed on the paper is electrically registered as a magnetic pattern on a card in the console. When the card is replayed in the console, the special typewriter automatically will reproduce the same wording as the typist had typed. Corrections can be made by back-spacing, which will cover over the incorrect character on the paper and at the same time correct the card. When completed, the cards can be placed in the console, fifty (50) cards at a time, and the typewriter will reproduce the information on the cards.

3. Using the Magnetic Card System

Once the cards are typed with one specification, that same specification can be reused by changing lines, the same as in the punch card system. The console can be adjusted to erase any line or lines and new information may be typed in their place.

C. MAGNETIC TAPE

1. There are magnetic-tape selector typewriters on the market that could be used for producing specifications, and they appear to have several advantages over the card system. The keyboard is the same as on any standard typewriter. The type is on a single ball, and depressing a key on the keyboard makes an electrical contact that revolves the ball and causes it to strike an inked ribbon, thus printing the proper character on the paper. The same character is also recorded on a master magnetic tape. The ball can be changed, and this permits the use of various styles of type. Upper- and lower-case letters and many symbols can be printed and underlined. Fifteen (15) pages of typing can be stored on one roll of tape one inch (1") in diameter.

2. When the master tape is played back, the information on the tape will be typed at a speed of over fifteen (15) letters or digits per second (15/sec). At the same time, identical information will be recorded on another new magnetic tape. The machine can be set to stop at any point and the typewriter can be used to add material to the new tape without changing the master tape. The machine can also be adjusted to skip material on the master tape. Thus, a new specification can be produced on new tape without altering the master tape, and

the new tape can be used to produce as many copies as necessary on paper.

D. THE DISK SYSTEM

1. General

The disk system is several times as expensive as the other systems but has the advantage of speed. Where the other systems reproduce one (1) letter at a time or about fifteen (15) lines per minute (15/min), the disk system can be made to reproduce two thousand lines per minute (2,000/min). That is forty (40) pages of fifty (50) lines each. This speed is possible because the machine prints an entire line at a time, not a single letter, as on a typewriter. In specification work there is no need for such high speed, and a less expensive machine that prints three hundred (300) lines, or six (6) pages a minute, should be fast enough.

2. Hardware

The hardware for the disk system consists of a keyboard, disks, a computer processing unit, and a printer.

3. Operation

a. The basic specification is typed on paper a line at a time. If an error is found, the line may be retyped. When the line is perfect, the typist presses a key and the entire line is added to the disk. The disk, when played back, will be reproduced on paper as a master specification.

b. The specification writer makes any changes desired in the master specification. It is possible to omit or add several lines or several pages, or to make changes in any line. When all the changes are made, the corrected pages are returned to the typist.

c. The typist types all the added material and this is recorded on a new disk. If one word is changed, the entire line is retyped.

d. The Computer Programmer then writes a program telling the computer which lines to omit and where new lines should be added.

e. When the program is given to the computer, one copy of the specification is run for checking.

f. The specification writer is required to check only rewritten work for accuracy, making sure the typing is correct and that it is inserted in the proper place.

33.03 WRITING SPECIFICATIONS FOR THE COMPUTER

A. MASTER COPY

1. As the master copy will be used on all specifications, it must be well-written and checked for errors.

2. Several paragraphs may be written covering the same subject in different ways. For example:

   "3.07 RAILROAD SIDING

   " The _____ Railroad has a siding at the job site. This siding may be used by the contractor and his subcontractor for the delivery of material. All materials shall be unloaded promptly so as not to delay other traffic."

   "3.07 RAILROAD SIDING

   " There is no railroad siding at the job site. The contractor will be required to arrange for motor shipment of his supplies and materials."

B. WRITER'S COPY

The writer's copy of each section of the specifications has the text identical with the master copy; however, blank lines are left to be filled in by the writer. In addition, each line is numbered in the margin to assist the computer operator. Some offices also have instructions on the writer's copy, such as, "Select one of the following."

C. PREPARING SPECIFICATIONS

The specification writer takes the writer's copy of each specification section and adds and deletes information as required to make a complete specification section. Unless the specification writer has a very legible handwriting, the information should be printed. The typist, when typing an entire text, can follow the meaning, and this often assists the transcriber in reading poor handwriting. The computer operator is copying words and is at times unfamiliar with the text.

D. TYPING

1. With the punch card system, the operator uses the collator to remove the cards for each line where changes were indicated on the writer's copy. New cards are typed and inserted in the proper place. One of the disadvantages of the punch card system is that some cards where no word change is required must be retyped to satisfy space requirements. On the magnetic-tape or disk system this is done automatically.

2. With the magnetic systems, the operator sets the cards or tape for each section of the specifications. The machine is set to stop when changes are required, and the operator types in the additions and

blanks out the deletions. When completed, the new copy is returned to the specification writer for checking.

E. CHECKING

One of the main advantages of computerized specifications is the time saved in checking. When a specification is retyped, every word and every comma must be checked for accuracy. Even so, errors do occur. With computerized specifications, the checking, once the master set is checked, can be confined to the lines that have been changed.

F. REPRODUCTION

When ready for printing, the cards or tapes can be placed in the computer and run automatically until the proper number of copies are made. Each copy is an original. Normal poor printing, blots, and blanks found is other methods are missing.

33.04   SHOULD WE USE IT?

The decision to use computerized specifications is a matter of economics. The large office with several full-time specification writers can hardly afford to be without them. The small office could hardly justify the high cost. Computers are extremely high-priced; however, they can be rented. The middle-sized office must determine the cost of maintaining standardized specifications and must balance high-cost equipment against the cost of the less efficient methods.

33.05   THE FUTURE SPECIFICATION WRITER

The future specification writer will be relieved of many of the routine jobs as computers and other aids come to the writer's assistance. However, with the advance in material technology and new methods of construction, his job will be one demanding a high degree of professional ability. The basics of writing will always remain.

Subcontractor's Estimate Sheet

Estimate No._____

ACME ROOFING AND SHEET METAL COMPANY

Due Date_____
Time_____

OWNER_____BUILDING_____

LOCATION_____

ARCHITECT_____CONTRACTOR_____

DECK_____ROOF_____TOTAL AREA_____ Sqs.

VAPOR SEAL_____BOND_____HEIGHT_____

INSULATION_____METAL_____

NO.	QUANTITY	UNIT		MATERIAL			LABOR		
				Unit		Total	Unit		Total
				Labor					
				Material					
				Set-Up & Cartage					
				Bond					
				Cost					
				Overhead & Profit ____%					
				Sales Tax					
				Quote $_____					

Form 1B

Suggested Trade Sections

I. EXPLANATION

A. As work performed by established subcontractors differs in the various parts of the country, and as construction methods are constantly changing in all areas, it is impossible to make a complete and accurate list of trade sections to properly cover all parts of the country. The following list is suggested to assist students to write specifications for class instruction.

B. Coordinating and referencing the work between the various trades require experience. As most students have no experience, the most common areas where coordination is required are listed. The list is not complete. The student should realize that each specification introduces special problems and that the following coordination is only a guide.

II. LIST

A. DEMOLITION

1. Items to Be Included in the Section

    a. Removals

    b. Temporary supports

    c. Protection of public and other work

    d. Weather protection

    e. Spreading dust and dirt

    f. Disposal of materials

2. Coordination

    a. When materials in a section of a structure to be demolished are to be removed, it is usually better to have the trade reusing the materials remove them. When this type of work is required, the demolition section should be coordinated with the trade involved.

    b. If mechanical or electrical service is to be maintained or disconnected, this section should be coordinated with the trade involved.

B. PILING AND CAISSONS

1. Work Involved

This section should include furnishing and driving all types of piles, including sheet piling and all types of caissons. It also includes the underpinning or moving of existing buildings

2. Coordination

    a. As some excavation may be required before piles are driven, the amount of work required by the piling and caisson subcontractor must be carefully coordinated with the work required by the excavating, filling, and grading subcontractor.

    b. Concrete is also required for caissons and some types of piles, and when concrete is required, it should be coordinated with the Concrete section.

C. EXCAVATING, FILLING, AND GRADING

1. Work Involved

    a. Removing trees

    b. Removing sod and topsoil and storing it for future use

    c. Grubbing

    d. Removing existing below-grade structure or utilities

    e. Bracing and shoving

    f. Rock excavating (often paid as a separate item)

    g. Placing drain tile

    h. Filling and backfilling

    i. Compacting soil

    j. Grading

2. Coordination

    a. This work should be coordinated with landscaping regarding the topsoil and resodding.

    b. As excavating is also required for other trades, this section should be coordinated with the Storm and Sanitary Sewers, Roads and Paving, Railroad Work, Fencing, Flagpoles, Swimming Pools, and Electrical Work sections.

D. CONCRETE

1. Work Involved

    a. Formwork, form ties, bracing, etc.

    b. Placing miscellaneous iron in forms

    c. Joints

        (1) Expansion joints

        (2) Contraction joints

        (3) Construction joints

    d. Reinforcing steel

        (1) Shop drawings

        (2) Bars

        (3) Wire mesh

        (4) Fabrication

        (5) Supports

            (a) Chairs, ties, bolsters, and spacers

            (b) Tie wire

        (6) Placing

            (a) Wiring

            (b) Splicing

    e. Concrete materials

        (1) Coarse aggregate

        (2) Fine aggregrate

        (3) Cement

        (4) Water

        (5) Admixtures

           (a) Retarders

           (b) Coloring

  f. Mixing concrete

  g. Preparing for placing

  h. Conveying concrete

  i. Depositing concrete

  j. Compacting concrete

  k. Testing

  l. Removal of forms

  m. Surface repairing

  n. Grouting

  o. Mud mats

  p. Cold-weather requirements

  q. Protecting

  r. Cleaning

2. Coordination

  a. General

Concrete is a building material that has many uses and is used by many trades. Subcontractors must know what concrete they are to furnish and what work will be done by other subcontractors. The trades where concrete could be used are shown in the following list. There are also trades that furnish material which is embedded in concrete. Who places this material in the forms is important. These trades are also listed.

  b. List of sections to be coordinated with the Concrete section

    (1) Piling and Caissons

    (2) Concrete Floor Finishing

    (3) Lightweight Concrete

    (4) Precast Concrete

    (5) Chimneys

    (6) Incinerators

    (7) Waterproofing and Dampproofing

      (a) Cutting Form Wires

      (b) Cement Plaster

    (8) Structural Steel (anchor bolts)

    (9) Miscellaneous Iron

    (10) Ornamental Iron

    (11) Carpentry (Formwork)

    (12) Storm and Sanitary Sewers

    (13) Roads and Paving

    (14) Fencing

    (15) Flagpoles

    (16) Swimming Pools

        (17) Plumbing

        (18) Electrical Work

E. CONCRETE FLOOR FINISHING

1. Work Involved

    a. Emery, flintrock, traprock, silica, quartz, iron, or iron-hardened floors

    b. Ground concrete floors

    c. Curing floors

    d. Hardening compounds for floors

2. Coordination

This section should be carefully coordinated with the Concrete section as to what materials are furnished, who is responsible for the bond between the two materials, and the work in each trade.

F. LIGHTWEIGHT CONCRETE

1. Foam Concrete

2. Lightweight Aggregate Concrete

G. PRECAST CONCRETE

1. Cement Tile Roof Deck

2. Precast Sills and Copings

3. Precast Prestressed Structural Units

H. MASONRY

1. Material

    a. Mortar

    b. Brick (all kinds)

    c. Concrete block

    d. Glass block

    e. Flue Lining

    f. Crock coping

    g. Wall reinforcing and ties

    h. Contraction joint materials

    i. Gypsum partition tile

2. Coordinate with

    a. Demolition (on alteration work)

    b. Stonework

    c. Chimneys

    d. Incinerators

    e. Waterproofing and Dampproofing

    f. Miscellaneous Iron (anchors)

g. Storm and Sanitary Sewers (catch basins)

I. STONEWORK

1. Material

a. All kinds of stone
b. Mortar
c. Expansion gaskets
d. Lead weather caps

2. Coordinate with

a. Masonry
b. Chimneys
c. Waterproofing and Dampproofing
d. Ornamental Metals (nonferrous anchors)
e. Slate, Marble, and Precast Terrazzo

J. CHIMNEYS

1. Large Concrete or Masonry Chimneys—Specialist to Construct

2. Metal Stocks

3. Coordinate with Concrete, Masonry, or Structural Steel Section

K. INCINERATORS

L. WATERPROOFING AND DAMPPROOFING

1. Types of Work

a. Soil waterproofing (Bentonite)
b. Mastic waterproofing
c. Membrane waterproofing
d. Cement plaster waterproofing
e. Weatherproofing with iron
f. Dampproofing with coated copper
g. Dampproofing with fabric
h. Concrete joint sealing
i. Plaster bond

2. Coordinate with

a. Excavating, Filling, and Grading (backfilling against waterproofing)
b. Concrete
c. Precast Concrete
d. Masonry
e. Stonework
f. Chimneys
g. Curtain Wall
h. Metal Siding

      i. Cement Asbestos

      j. Gunite

      k. Metal Sash

      l. Carpentry and Millwork

M. STRUCTURAL STEEL

1. Items Included

      a. Anchor bolts

      b. Base plates and bearing plates

      c. Bolts, rivets, and other attachments

      d. Structural sections

      e. Structural tubing

2. Coordination

      a. Concrete (anchor bolts)

      b. Miscellaneous Iron

      Care must be used to define what is structural steel and what is miscellaneous iron.

      c. Cranes (crane rails and hook bolts)

      d. Monorails

      e. Curtain Wall

      f. Elevators and Electric Stairways

N. BAR JOIST

1. Joist

2. Bearing Plates

3. Bridging

4. Anchors

O. MISCELLANEOUS IRON

1. Items Included

      a. Anchor bolts

      b. Pipe sleeves

      c. Inserts

      d. Pulling eyes (to pull wire through conduit)

      e. Checker plate

      f. Grating

      g. Chains

      h. Ladders

      i. Metal stairs

      j. Hand railing

      k. Metal stair nosings

      l. Guard posts and bumpers

      m. Pit frames and covers, hatch covers

II. O. 1. (Cont.)

    n. Access panels

    o. Louvers

    p. Structural door frames

    q. Loose lintels

    r. Thresholds

    s. All other items of steel or iron not specified in other sections

2. Coordination

This section will have to be coordinated with most sections in the specifications.

P. CRANES

1. Items Included

    a. Crane rails

    b. Hook bolts and clamps

    c. Splices

    d. Bumpers

2. Coordination

This section must be coordinated with sections specifying structural steel, miscellaneous iron, and electrical work.

Q. MONORAILS

1. Items Included

    a. Hangers

    b. Clamps

    c. Track

    d. Switches

    e. Bumpers

    f. Hoists (both hand-operated and electric)

    g. Trolleys

2. Coordination

This section should be coordinated with Structural Steel, Miscellaneous Iron, and Electrical Work.

R. HYDRAULIC EQUIPMENT

S. ORNAMENTAL METAL

1. Items Included

    a. Aluminum

    b. Brass

    c. Bronze

    d. Stainless steel

    e. Cast iron

    f. Wrought iron

II. S. 1. (Cont.)

    g. Porcelain enamel

  2. Coordination

  This section should be coordinated with the Miscellaneous Iron section.

T. BANK EQUIPMENT

  1. Items Included

    a. Safes
    b. Tellers' cages
    c. Safe deposit boxes

  2 Coordination

  This section should be coordinated with the sections on Miscellaneous Iron and Ornamental Metals.

U. CELLULAR STEEL

V. STEEL DECKING

W. POURED ROOF DECKING

  1. Items Included

    a. Steel-supported system
      (1) Galvanized steel deck
      (2) Lightweight concrete
    b. Self-supporting system
      (1) Bulb tees
      (2) Form board
      (3) Reinforcing
      (4) Lightweight concrete or gypsum

  2. Coordination

  This section should be coordinated with Lightweight Concrete and Miscellaneous Iron.

X. ROOFING AND SHEET METAL

  1. Items Included

    a. Vapor seals
    b. Roof insulation
    c. Cant strips
    d. Roofing felts
    e. Asphalt and tar
    f. Gravel and slag
    g. Sprayed roofing materials
    h. Roof sumps
    i. Gutters
    j. Downspouts

II. X. 1. (Cont.)

     k. Flashing and counter flashing

     l. Other miscellaneous sheet metal

    m. Shingles

2. Coordination

    a. Waterproofing and Dampproofing

    b. Ornamental Metal

    c. Curtain Walls (flashing)

    d. Kitchen Equipment (metal work)

    e. Laboratory Furniture (metal work)

    f. Plumbing (roof sumps)

Y. CURTAIN WALLS

1. Items Included

    a. Grid system

    b. Panels

    c. Sash and screens

    d. Doors

    e. Flashing

2. Coordination

    a. Waterproofing and Dampproofing

    b. Structural Steel

    c. Miscellaneous Iron

    d. Ornamental Metals

    e. Roofing and Sheet Metal

    f. Metal Sash

    g. Hollow Metal Work

    h. Caulking

    i. Glass and Glazing

Z. METAL SIDING

AA. CEMENT ASBESTOS

AB. GUNITE

AC. METAL SASH

AD. CARPENTRY AND MILLWORK

1. General

This section includes all wood and work normally installed by the carpenter. Because it is such an all-inclusive trade, only a few of the items are listed to give the student an idea of the work involved.

2. Wood Framing

    a. Sills

II. AD. 2. **(Cont.)**

      b. Plates

      c. Joists

      d. Studs

      e. Siding

      f. Wood decks

      g. Insulation (when nailed to studs or joists)

3. Fascia

4. Blocking and Nailing Strips

5. Furring

6. Wood Grounds

7. Wood Bumpers

8. Wood Stairways and Stair Rails

9. Sub Flooring and Flooring

10. Drywall Construction

11. Wood Doors and Frames

12. Wood Sash

13. Wall Panels

14. Caulk Boards

15. Paneling

16. Trim

17. Cabinets and Shelving

18. Counters

19. Drawers and Tables

20. Prime or Back Painting

21. Rough Hardware (Nails, Screws, etc.)

AE. HOLLOW METAL WORK

    1. Items Included

      a. Metal doors

      b. Metal trim

    2. Coordinate with

    This section should be coordinated with Miscellaneous Iron and Finished Hardware.

AF. FIRE DOORS

1. Items Included

a. Hollow metal fire doors
b. Tin-clad fire doors
c. Kalamein fire doors
d. Plywood fire doors
e. Frames for fire doors

2. Coordinate with

a. Miscellaneous Iron
b. Carpentry and Millwork
c. Hollow Metal Work
d. Glass and Glazing
e. Finished Hardware
f. Painting and Finishing

AG. OVERHEAD AND VERTICAL-LIFT DOORS

1. Items Included

a. Doors and glazing
b. Guides
c. Hardware
d. Weatherstripping
e. Operators
   (1) Motors
   (2) Limit switches
   (3) Solenoid brakes
   (4) Disconnect switch
   (5) Push buttons
   (6) Wire

2. Coordinate with

a. Miscellaneous Iron
b. Glass and Glazing
c. Electrical Work

AH. ROLLING METAL CURTAINS

1. Items Included

a. Curtains
b. Guides
c. Roller shafts, hoods, and brackets
d. Operators

2. Coordinate with

a. Miscellaneous Iron
b. Electrical Work

II. (Cont.)

AI. CAULKING

AJ. GLASS AND GLAZING

1. Items Included

    a. All types of glass
    b. Mirrors
    c. Glazing compounds
    d. Glass doors

2. Coordinate with

    a. Metal Sash
    b. Carpentry and Millwork
    c. Hollow Metal Work
    d. Fire Doors
    e. Overhead and Vertical-Lift Doors
    f. Metal Casework

AK. LATH AND PLASTERING

1. Items Included

    a. Furring
      (1) Inserts
      (2) Hangers
      (3) Runner channels
      (4) Furring channels
      (5) Tie wire
      (6) Clips
    b. Lathing
      (1) Various types of lath
      (2) Corner bead
      (3) Expansion joints
    c. Plastering
      (1) Gypsum
      (2) Hydrated lime
      (3) Water
      (4) Keens cement
      (5) Gauging plaster
      (6) Sands

AL. ACOUSTICAL TREATMENT

This section should be coordinated with the Lathing and Plastering section if the supports for the acoustical are specified therein and with the Electrical section if light fixtures are fitted in the ceiling.

AM. INTERIOR TILE WORK

1. Items Included

    a. Floor brick (mill pavers)

II. AM. 1. (Cont.)

      b. Quarry tile

      c. Glazed tile

      d. Ceramic tile

      e. Mortar

2. Coordinate with

      a. Masonry

      b. Waterproofing and Dampproofing (underlayment)

      c. Plumbing (floor drains)

AN. CEMENT ENAMEL

AO. SLATE, MARBLE, AND PRECAST TERRAZZO

AP. POURED TERRAZZO

    1. Sand

    2. Felt

    3. Mesh

    4. Pigment

    5. Divider Strips

    6. Marble Chips

    7. Water

AQ. WOOD BLOCK FLOORS

AR. ASPHALT FLOORS

AS. RESILIENT FLOORS

    1. Asphalt Tile

    2. Vinyl Tile

    3. Cork

    4. Linoleum

AT. WIRE PARTITIONS

    1. Items Included

      a. Type of partition, wire, posts, bases, frames, etc.

      b. Doors

      c. Hardware

      d. Attachments and supports

AU. FOLDING PARTITIONS

This includes wood, metal, and fabric interior partitions. The track, trolleys, and hardware should be included under this heading.

AV. MOVABLE PARTITIONS

Various types of factory-fabricated partitions are included under this heading. As glass and hardware are usually furnished with them, this section should be coordinated with Glass and Glazing and Hardware.

AW. METAL TOILET STALLS

1. Items Included

    a. Supports (for hanging type)
    b. Dividers, pilasters, and doors
    c. Hardware

2. Coordinate with

    a. Miscellaneous Iron
    b. Hardware

AX. WASHROOM EQUIPMENT

    a. Soap dispensers
    b. Towels
    c. Waste disposal
    d. Sanitary napkin dispensers
    e. Paper holders

AY. LAUNDRY EQUIPMENT

AZ. KITCHEN EQUIPMENT

1. Items Included

    a. Dishwashers
    b. Garbage disposal units
    c. Refrigerator
    d. Broilers
    e. Deep-fat fryer
    f. Grill
    g. Range
    h. Canopies or hoods
    i. Sinks
    j. Bain Marie
    k. Hot-food wells
    l. Serving counter
    m. Coffee urn
    n. Ice cream cabinet
    o. Peeler
    p. Ice machine
    q. Meat grinder

II. AZ. 1.   (Cont.)

     r. Slicers and cutters

     s. Mixers

     t. Water cooler

2. Coordinate with

     a. Ornamental Metals

     b. Metal Casework

     c. Plumbing

     d. Electrical Work

BA. THERMAL INSULATION AND COLD STORAGE WORK

BB. LABORATORY FURNITURE

1. Items Included

     a. Base units

     b. Pipe racks

     c. Shelves

     d. Drawers

     e. Doors

     f. Mouldings

     g. Waste chutes

     h. Hardware

        (1) Door and drawer pulls

        (2) Hinges

     i. Table tops

     j. Fume hoods

     k. Racks

     l. Fixtures and fittings

        (1) Water fixtures

        (2) Steam cocks

        (3) Distilled water fixtures

        (4) Gas and air cocks

        (5) Remote control valves

        (6) Index buttons

        (7) Electrical outlets

2. Coordinate with

A large part of the installation of laboratory furniture involves plumbing, and this section should be carefully coordinated with the Plumbing section. It should also be coordinated with the Electrical Work.

BC. METAL CASEWORK

1. Wardrobe Cabinets

2. Chart and Magazine Cabinets

II. BC. (Cont.)

    3. Hospital Cabinets

    4. Filing Cabinets

BD. LOCKERS AND METAL SHELVING

BE. FINISHED HARDWARE

    1. Items Included

      a. Hinges

      b. Pivots

      c. Lockets

      d. Latch sets

      e. Push plates

      f. Door pulls

      g. Friction catches

      h. Flush bolts

      i. Anti-panic exit devices

      j. Door closers

      k. Door holders

      l. Door stops

      m. Barrel bolts

      n. Hasps

      o. Padlocks

      p. Key boards

      q. Letter-box plates

      r. Coat and hat hooks

    2. Coordinate with

      a. Miscellaneous Iron

      b. Metal Sash

      c. Carpentry and Millwork

      d. Hollow Metal Work

      e. Fire Doors

      f. Overhead and Vertical-Lift Doors

      g. Rolling Metal Curtains

      h. Wire Partitions

      i. Folding Partitions

      j. Movable Partitions

      k. Metal Toilet Stalls

      l. Laboratory Furniture

      m. Metal Casework

BF. POSTAL SPECIALTIES

BG. GYMNASIUM EQUIPMENT

BH. THEATRE SEATING

II. (Cont.)

BI. STAGE EQUIPMENT

BJ. AUDIO VISUAL EQUIPMENT

    1. Items Included

        a. Sound equipment

        b. Wiring

        c. Projectors

    2. Coordinate With

        a. Stage Equipment

        b. Electrical Work

BK. ORGANS, CHIMES, AND BELLS

BL. WALL COVERING

    1. Wallpaper

    2. Vinyl Sheets

    3. Photographs

BM. SANDBLASTING AND CLEANING

BN. PAINTING AND FINISHING

BO. MATS AND CARPETS

BP. SHADES AND VENETIAN BLINDS

BQ. FURNISHINGS

BR. PLUMBING

    1. Work Included

        a. Fixtures

            (1) Vitreous china

                (a) Water closets

                (b) Urinals

                (c) Lavatories

                (d) Service sinks

                (e) Drink fountain

            (2) Enameled cast-iron plumbing fixtures

                (a) Lavatories

                (b) Kitchen sinks

                (c) Sink-and-laundry-tray combinations

                (d) Laundry trays

                (e) Service sinks

                (f) Bathtubs

            (3) Porcelain-enameled steel fixtures

        (a) Lavatories
        (b) Kitchen sinks
        (c) Sink-and-tray combinations
        (d) Bathtubs
     (4) Miscellaneous fixtures
        (a) Scullery sinks and pot-washing sinks
        (b) Concrete laundry trays
        (c) Stone composition wash fountains
     (5) Wall supports for fixtures
  b. Shower baths
     (1) Curtains
     (2) Steel cabinets
  c. Toilet seats
     (1) Open front with cover
     (2) Open front without cover
     (3) Closed front with cover
     (4) Closed front without cover
     (5) Extended back
     (6) Square back
  d. Trim
     (1) Faucets
     (2) Drain fittings
     (3) Shower heads
     (4) Traps
  e. Valves
  f. Pipe
     (1) Acid-resisting
     (2) Cast-iron
     (3) Copper
     (4) Brass
     (5) Galvanized iron
  g. Fittings
     (1) Acid-resisting
     (2) Cast-iron soil pipe
     (3) Cast-iron threaded fittings
     (4) Drainage fittings
     (5) Fittings for brass and copper pipe
     (6) Fittings for copper tubing
     (7) Malleable iron fittings
     (8) Nipples
     (9) Unions
  h. Insulation
  i. Hot water heaters
  j. Flashing
  k. Shower pans
  l. Roof drains

    m. Grease interceptors

    n. Sump pumps

    o. Hose faucets

    p. Sleeves and hangers

    q. Wall hydrants

    r. Floor, wall, and ceiling plates

    s. Booster pumps

    t. Chilled water systems

2. Coordinate with

    a. Demolition (removing plumbing)

    b. Excavating, Filling, and Grading

    c. Concrete (pipe sleeves)

    d. Roofing and Sheet Metal (roof sumps)

    e. Laundry Equipment

    f. Kitchen Equipment

    g. Laboratory Furniture

    h. Painting and Finishing

    i. Storm and Sanitary Sewers

    j. Swimming Pools

BS. FIRE PROTECTION

1. Items Included

    a. Automatic sprinkler systems

    b. Manual armed sprinkler systems

    c. Automatic low-pressure carbon dioxide system

    d. Vapor detection system

    e. Hose and cabinets

    f. Fire extinguishers

2. Coordinate with

    a. Lathing and Plastering

    b. Acoustical Treatment

    c. Painting and Finishing

    d. Process Piping

    e. Plumbing

    f. Heating, Ventilating, and Air Conditioning

    g. Electrical Work

BT. PROCESS PIPING

This section includes all piping for chemical manufacturing and distribution.

BU. HEATING, VENTILATING, AND AIR CONDITIONING

1. Note

In some areas, the sheet metal work for the mechanical trades is performed by a separate contractor who is not involved in heating or cooling. In such areas, a separate section headed "Sheet Metal Ducts" might be desirable.

2. Work Required

a. Heating
   (1) Heat distribution system
   (2) Direct gas-fired units
   (3) Forced hot water coal fired
   (4) Forced hot water gas fired
   (5) Forced hot water oil fired
   (6) Forced hot water steam converter
   (7) Forced hot air coal fired
   (8) Forced hot air gas fired
   (9) Forced hot air oil fired
   (10) Forced hot air steam coil air-heating unit
   (11) Steam system
   (12) Central heat from utilities

b. Ventilating
   (1) Mechanical system
   (2) Roof ventilators, gravity-type

c. Air conditioning
   (1) Evaporative system
   (2) Compressor system
   (3) Heat pumps

BV. DUST-COLLECTING EQUIPMENT

BW. BOILER HOUSE EQUIPMENT

1. Items Included

a. Draft gauges
b. Exhaust heads
c. Expansion joints
d. Fans
e. Feed water heater
f. Feed water regulator
g. Insulation
h. Low water cutoff
i. Motors
j. Pipe and fittings
k. Pipe covering
l. Pipe supports
m. Pipe threads
n. Pressure gages
o. Refractories

II. BW. 1. (Cont.)

    p. Steam drives
       (1) Steam turbines
       (2) Steam engines
    q. Strainers
    r. Thermometers
    s. Traps
    t. Valves
    u. Water column
    v. Water meter
    w. Boilers
    x. Boiler fittings
    y. Panels and instruments
    z. Control equipment
  aa. Oil burner
  ab. Pumps
  ac. Firebox
  ad. Drums
  ae. Tubes
  af. Access doors
  ag. Anchors
  ah. Smoke alarm and recorder
  ai. Ignition system
  aj. Fuel oil storage tanks
  ak. Breaching
  al. Blowoff tank
  am. Surge tank
  an. Sleeves
  ao. Gas-burning equipment
  ap. Heat exchangers

2. Coordinate with

    a. Masonry
    b. Incinerators
    c. Miscellaneous Iron
    d. Thermo Insulation and Cold Storage Work
    e. Process Piping
    f. Plumbing

BX. WELLS

BY. WATER SUPPLY

BZ. STORM AND SANITARY SEWERS

CA. SWIMMING POOLS

CB. TENNIS COURTS

II. (Cont.)

CC. PLAYGROUND EQUIPMENT

CD. TUNNELING

CE. MARINE WORK

CF. RAILROAD WORK

1. Items Included

    a. Grading
    b. Ties
    c. Rails
    d. Switches and frogs
    e. Signals
    f. Bumpers
    g. Derailer equipment
    h. Splice bars
    i. Tie plates
    j. Spikes
    k. Crossings
    l. Ballast

2. Coordinate with

    a. Excavating, Filling, and Grading
    b. Cranes
    c. Roads and Paving

CG. ROADS AND PAVING

1. Items Included

    a. Subbase
    b. Base
    c. Concrete paving
        (1) Curbs
        (2) Joint cutting
    d. Asphalt paving
        (1) Leveling course
        (2) Wearing courses

2. Coordinate with

    a. Excavating, Filling, and Grading
    b. Concrete
    c. Waterproofing and Dampproofing

CH. FENCING

1. Items Included

    a. Excavating

II. CH. 1. (Cont.)

      b. Concrete

      c. Line posts

      d. End posts and gateposts

      e. Rails

      f. Bracing

      g. Fabric

      h. Fabric ties

      i. Gates

2. Coordinate with

      a. Excavating, Filling, and Grading

      b. Concrete

      c. Hardware

CI. FLAGPOLES

CJ. LANDSCAPING

1. Items Included

      a. Placing topsoil

      b. Fertilizing

      c. Planting

      d. Sodding

      e. Seeding

2. Coordinate with

      a. Excavating, Filling, and Grading

      b. Storm and Sanitary Sewers

      c. Fencing

      d. Plumbing

CK. ELECTRICAL WORK

1. Work Included

      a. Generators

      b. Overhead lines and poles

      c. Underlines and conduit

      d. Busways and busbays

      e. Meters

      f. Transformers

      g. Instruments

      h. Insulators

      i. Lightning arrestors

      j. Luminaires

      k. Fuses

      l. Disconnect switches

II. CK. 1.   (Cont.)

    m. Circuit breakers

    n. Relays

    o. Switch gear

    p. Substations

    q. Wire

    r. Cable

    s. Floodlights

    t. Lamps

    u. Panelboards

    v. Potheads

    w. Ballast and fluorescent lamps

    x. Fixtures

    y. Motors

    z. Motor controls

   aa. Outlet boxes

   ab. Receptacles

   ac. Computers

2. Coordinate with

The electrical should be coordinated with all other sections, as the electrical work affects almost every part of the work.

CL. CATHODIC PROTECTION

CM. ELEVATORS AND ELECTRIC STAIRWAYS

1. Items Included

    a. Cables

    b. Wire rope

    c. Controller

    d. Electric power door operator

    e. Governor

    f. Hoistway door interlocks and electric contacts

    g. Hoisting machine

    h. Motor generator set

    i. Car safety and governor

    j. Car

    k. Counterweight

    l. Guide rails

    m. Supporting beams

    n. Break

    o. Sheaves

    p. Bed plate

    q. Car selective system

    r. Car lights and switch

    s. Car call registration lights

II. CM. 1. (Cont.)

      t. Door open button
      u. Emergency alarm
      v. Fan
      w. Automatic leveling device
      x. Car position indicators
      y. Landing position indicators
      z. Telephone

2. Coordinate with

      a. Concrete
      b. Structural Steel
      c. Miscellaneous Iron
      d. Hydraulic Equipment
      e. Ornamental Metals
      f. Painting and Finishing
      g. Electrical Work
      h. Stage Equipment

CN. STAGE EQUIPMENT

CO. X-RAY EQUIPMENT

CP. TELEPHONES

CSI Trade Divisions

UNIFORM CONSTRUCTION INDEX

Specification Format

DIVISION 1 - GENERAL REQUIREMENTS
- Summary of work
- Alternatives
- Project meetings
- Submittals
- Quality control
- Temporary facilities & controls
- Material & equipment
- Project closeout

DIVISION 2 - SITE WORK
- Subsurface exploration
- Clearing
- Demolition
- Earthwork
- Soil treatment
- Pile foundations
- Caissons
- Shoring
- Site drainage
- Site utilities
- Paving & surfacing
- Site improvements
- Landscaping
- Railroad work
- Marine work
- Tunneling

DIVISION 3 - CONCRETE
- Concrete formwork
- Expansion & contraction joints
- Concrete reinforcement
- Cast-in-place concrete
- Specially finished concrete
- Specially placed concrete
- Precast concrete
- Cementitious decks

DIVISION 4 - MASONRY
- Mortar
- Masonry accessories
- Unit masonry
- Stone
- Masonry restoration & cleaning
- Refractories

DIVISION 5 - METALS
- Structural metal framing
- Metal joists
- Metal decking
- Lightgage metal framing
- Metal fabrications
- Ornamental metal
- Expansion control

DIVISION 6 - WOOD & PLASTICS
- Rough carpentry
- Heavy timber construction
- Trestles
- Prefabricated structural wood
- Finish carpentry
- Wood treatment
- Architectural woodwork
- Prefabricated structural plastics
- Plastic fabrications

DIVISION 7 - THERMAL & MOISTURE PROTECTION
- Waterproofing
- Dampproofing
- Insulation
- Shingles & roofing tiles
- Preformed roofing & siding
- Membrane roofing
- Traffic topping
- Flashing & sheet metal
- Roof accessories
- Sealants

DIVISION 8 - DOORS & WINDOWS
- Metal doors & frames
- Wood & plastic doors
- Special doors
- Entrances & storefronts
- Metal windows
- Wood & plastic windows
- Special windows
- Hardware & specialties
- Glazing
- Window walls/curtainwalls

DIVISION 9 - FINISHES
- Lath & plaster
- Gypsum wallboard
- Tile
- Terrazzo
- Acoustical treatments
- Suspension systems
- Wood flooring
- Resilient flooring
- Carpeting
- Special flooring
- Floor treatment
- Special coatings
- Painting
- Wall covering

DIVISION 10 - SPECIALTIES
- Chalkboards & tackboards
- Compartments & cubicles
- Louvers & vents
- Grilles & screens
- Wall & corner guards
- Access flooring
- Specialty modules
- Pest control
- Fireplaces
- Flagpoles
- Identifying devices
- Pedestrian control devices
- Lockers
- Protective covers
- Postal specialties
- Partitions
- Scales

Storage shelving
Sun control devices
  (Exterior)
Telephone enclosures
Toilet & bath
  accessories
Wardrobe specialties

DIVISION 11 - EQUIPMENT
Built-in maintenance
  equipment
Bank & vault equipment
Commercial equipment
Checkroom equipment
Darkroom equipment
Ecclesiastical equipment
Educational equipment
Food service equipment
Vending equipment
Athletic equipment
Industrial equipment
Laboratory equipment
Laundry equipment
Library equipment
Medical equipment
Mortuary equipment
Musical equipment
Parking equipment
Waste handling
  equipment
Loading dock
  equipment
Detention equipment
Residential equipment
Theater equipment
Registration equipment

DIVISION 12 - FURNISHINGS
Artwork
Cabinets & storage
Window treatment
Fabrics
Furniture
Rugs & mats
Seating
Furnishing accessories

DIVISION 13 - SPECIAL CONSTRUCTION
Air supported structures
Integrated assemblies
Audiometric room
Clean room
Hyperbaric room
Incinerators
Instrumentation
Insulated room
Integrated ceiling
Nuclear reactors
Observatory
Prefabricated structures
Special purpose rooms
  & buildings
Radiation protection
Sound & vibration
  control
Vaults
Swimming pool

DIVISION 14 - CONVEYING SYSTEMS
Dumbwaiters
Elevators
Hoists & cranes
Lifts
Material handling
  systems
Turntables
Moving stairs & walks
Pneumatic tube systems
Powered scaffolding

DIVISION 15 - MECHANICAL
General provisions
Basic materials &
  methods
Insulation
Water supply &
  treatment
Waste water disposal &
  treatment
Plumbing
Fire protection

Power or heat
  generation
Refrigeration
Liquid heat transfer
Air distribution
Controls &
  instrumentation

DIVISION 16 - ELECTRICAL
General provisions
Basic materials &
  methods
Power generation
Power transmission
Service & distribution
Lighting
Special systems
Communications
Heating & cooling
Controls &
  instrumentation

Sample Technical Section
of a Specification

SECTION V

MASONRY

5.01 GENERAL NOTE

The General Conditions and the Special Conditions apply to those bidding or performing work under this section of the specifications.

5.02 SCOPE OF THE WORK

Unless otherwise specified, the Contractor or his Subcontractor shall furnish all materials, tools, equipment, apparatus, appliances, transportation, labor and supervision required to furnish and place all the masonry shown on the drawings.

5.03 WORK NOT INCLUDED IN THIS SECTION

A. Dovetail slots, to receive the dovetail anchors furnished by the mason, are specified in the Concrete Section. Concrete work is specified in Section IV.

B. The louvers are specified in Section VII.

C. Caulking is specified in Section X.

D. Lintels and other miscellaneous iron are specified in Section VIII.

E. Interior tile work is specified in Section XIV.

F. Placing membrane over lintels, under sills, against concrete is dampproofing and is specified in Section VI. The nailing of felt on siding for brick veneer is also specified in Section VI.

5.04 MATERIALS

A. Mortar:

1. Standard_Gray:

a. Materials:

(1) Portland Cement:

All Portland cement shall conform to the requirements of Specification C 150-64, Type I, of the American Society for Testing Materials.

(2) Hydrated Lime:

All hydrated lime shall conform to the requirements of Type S of Specification C 207-49 of the American Society for Testing Materials and shall be at least ninety-two percent (92%) hydrated.

5-1

5.04 A. 1. a. (Cont'd)

        (3) Sand:

All sand used for gray mortar shall conform to the requirements of Specification C 144-62T of the American Society for Testing Materials.

        (4) Water:

All water shall be clean and free from any substance injurious to mortar. In general, water that is suitable for drinking will be suitable for making mortar.

    b. Mixing:

        (1) All standard gray mortar shall be a mixture of one (1) part of Portland cement, one (1) part of hydrated lime putty, and six (6) parts of sand by volume. The use of prepared mortars will not be permitted.

        (2) The ingredients shall be equally mixed by measuring devices approved by the Contracting Officer. Hand mixing will be permitted only for small quantities and with the permission of the Contracting Officer. All other mortar shall be machine mixed. The mortar for grout and pointing shall be mixed in as stiff consistency as can be worked into the joints.

        (3) Retempering will not be permitted. Mortar should not be used more than one (1) hour after mixing.

  2. White:

    a. Material:

        (1) White Cement:

All white cement shall be non-staining, water repellent, white Portland Cement, conforming to Federal Specification SS-C-1816, Type I.

        (2) White Sand:

All sand for white mortar shall be white silica sand of proper grading for the joint widths specified.

        (3) Water:

All water used with white cement shall be clean and pure.

5-2

5.04   A.   2.   (Cont'd)

        b.   Mixing:
           • • • •
          All white mortar shall be a mixture of one (1) part of white
          cement, two (2) parts of sand and sufficient water to make
          a workable mix.

   3.   Refractory:

      All refractory mortar shall conform to Federal Specification
      HH-M-61la, Type I, Grade A.

B.   Brick:

   1.   Face Brick:

      All face brick shall match the existing buildings in range
      of color, size, surface texture and other qualities.

   2.   Refractory Brick:

      All refractory brick shall conform to Federal Specification
      HH-B-671d, Class 4.

   3.   Common Brick:

      All common brick shall be solid clay brick conforming to
      Federal Specification SS-B-656, Grade M.

   4.   Concrete Brick:

      All concrete brick shall be made from concrete with an
      ultimate compressive strength of not less than three
      thousand pounds per square inch (3,000 lbs/sq in) twenty-
      eight (28) days after pouring.

C.   Concrete Masonry Units:

   1.   All concrete masonry units shall be made with a mixture of
      Portland Cement, sand, gravel, and water. These materials
      shall be free from injurious ingredients which could effect
      the strength, appearance or durability of the block.

   2.   The block shall be smooth on all faces (not rock faced).

   3.   No cinders shall be used as aggregate in concrete blocks.

   4.   Units shall be of nominal size and shape including all
      closers, jamb units, headers and special shapes and sizes
      required to complete the work as indicated. Units shall
      be sawed and free from cracks, chipped edges, and other

5.04 C. 4. (Cont'd)

defects that would interfere with their proper setting or impair the strength, appearance, or durability of the structure.

5. All units shall be free of any delerterious matter that will stain plaster or corrode metal. Only concrete masonry units that have been subjected during manufacture to a saturated steam pressure of not less than one hundred and twenty pounds per square inch (120 lbs/sq in) for five (5) hours or more shall be used as soon as cooled. Units shall be delivered to the job site in air-dry condition.

6. The walls of all units shall not be less than one and one-quarter inches ($1\frac{1}{4}$") thick.

7. In all other respects all units shall conform to Specification C 90-59 of the American Society for Testing Materials.

D. Wall Coping:

All wall coping shall be double slant, salt glazed, hard burned clay in mingled brown colors. The units shall be sound, free from fractures, cracks, blisters, and warping, and shall be of standard size and proper width to overlap the wall masonry. Starters, tee sections, ells and ends shall be furnished as required.

E. Structural Facing Tile:

1. All structural facing tile shall conform in every respect to the specifications of the Facing Tile Institute for Series 4D standard quality, ceramic glazed structural facing tile. The face shall be five and one-third inches by eight inches (5-1/3" x 8") and the depth shall be as shown on the drawings or as required.

2. All of the special shapes shall be furnished as required for the corners, jambs, sills, etc.

3. Exterior corners, jambs, sills, etc., shall be bullnose and the interior corners shall be coved internal fittings.

4. The base course shall be coved.

5. The color of the Office Building toilets, Dispensary and Kitchen will be similar to Type 5201 of the National Fire-proofing Corporation and the janitor's closet and locker room toilets will be Type 1610.

5-4

5.04 (Cont'd)

F. Wall Reinforcing:

All wall reinforcing shall be extra heavy "Dur-O-Wall" as manufactured by the Cedar Rapids Block Company of Cedar Rapids, Iowa;
heavy "Duo-Wire" as manufactured by Light Weight Aggregate Corporation of Livonia, Michigan; "Wal-Lok" as manufactured by the
Lenawee Peerless Company of Adrian, Michigan or an equal approved
by the Contracting Officer.

G. Anchors:

1. Dovetail:

   Dovetail anchors shall number sixteen gauge (#16) galvanized
   metal cut with a dovetail to fit the anchor slots specified in
   Section IV.

2. Brick Ties:

   All brick ties shall be three-quarter inch by sixteen gauge
   (3/4" x 16 ga) corrugated galvanized iron.

3. Wall Anchors:

   All wall anchors shall be three sixteenths of an inch diameter
   (3/16" d) wire with a thirty percent (30%) copper sheathed
   finish. The anchors shall be bent in the form of a Zee with
   a moisture drip in the center.

H. Anchor Sockets:

All anchor sockets to hold the anchors supporting the runner channels
shall be made of twenty-four gauge sheet steel zink plated after
forming. The socket shall be four inches (4") long and seven-sixteenths
inches (7/16") thick, with the front portion being formed to fit and
hold the anchor specified under Lathing and Plastering.

I. Expansion Joint Filler:

All joint filler shall be a premoulded expansion joint filler conforming to Federal Specification HH-F-334.

J. Control Joint Material:

1. Felt:

   All felt shall be a fifteen pound (15 lb) asphalt saturated rag
   felt conforming to Federal Specification HH-F-101, Type I,#15.

5-5

5.04 J. (Cont'd)

2. Strip:

The strip shall be a specially shaped, nonabsorvent expanded, polyvinyl chloride strip one half by one inch ($\frac{1}{2}$" x 1") in size, made to fit the control joint shown on the drawings.

5.05 SAMPLES

A. At least two (2) samples of concrete block, face brick, common brick, and structural facing tile shall be submitted to the Contracting Officer for approval.

B. These samples shall show the extreme variation in size and color that may occur in the material furnished in the field.

C. All material furnished shall fall within the range of the approved samples.

D. No material shall be sent to the job site until the samples have been approved.

5.06 DELIVERY AND STORAGE OF MATERIALS

A. All materials shall be delivered to the job site and stored until ready for use.

B. All cement shall be delivered to the job site in unbroken bags in good condition and in full weight. Damaged or fractional packages will be rejected. Immediately upon receipt all cement shall be stored in a weathertight and properly ventilated structure. Reinforcement shall be stored off the ground in such a manner as to prevent distortion. Brick and block shall be neatly piled where directed.

5.07 LAYING WALLS

A. Precautions:

1. Masonry shall not be erected when the ambient temperature is below thirty-five degrees Farenheit (35°F), except by written permission of the Contracting Officer. No frozen work shall be built upon. No units having a film of water or frost on its surface shall be laid in the walls. Masonry shall be protected from freezing for forty-eight (48) hours after being laid. Masonry shall be laid plumb, true to line, with level courses accurately spaced with a story pole and with each course breaking joints with the course next below.

2. In rainy weather all work shall be performed under cover.

5-6

3. When work is not in progress the top of all exposed masonry
    shall be kept covered with a non-staining waterproof covering.
    When the work is resumed the top surfaces shall be cleaned of
    all loose mortar.

4. In dry weather, the tops of the walls under construction shall
    be moistened before continuing with their construction.

B. Joint Filler:

1. Where separation is required between existing and new construc-
    tion, and at all expansion joints, joint filler, as hereinbefore
    specified, shall be used.

2. The joint filler shall be secured to the existing work before
    masonry is placed. It shall extend through the entire wall and
    to within three quarters of an inch (3/4") of the surface to
    permit caulking.

C. Workmanship:

1. General:

    a. All work shall be laid to true lines, plumb, level and
        square except where otherwise indicated on the drawings.
        The joints, except in hollow open-end masonry, shall be
        filled with mortar.

    b. Each unit may be adjusted to its final position in the wall
        while mortar is still soft and plastic. Any unit which is
        disturbed after mortar has stiffened shall be removed and
        relaid with fresh mortar.

    c. Corners and reveals shall be plumb and true. Spaces around
        metal door frames and other built-up items shall be solidly
        filled with mortar as the walls are laid up. Anchors, wall
        plugs, accessories, flashings, and other items required to
        be built in with masonry shall be built in as the masonry
        work progresses. Cutting and fitting of masonry required
        to accommodate the work of others shall be done by masonry
        mechanics with masonry saws. Mortar that has stiffened be-
        cause of chemical reaction (hydration) shall not be used.

    d. Mortar shall be used and placed in final position within
        two and one-quarter ($2\frac{1}{4}$) hours after mixing where air temp-
        erature is eighty degrees Farenheit (80°F), or higher and
        within three and one-quarter ($3\frac{1}{4}$) hours after mixing where
        air temperature is less than eighty degrees Fahrenheit (80°F).
        Mortar not used within these time intervals shall be discar-
        ded. Brick and concrete masonry units shall be wetted before
        laying. Jamb units shall be of the sizes and shapes required

5-7

5.07 C. 1. d. (Cont'd)

to bond with wall units. No cells shall be left open in face surfaces.

2. Use of Mortar:

a. All structural facing tile shall be laid in white mortar.

b. All refractory brick shall be set in refractory mortar.

c. All other masonry materials shall be laid in standard grey mortar.

3. Joints:

a. All exterior joints shall be tooled slightly concave so that the mortar will be thoroughly compacted and pressed against the edges of the masonry. The tool used to form the concave surface shall be made of stainless steel.

b. All interior joints and joints in masonry which are not exposed shall be struck flush.

c. All joints shall be of the width shown on the drawings and brick joints shall be completely filled with mortar.

D. Solid Wall Construction:

1. Brick:

a. Type of Brick:

Only face brick shall be used on exposed surfaces. Common brick or concrete brick may be used for backup or on walls covered with plaster or other material unless otherwise noted.

b. Bond:

(1) Exterior brick shall be laid in Flemish bond.

(2) Interior walls shall be laid in common bond.

c. Reinforcing:

Starting with the second course and every third course thereafter, shall have the wall reinforcing, hereinbefore specified, laid in the joints of the brick. Reinforcing shall lap eight inches (8") at the splices and the corner shall be made by cutting the inside bar and bending the outer bar to make a continuous piece.

5-8

    d. Anchor Sockets:

        Anchor sockets, hereinbefore specified, shall be placed in all walls to receive plaster. They shall be placed to properly carry the furring anchors. They shall be level and spaced not over four feet on center (4'-0" oc) and additional sockets shall be placed as required to carry end spans of runner channels.

2. Parapet Walls:

    a. All parapet walls shall be laid with face brick throughout. No common brick shall be used.

    b. All parapet walls shall be capped with the wall coping hereinbefore specified. The coping shall be properly set in mortar with lapped watertight joints.

3. Concrete Masonry Units:

    a. Laying:

        All concrete block shall be laid with the cells vertical in the wall in such a manner that the main bearing webs come in proper relation for bearing out the units below.

    b. Lintels and Other Steel:

        (1) General:

            Where steel bears on concrete block, the two courses of block directly under the steel shall be cast solid.

        (2) Option:

            At the option of the Contractor, concrete brick as hereinbefore specified may be substituted for concrete block. Not less than six (6) courses of brick shall be used under the steel. Each course of brick above the bottom course shall bear entirely upon another course of brick.

    c. Expansion Bolts:

        Where expansion bolts are required in block for any reason, the block shall be cast solid. Expansion bolts will not be permitted in hollow block, however toggle bolts may be used when approved by the Contracting Officer.

    d. Reinforcing:

        Starting with the second course and every second course thereafter, steel reinforcing, as hereinbefore specified, shall be

5.07 D. 3. d. (Cont'd)

laid in the joints of the concrete blocks. Steel reinforcing
shall lap eight inches (8") at splices and the corner shall
be made by cutting the inside bar and bending the outer bar
to make a continuous piece as recommended by the manufacturer.

e. Anchor Sockets:

Anchor sockets, hereinbefore specified, shall be placed in all
walls to receive plaster. They shall be placed to properly
carry the furring anchors. They shall be level and spaced
not over four feet on center (4'-0" o c) and additional sockets
shall be placed as required to carry end spans of runner channels.

f. Joints:

(1) Masonry Joints:

Joints in all concrete masonry shall be struck flush.

(2) Control Joints:

(a) Control joints shall be placed as shown on the drawings.

(b) Building paper shall be placed in the joint as shown
on the drawings to prevent bond between the mortar
and the block.

(c) The filler shall be a polyvinyl strip as hereinbefore specified and shall be placed on each side of
the vertical joint as shown on the drawings.

(d) The opening in the blocks at the control joint will
be caulked.

(e) Reinforcing shall not run through the control joints.

(f) In no case shall control joints be spaced greater than
thirty five feet on center (35'-0" oc).

4. Structural Facing Tile:

a. Laying Tile:

All tile shall be laid with white mortar in regular bond with
the vertical joint broken to form true, evenly spaced lines.
No piece of tile shorter than four inches (4") shall be permitted
at any vertical angle or corner jamb. One (1) piece units shall
be used for caps and end pieces of partitions. Base courses

5-10

shall start on the top of structural slabs and be shimmed up
as required to make the coves level with the finished floor.
Partitions with double faced units shall be laid to a line
with the more important side laid flush.

b. Special Units:

(1) Special units of ceramic tile shall be properly fitted
in the structural facing tile where shown on the drawings.

(2) In the shower rooms one (1) soap dish shall be furnished
with each shower head.

c. Cutting:

Necessary cuts on the job shall be made with a power driven
saw in such a manner to produce clean-cut edges. The necessary cutting for mechanical and electrical work, brackets
and toilet fixtures shall be performed in a neat and workmanlike manner. Tile with chipped or irregular cut surfaces
will not be accepted.

d. Joints:

Joints shall be approximately one-quarter inch ($\frac{1}{4}$") wide,
except where otherwise shown on the drawings or directed by
the Contracting Officer. The joints shall be struck flush
and tooled to compress the mortar against the tile. Joints
between the back of metal door trim and the face of the tile
shall be left open to receive caulking.

E. Cavity Walls:

1. Laying Block:

Where cavity walls are required, the concrete block shall be
built up first in the same manner as specified for solid walls.
Reinforcing shall be placed in the same manner.

2. Wall Anchors:

Wall anchors, hereinbefore specified, shall be placed in each
course of block two feet (2'-0") on center to bond the block
and the brick facing. These anchors shall extend not less than
two inches (2") into the block joints.

3. Pargeting:

The entire block wall shall be pargeted with mortar one quarter
of an inch ($\frac{1}{4}$") thick. The mortar shall be pressed against the
block and bonded to it.

5-11

5.07 E. (Cont'd)

    4. Laying Brick:

After the block has been pargeted a reasonable height, face brick
shall be laid properly anchored to the block. The cavity between
the brick and block shall be kept clear of mortar droppings and
extra care shall be used to accomplish this.

    5. Weep Holes:

Weep holes shall be placed in the bottom joint of brick work at
not over two feet on center (2'-0" oc). They shall be formed by
inserting a lubricated cord or a flexible tubing in soft mortar
and removing after the mortar has taken its initial set. The cord
or tubing shall be of sufficient length and height to extend
through all dropping.

F. Brick Veneer Walls:

    1. General:

        a. No brick shall be placed until the dampproofing has been
           inspected and approved.

        b. The brick shall be laid using stretcher coursing throughout.

    2. With Concrete Backup:

Dovetail anchors shall be placed in every third course at each
dovetail slot. The anchors shall be properly inserted and anchored in the dovetail slot and extend into the brick joint.
The anchors shall be cut so that no metal is within one inch (1")
of the surface.

    3. With Wood Backup:

The galvanized metal bonding ties, hereinbefore specified shall
be placed in every third course of brick at two feet (2'-0")
on center to bond the backup and the brick facing. These anchors
shall extend not less than two inches (2") into the brick and be
nailed to the wood sheathing at studs with galvanized nails.

G. Stack Lining:

    1. The stacks shall be lined with refractory brick set in refractory
       mortar.

    2. The mortar shall be used as it comes from the container with a
       moderate amount of tempering with clean, pure water.

5-12

5.07 G. (Cont'd)

    3. The brick shall be laid in stretcher bond properly anchored to the brick stack. The joints shall be one quarter inch ($\frac{1}{4}$") wide and struck flush.

5.08 SETTING SPLASH BLOCKS

Splash blocks shall be placed on the ground under each downspout.

5.09 BUILT-IN WORK

A. All built-in work, whether in facing tile, block or brick work, such as frames, louvers, brackets and other items shall be properly built-in. In no case, and under no circumstances shall built-in bearing plates, joints, be set closer than one inch (1") from the outside of the wall.

B. The Masonry Subcontractor shall check to see that all items are properly set and shall report improper work to the Contracting Officer before proceeding.

C. The exact size of the opening for ducts, pipe, and the wash room equipment shall be obtained. Openings shall be accurately and properly built to receive them.

D. All work to be built into the masonry shall be accurately located and built in tight in a skillful and workmanlike manner.

E. All ducts and pipes including those above the ceiling shall be built-in with air tight joints.

5.10 POINTING

Before completion of the work, all defects in joints of exposed exterior masonry surfaces shall be raked out as necessary, filled with mortar, and retooled.

5.11 CLEANING

A. At the completion of the job, all brick shall be cleaned using a stiff wire brush to remove all spots and stains.

B. All exterior brick work shall be cleaned using a five percent (5%) solution of muriatic acid. This shall be preceded and followed by a copious bath of fresh, clean water.

C. The greatest care shall be taken to protect glass, stone and other materials that may be damaged by this acid. The Contractor will be responsible for any material damaged by his negligence.

5-13

Sample Section
of Alternates

Section E

ALTERNATES

4.01 INSTRUCTIONS TO BIDDERS

The Contractor is requested to bid on the following alternates. With the exception of the requirements stated below, all work shall conform to the specifications as written for this purpose.

4.02 ALTERNATE NO. 1

Alternate No. 1 consists of deleting the resilient flooring shown for the first floor and replacing it with ceramic tile. The tile shall be as specified in Section XII and as shown on the drawing A-7. The concrete slab specified for the resilient flooring shall be held down to permit the ceramic tile to be placed as specified level with the adjacent quarry tile floor. Metal strips, as specified, shall be used to separate ceramic tile from other types of flooring. The patterns of the tile in various rooms is shown on drawing A-7 marked "Alternate One." The colors used on the first floor will be the same as corresponding areas on the second floor.

4.03 ALTERNATE NO. 2

A. General:

Alternate No. 2 consists of deleting the resilient flooring shown for the first floor and replacing it with terrazzo. The concrete slab specified for the resilient flooring shall be held down to permit the terrazzo to be finished flush with the adjacent quarry tile floor when placed as specified herein. Details of the floor shall be as shown on the drawings for Alternate 2 and as specified herein.

B. Terrazzo Floors:

1. General Note:

The General and Special Conditions apply to those bidding or performing terrazzo work.

E-1

4.03   B.   (Cont'd.)

    2. Scope of the Work:

       Unless otherwise specified, the contractor or his
       subcontractor shall furnish all materials, tools,
       equipment, apparatus, appliances, transportation,
       labor, and supervision required to place all of the
       terrazzo floors shown on the drawings.

    3. Work Not Included in This Section:

       a. The structural concrete slab is specified in
          Section VI.

       b. The Structural Facing Tile Base is specified in
          Section VIII.

    4. Materials:

       a. Sand:

         (1) All sand used for terrazzo work shall be
             clean, hard, sharp, uncoated aggregate, free
             from deleterious substances and shall be
             well-graded from coarse to fine.

         (2) All sand shall conform to Federal Specifica-
             tion SS-A-281, and shall pass a one-eighth
             inch (1/8") screen.

       b. Felt:

         (1) All felt shall be an asphalt saturated rag
             felt weighing not less than fifteen pounds
             per hundred square feet (15 lbs/100 sq. ft.).

       c. Wire Reinforcing:

       All wire reinforcing shall be one and one half
       inches by one and one half inches (1½ x 1½")
       galvanized wire mesh conforming to Federal Speci-
       fication RR-W-370 with wire not thinner than
       nineteen gauge (#19 ga.).

E-2

    d. Cement:

        (1) White Cement:

            White cement shall be non-staining, water repellent, white Portland cement, conforming to Federal Specification SS-C-1816, Type 1.

        (2) Natural Gray Portland Cement:

            All natural gray Portland cement shall conform to requirements of Specification C-150-73, Type I, of the American Society for Testing Materials.

    e. Pigment:

        Coloring material shall be the best quality of mineral pigment of high purity, shall be finely ground, sunproof, and limeproof, and shall have a specific gravity similar to that of Portland cement. Coloring material shall not exceed five percent (5%), by weight, of the cement used.

    f. Divider Strips:

        All division strips shall be zinc alloy standard division strips one-eighth inch (1/8") thick and not less than one and one-quarter inch (1-1/4") in depth with approved anchoring features.

    g. Marble Chips:

        Marble chips shall have an abrasive hardness of not less than sixteen (16), as determined by the test for wear resistance in National Bureau of Standards Report BMS98. All chips shall pass a three-eighths inch (3/8") mesh screen.

    h. Water:

        Water shall be fresh, clean, and free from acid, alkali, sewage, and organic matter.

i. Cleaning Compound:

Cleaning compound used for all cleaning of terrazzo shall be an approved neutral chemical cleaner free from acids and strong alkalis or other material that would affect the color or otherwise damage the terrazzo.

j. Preservative Treatment:

Preservative material for terrazzo floors shall be an approved material of a type required to produce a waterproof finish that will not be impaired by immersion in water at room temperature for a period of two and one half ($2\frac{1}{2}$) hours, approximately eighteen (18) hours after the floor is finished by buffing, as specified. The preservative material shall not discolor the terrazzo nor leave a tacky or sticky finish film on the surface after buffing.

5. Color:

Areas marked "Color 1" on the floor plans shall match the color of plate 207 of the third edition of the Terrazzo and Mosaic Catalogue published by the National Terrazzo and Mosaic Association. Areas marked "Color 2" shall conform to plate 203 and areas marked "Color 3" shall conform to plate 237 of the same catalogue.

6. Samples:

a. The contractor shall furnish not less than two (2) samples of each color not less than six inches (6") square.

b. The samples shall show the extreme variation in quality, color, quantity of chips, etc., that may appear in the finished floor.

c. The finished floors shall fall within the range of these samples.

E-4

4.03 B. (Cont'd.)

7. Inspecting the Surfaces:

Before starting the work, the Terrazzo Subcontractor shall inspect the concrete subfloor, making sure that it is dry and ready to receive the topping.

8. Mixing:

a. Concrete Bed Coats:

The concrete bed coat shall consist of a mixture of one (1) part of natural gray Portland cement and four (4) parts of sand. This mixture shall be well mixed, dry, and then shall have sufficient water added to result in a dry mixture.

b. Terrazzo Topping:

The terrazzo topping shall consist of a mixture of white cement and marble chips in a proportion that eighty percent (80%) of the topping will consist of chips.

9. Application:

a. Preparing the Bed:

A one-quarter inch (1/4") bed of sand shall be spread evenly over the rough slabs to prevent a bond between the rough slabs and the terrazzo floor.

b. Laying felt:

Felt, hereinbefore specified, shall be laid over the sand fill lapping the edges of not less than three inches (3").

c. Concrete Underbed:

The wire mesh shall be placed above the felt and a two and one eighth inch (2-1/8") concrete underbed shall be poured.

E-5

        d. Division Strips:

            (1) The division strips hereinbefore specified shall be installed according to the strip maker's directions, and set absolutely true to line, neatly joined together, carefully leveled up and properly anchored and bedded in the screen beds.

            (2) Division strips shall be placed as shown on the drawings.

        e. Topping:

The terrazzo finishing shall be placed throughout all areas to a thickness of not less than five-eighths inch (5/8"). The mixture shall be rolled into a compact mass until all superfluous cement and water are extracted. The terrazzo shall be hand troweled to a surface even with the tops of metal strip. The surface shall be kept moist for a period of not less than six (6) days.

        f. Grinding:

After the terrazzo floor has hardened, it shall be ground by machine using a Number twenty-four (#24) grit and abrasive stones for the initial rubbing. It shall then be resurfaced, using a Number eight (#8) grit or final abrasive stone after which a light grouting of neat Portland cement of the same kind and color as the matrix shall be applied to the surface filling all floors. The grouting shall remain until the time of final cleaning.

    10. Leveling the Slab:

Terrazzo floors shall be ground level. They shall not vary more than one-sixteenth inch (1/16") when measured with a six foot (6'0") straight edge.

E-6

4.03 B. (Cont'd.)

11. Damaged or Defective Work:

Damaged or defective terrazzo floor shall be replaced by new material.

12. Protection:

For a period of at least five (5) days, after the
completion of the troweling, the use of the floors
shall not be permitted.

13. Cleaning:

The floors shall have the grout coat removed by
machines using stone no coarser than Number eighty
(#80) grit. This cleaning and final stoning shall
not take place sooner than seventy-two (72) hours
after the floor has been grouted, after which it
must be cleaned thoroughly. The use of acids will
not be permitted.

4.04 ALTERNATE NO. 3

Alternate No. 3 consists of omitting all work on the retaining
wall shown in the front of the building. If this alternate
is accepted, the ground shall be graded as shown on the detail
on drawing A-2 marked "Alternate 3."

E-7

Sample of an Addendum

WALKER, HOME & LEVER
ARCHITECTS & ENGINEERS
2000 Bankrup Bank Building
Feeling, Ill.

OWNER: Little Leak Pipe Company   ADDENDUM: No. 2
BUILDING: Office   DATED: February 5, 1975
LOCATION: Wier, Ill.   PROJECT NO: UR 1-2

XXXXXXXXXXXXXXXXXXXXXXXXXXXXXXXXXXXXXXXXXXXXXXXXXXXXXXXXXXXXXXXXXXXXX

I.   INSTRUCTIONS

     1. This Supplement to the Plans and Specifications
        is issued prior to the receipt of bids. All
        work covered in this Supplement shall be included
        in the original quotation and the Supplement will
        be considered one of the Contract Documents.

     2. All work performed under this Supplement shall
        be subject to the General Conditions of the Con-
        tract and the Specifications for similar work
        in connection with this project.

II. DRAWINGS

     A. Drawing number Al revision 1 dated February 1, 1968
        issued with this addendum replaces drawing Al dated
        January 15, 1968.

     B. Drawing number S2 revision 2 dated February 1, 1968
        issued with this addendum replaces drawing S2 revision
        dated January 21, 1968.

III. SPECIFICATIONS

     With this Supplement are issued the following pages. These
     sheets have been revised and shall become a part of the
     Specification. The Contractor shall insert these sheets
     in their proper location in the Specification Book and re-
     move and destroy the applicable corresponding pages. The
     Addendum sheets shall be bound in the back of the book.

     Section Title   Page No.
     V   Masonry   5 - 8
     VI   Miscellaneous Iron 6 - 2
     X   Interior Tile   10 - 2, 10 - 3, & 10 - 5

                      END OF ADDENDUM

Sample of a Bulletin

OWNER:	Ups & Downs — Stock Brokers	BULLETIN:	No. 5
BUILDING:	Office	DATED:	March 15, 1975
LOCATION:	Hi, Texas	PROJECT NO.	UP 4

XXXXXXXXXXXXXXXXXXXXXXXXXXXXXXXXXXXXXXXXXXXXXXXXXXXXXXXXXXXXXXXXXXX
This Is a Request for a Price; It Is Not an Order
XXXXXXXXXXXXXXXXXXXXXXXXXXXXXXXXXXXXXXXXXXXXXXXXXXXXXXXXXXXXXXXXXXX

I. GENERAL

A. This Bulletin is issued after the award of the contract
   to inform the Contractor of certain proposed modifications to the work.

B. The General Conditions, Special Conditions, and Specifications shall govern for all work, unless otherwise
   mentioned.

C. The Contractor shall submit to the Owner an itemized
   proposal stating the amount of cost to be added to
   or deducted from the contract.

D. The final completion date is not to be affected by reason
   of this Bulletin.

II. DRAWING CHANGES

A. Architectural Drawings

   1. Drawing A4, Revision 2; Second-Floor Plan

      The partition between room 223 and room 225 is
      deleted. The new larger room is numbered 223 and
      named "Controller's Office."

   2. Drawing A17, Revision 1; Room Elevations

      The elevations of room 223 are revised and the
      west elevation of room 225 is changed to read:

west elevation of room 223. Other elevations of room 225 are deleted.

3. Drawing A27, Revision 4; Door Schedule

Door 272 is deleted.

B. Plumbing Drawing P2

1. The drinking fountain is relocated on the west side of door 237 as shown on the architectural drawings, and the piping has been changed as required.

2. A sink with required piping is located in room 321 to agree with drawing A3.

III. SPECIFICATION CHANGES

A. Refer to Section IV, Concrete

1. Subsection 4.04

This subsection is deleted.

2. Article 4.05 E

This article is deleted and the following is substituted in lieu thereof.

"E Face Brick

All face brick shall be Kingsport Mission Pinks 1-181 brick."

B. Refer to Section XXI, Roofing and Sheet Metal

The following is added to paragraph 21.06 D. 4.

"The aluminum fascia for the main entrance canopy shall receive a black anodized finish to match other existing work."

End of Bulletin

Bid Bond

THE AMERICAN INSTITUTE OF ARCHITECTS

AIA Document A310

Bid Bond

KNOW ALL MEN BY THESE PRESENTS, that we

as Principal, hereinafter called the Principal, and

a corporation duly organized under the laws of the State of
as Surety, hereinafter called the Surety, are held and firmly bound unto

as Obligee, hereinafter called the Obligee, in the sum of

Dollars ($),
for the payment of which sum well and truly to be made, the said Principal and the said Surety, bind
ourselves, our heirs, executors, administrators, successors and assigns, jointly and severally, firmly by
these presents.

WHEREAS, the Principal has submitted a bid for

NOW, THEREFORE, if the Obligee shall accept the bid of the Principal and the Principal shall enter into a Contract
with the Obligee in accordance with the terms of such bid, and give such bond or bonds as may be specified in the bidding
or Contract Documents with good and sufficient surety for the faithful performance of such Contract and for the prompt
payment of labor and material furnished in the prosecution thereof, or in the event of the failure of the Principal to enter
such Contract and give such bond or bonds, if the Principal shall pay to the Obligee the difference not to exceed the penalty
hereof between the amount specified in said bid and such larger amount for which the Obligee may in good faith contract
with another party to perform the Work covered by said bid, then this obligation shall be null and void, otherwise to remain
in full force and effect.

Signed and sealed this   day of   19

_____   { _____
                                         {   (Principal)   (Seal)
            (Witness)   {
                                         { _____
                                         {   (Title)

_____   { _____
                                         {   (Surety)   (Seal)
            (Witness)   {
                                         { _____
                                         {   (Title)

AIA DOCUMENT A310 • BID BOND • AIA ® • FEBRUARY 1970 ED • THE AMERICAN
INSTITUTE OF ARCHITECTS, 1735 N.Y. AVE., N.W., WASHINGTON, D. C. 20006

AIA General Conditions of the Contract for Construction

THE AMERICAN INSTITUTE OF ARCHITECTS

AIA Document A201

General Conditions of the Contract for Construction

*THIS DOCUMENT HAS IMPORTANT LEGAL CONSEQUENCES; CONSULTATION
WITH AN ATTORNEY IS ENCOURAGED WITH RESPECT TO ITS MODIFICATION*

TABLE OF ARTICLES

This document has been approved and endorsed by The Associated General Contractors of America.

AIA DOCUMENT A201 • GENERAL CONDITIONS OF THE CONTRACT FOR CONSTRUCTION • TWELFTH EDITION • APRIL 1970 ED.
AIA® • © 1970 • THE AMERICAN INSTITUTE OF ARCHITECTS, 1735 NEW YORK AVENUE, N.W., WASHINGTON, D.C. 20006

INDEX

AIA DOCUMENT A201 • GENERAL CONDITIONS OF THE CONTRACT FOR CONSTRUCTION • TWELFTH EDITION • APRIL 1970 ED.
AIA® • © 1970 • THE AMERICAN INSTITUTE OF ARCHITECTS, 1735 NEW YORK AVENUE, N.W., WASHINGTON, D.C. 20006

AIA DOCUMENT A201 • GENERAL CONDITIONS OF THE CONTRACT FOR CONSTRUCTION • TWELFTH EDITION • APRIL 1970 ED.
AIA® • © 1970 • THE AMERICAN INSTITUTE OF ARCHITECTS, 1735 NEW YORK AVENUE, N.W., WASHINGTON, D.C. 20006

GENERAL CONDITIONS OF THE CONTRACT FOR CONSTRUCTION

ARTICLE 1

CONTRACT DOCUMENTS

1.1 DEFINITIONS

1.1.1 THE CONTRACT DOCUMENTS

The Contract Documents consist of the Agreement, the Conditions of the Contract (General, Supplementary and other Conditions), the Drawings, the Specifications, all Addenda issued prior to execution of the Contract, and all Modifications thereto. A Modification is (1) a written amendment to the Contract signed by both parties, (2) a Change Order, (3) a written interpretation issued by the Architect pursuant to Subparagraph 1.2.5, or (4) a written order for a minor change in the Work issued by the Architect pursuant to Paragraph 12.3. A Modification may be made only after execution of the Contract.

1.1.2 THE CONTRACT

The Contract Documents form the Contract. The Contract represents the entire and integrated agreement between the parties hereto and supersedes all prior negotiations, representations, or agreements, either written or oral, including the bidding documents. The Contract may be amended or modified only by a Modification as defined in Subparagraph 1.1.1.

1.1.3 THE WORK

The term Work includes all labor necessary to produce the construction required by the Contract Documents, and all materials and equipment incorporated or to be incorporated in such construction.

1.1.4 THE PROJECT

The Project is the total construction designed by the Architect of which the Work performed under the Contract Documents may be the whole or a part.

1.2 EXECUTION, CORRELATION, INTENT AND INTERPRETATIONS

1.2.1 The Contract Documents shall be signed in not less than triplicate by the Owner and Contractor. If either the Owner or the Contractor or both do not sign the Conditions of the Contract, Drawings, Specifications, or any of the other Contract Documents, the Architect shall identify them.

1.2.2 By executing the Contract, the Contractor represents that he has visited the site, familiarized himself with the local conditions under which the Work is to be performed, and correlated his observations with the requirements of the Contract Documents.

1.2.3 The Contract Documents are complementary, and what is required by any one shall be as binding as if required by all. The intention of the Documents is to include all labor, materials, equipment and other items

as provided in Subparagraph 4.4.1 necessary for the proper execution and completion of the Work. It is not intended that Work not covered under any heading, section, branch, class or trade of the Specifications shall be supplied unless it is required elsewhere in the Contract Documents or is reasonably inferable therefrom as being necessary to produce the intended results. Words which have well-known technical or trade meanings are used herein in accordance with such recognized meanings.

1.2.4 The organization of the Specifications into divisions, sections and articles, and the arrangement of Drawings shall not control the Contractor in dividing the Work among Subcontractors or in establishing the extent of Work to be performed by any trade.

1.2.5 Written interpretations necessary for the proper execution or progress of the Work, in the form of drawings or otherwise, will be issued with reasonable promptness by the Architect and in accordance with any schedule agreed upon. Either party to the Contract may make written request to the Architect for such interpretations. Such interpretations shall be consistent with and reasonably inferable from the Contract Documents, and may be effected by Field Order.

1.3 COPIES FURNISHED AND OWNERSHIP

1.3.1 Unless otherwise provided in the Contract Documents, the Contractor will be furnished, free of charge, all copies of Drawings and Specifications reasonably necessary for the execution of the Work.

1.3.2 All Drawings, Specifications and copies thereof furnished by the Architect are and shall remain his property. They are not to be used on any other project, and, with the exception of one contract set for each party to the Contract, are to be returned to the Architect on request at the completion of the Work.

ARTICLE 2

ARCHITECT

2.1 DEFINITION

2.1.1 The Architect is the person or organization licensed to practice architecture and identified as such in the Agreement and is referred to throughout the Contract Documents as if singular in number and masculine in gender. The term Architect means the Architect or his authorized representative.

2.1.2 Nothing contained in the Contract Documents shall create any contractual relationship between the Architect and the Contractor.

2.2 ADMINISTRATION OF THE CONTRACT

2.2.1 The Architect will provide general Administration of the Construction Contract, including performance of the functions hereinafter described.

AIA DOCUMENT A201 • GENERAL CONDITIONS OF THE CONTRACT FOR CONSTRUCTION • TWELFTH EDITION • APRIL 1970 ED.
AIA® • © 1970 • THE AMERICAN INSTITUTE OF ARCHITECTS, 1735 NEW YORK AVENUE, N.W., WASHINGTON, D.C. 20006

2.2.2 The Architect will be the Owner's representative during construction and until final payment. The Architect will have authority to act on behalf of the Owner to the extent provided in the Contract Documents, unless otherwise modified by written instrument which will be shown to the Contractor. The Architect will advise and consult with the Owner, and all of the Owner's instructions to the Contractor shall be issued through the Architect.

2.2.3 The Architect shall at all times have access to the Work wherever it is in preparation and progress. The Contractor shall provide facilities for such access so the Architect may perform his functions under the Contract Documents.

2.2.4 The Architect will make periodic visits to the site to familiarize himself generally with the progress and quality of the Work and to determine in general if the Work is proceeding in accordance with the Contract Documents. On the basis of his on-site observations as an architect, he will keep the Owner informed of the progress of the Work, and will endeavor to guard the Owner against defects and deficiencies in the Work of the Contractor. The Architect will not be required to make exhaustive or continuous on-site inspections to check the quality or quantity of the Work. The Architect will not be responsible for construction means, methods, techniques, sequences or procedures, or for safety precautions and programs in connection with the Work, and he will not be responsible for the Contractor's failure to carry out the Work in accordance with the Contract Documents.

2.2.5 Based on such observations and the Contractor's Applications for Payment, the Architect will determine the amounts owing to the Contractor and will issue Certificates for Payment in such amounts, as provided in Paragraph 9.4.

2.2.6 The Architect will be, in the first instance, the interpreter of the requirements of the Contract Documents and the judge of the performance thereunder by both the Owner and Contractor. The Architect will, within a reasonable time, render such interpretations as he may deem necessary for the proper execution or progress of the Work.

2.2.7 Claims, disputes and other matters in question between the Contractor and the Owner relating to the execution or progress of the Work or the interpretation of the Contract Documents shall be referred initially to the Architect for decision which he will render in writing within a reasonable time.

2.2.8 All interpretations and decisions of the Architect shall be consistent with the intent of the Contract Documents. In his capacity as interpreter and judge, he will exercise his best efforts to insure faithful performance by both the Owner and the Contractor and will not show partiality to either.

2.2.9 The Architect's decisions in matters relating to artistic effect will be final if consistent with the intent of the Contract Documents.

2.2.10 Any claim, dispute or other matter that has been referred to the Architect, except those relating to artistic effect as provided in Subparagraph 2.2.9 and except any

which have been waived by the making or acceptance of final payment as provided in Subparagraphs 9.7.5 and 9.7.6, shall be subject to arbitration upon the written demand of either party. However, no demand for arbitration of any such claim, dispute or other matter may be made until the earlier of:

2.2.10.1 The date on which the Architect has rendered his written decision, or

    .2 the tenth day after the parties have presented their evidence to the Architect or have been given a reasonable opportunity to do so, if the Architect has not rendered his written decision by that date.

2.2.11 If a decision of the Architect is made in writing and states that it is final but subject to appeal, no demand for arbitration of a claim, dispute or other matter covered by such decision may be made later than thirty days after the date on which the party making the demand received the decision. The failure to demand arbitration within said thirty days' period will result in the Architect's decision becoming final and binding upon the Owner and the Contractor. If the Architect renders a decision after arbitration proceedings have been initiated, such decision may be entered as evidence but will not supersede any arbitration proceedings unless the decision is acceptable to the parties concerned.

2.2.12 The Architect will have authority to reject Work which does not conform to the Contract Documents. Whenever, in his reasonable opinion, he considers it necessary or advisable to insure the proper implementation of the intent of the Contract Documents, he will have authority to require special inspection or testing of the Work in accordance with Subparagraph 7.8.2 whether or not such Work be then fabricated, installed or completed. However, neither the Architect's authority to act under this Subparagraph 2.2.12, nor any decision made by him in good faith either to exercise or not to exercise such authority, shall give rise to any duty or responsibility of the Architect to the Contractor, any Subcontractor, any of their agents or employees, or any other person performing any of the Work.

2.2.13 The Architect will review Shop Drawings and Samples as provided in Subparagraphs 4.13.1 through 4.13.8 inclusive.

2.2.14 The Architect will prepare Change Orders in accordance with Article 12, and will have authority to order minor changes in the Work as provided in Subparagraph 12.3.1.

2.2.15 The Architect will conduct inspections to determine the dates of Substantial Completion and final completion, will receive and review written guarantees and related documents required by the Contract and assembled by the Contractor and will issue a final Certificate for Payment.

2.2.16 If the Owner and Architect agree, the Architect will provide one or more Full-Time Project Representatives to assist the Architect in carrying out his responsibilities at the site. The duties, responsibilities and limitations of authority of any such Project Representative shall be as set forth in an exhibit to be incorporated in the Contract Documents.

AIA DOCUMENT A201 • GENERAL CONDITIONS OF THE CONTRACT FOR CONSTRUCTION • TWELFTH EDITION • APRIL 1970 ED. AIA® • © 1970 • THE AMERICAN INSTITUTE OF ARCHITECTS, 1735 NEW YORK AVENUE, N.W., WASHINGTON, D.C. 20006

2.2.17 The duties, responsibilities and limitations of authority of the Architect as the Owner's representative during construction as set forth in Articles 1 through 14 inclusive of these General Conditions will not be modified or extended without written consent of the Owner, the Contractor and the Architect.

2.2.18 The Architect will not be responsible for the acts or omissions of the Contractor, any Subcontractors, or any of their agents or employees, or any other persons performing any of the Work.

2.2.19 In case of the termination of the employment of the Architect, the Owner shall appoint an architect against whom the Contractor makes no reasonable objection whose status under the Contract Documents shall be that of the former architect. Any dispute in connection with such appointment shall be subject to arbitration.

ARTICLE 3

OWNER

3.1 DEFINITION

3.1.1 The Owner is the person or organization identified as such in the Agreement and is referred to throughout the Contract Documents as if singular in number and masculine in gender. The term Owner means the Owner or his authorized representative.

3.2 INFORMATION AND SERVICES REQUIRED OF THE OWNER

3.2.1 The Owner shall furnish all surveys describing the physical characteristics, legal limits and utility locations for the site of the Project.

3.2.2 The Owner shall secure and pay for easements for permanent structures or permanent changes in existing facilities.

3.2.3 Information or services under the Owner's control shall be furnished by the Owner with reasonable promptness to avoid delay in the orderly progress of the Work.

3.2.4 The Owner shall issue all instructions to the Contractor through the Architect.

3.2.5 The foregoing are in addition to other duties and responsibilities of the Owner enumerated herein and especially those in respect to Payment and Insurance in Articles 9 and 11 respectively.

3.3 OWNER'S RIGHT TO STOP THE WORK

3.3.1 If the Contractor fails to correct defective Work or persistently fails to supply materials or equipment in accordance with the Contract Documents, the Owner may order the Contractor to stop the Work, or any portion thereof, until the cause for such order has been eliminated.

3.4 OWNER'S RIGHT TO CARRY OUT THE WORK

3.4.1 If the Contractor defaults or neglects to carry out the Work in accordance with the Contract Documents or fails to perform any provision of the Contract, the Owner may, after seven days' written notice to the Contractor and without prejudice to any other remedy he

may have, make good such deficiencies. In such case an appropriate Change Order shall be issued deducting from the payments then or thereafter due the Contractor the cost of correcting such deficiencies, including the cost of the Architect's additional services made necessary by such default, neglect or failure. The Architect must approve both such action and the amount charged to the Contractor. If the payments then or thereafter due the Contractor are not sufficient to cover such amount, the Contractor shall pay the difference to the Owner.

ARTICLE 4

CONTRACTOR

4.1 DEFINITION

4.1.1 The Contractor is the person or organization identified as such in the Agreement and is referred to throughout the Contract Documents as if singular in number and masculine in gender. The term Contractor means the Contractor or his authorized representative.

4.2 REVIEW OF CONTRACT DOCUMENTS

4.2.1 The Contractor shall carefully study and compare the Contract Documents and shall at once report to the Architect any error, inconsistency or omission he may discover. The Contractor shall not be liable to the Owner or the Architect for any damage resulting from any such errors, inconsistencies or omissions in the Contract Documents. The Contractor shall do no Work without Drawings, Specifications or Modifications.

4.3 SUPERVISION AND CONSTRUCTION PROCEDURES

4.3.1 The Contractor shall supervise and direct the Work, using his best skill and attention. He shall be solely responsible for all construction means, methods, techniques, sequences and procedures and for coordinating all portions of the Work under the Contract.

4.4 LABOR AND MATERIALS

4.4.1 Unless otherwise specifically noted, the Contractor shall provide and pay for all labor, materials, equipment, tools, construction equipment and machinery, water, heat, utilities, transportation, and other facilities and services necessary for the proper execution and completion of the Work.

4.4.2 The Contractor shall at all times enforce strict discipline and good order among his employees and shall not employ on the Work any unfit person or anyone not skilled in the task assigned to him.

4.5 WARRANTY

4.5.1 The Contractor warrants to the Owner and the Architect that all materials and equipment furnished under this Contract will be new unless otherwise specified, and that all Work will be of good quality, free from faults and defects and in conformance with the Contract Documents. All Work not so conforming to these standards may be considered defective. If required by the Architect, the Contractor shall furnish satisfactory evidence as to the kind and quality of materials and equipment.

4.6 TAXES

4.6.1 The Contractor shall pay all sales, consumer, use and other similar taxes required by law.

AIA DOCUMENT A201 • GENERAL CONDITIONS OF THE CONTRACT FOR CONSTRUCTION • TWELFTH EDITION • APRIL 1970 ED.
AIA® • © 1970 • THE AMERICAN INSTITUTE OF ARCHITECTS, 1735 NEW YORK AVENUE, N.W., WASHINGTON, D.C. 20006

4.7 PERMITS, FEES AND NOTICES

4.7.1 The Contractor shall secure and pay for all permits, governmental fees and licenses necessary for the proper execution and completion of the Work, which are applicable at the time the bids are received. It is not the responsibility of the Contractor to make certain that the Drawings and Specifications are in accordance with applicable laws, statutes, building codes and regulations.

4.7.2 The Contractor shall give all notices and comply with all laws, ordinances, rules, regulations and orders of any public authority bearing on the performance of the Work. If the Contractor observes that any of the Contract Documents are at variance therewith in any respect, he shall promptly notify the Architect in writing, and any necessary changes shall be adjusted by appropriate Modification. If the Contractor performs any Work knowing it to be contrary to such laws, ordinances, rules and regulations, and without such notice to the Architect, he shall assume full responsibility therefor and shall bear all costs attributable thereto.

4.8 CASH ALLOWANCES

4.8.1 The Contractor shall include in the Contract Sum all allowances stated in the Contract Documents. These allowances shall cover the net cost of the materials and equipment delivered and unloaded at the site, and all applicable taxes. The Contractor's handling costs on the site, labor, installation costs, overhead, profit and other expenses contemplated for the original allowance shall be included in the Contract Sum and not in the allowance. The Contractor shall cause the Work covered by these allowances to be performed for such amounts and by such persons as the Architect may direct, but he will not be required to employ persons against whom he makes a reasonable objection. If the cost, when determined, is more than or less than the allowance, the Contract Sum shall be adjusted accordingly by Change Order which will include additional handling costs on the site, labor, installation costs, overhead, profit and other expenses resulting to the Contractor from any increase over the original allowance.

4.9 SUPERINTENDENT

4.9.1 The Contractor shall employ a competent superintendent and necessary assistants who shall be in attendance at the Project site during the progress of the Work. The superintendent shall be satisfactory to the Architect, and shall not be changed except with the consent of the Architect, unless the superintendent proves to be unsatisfactory to the Contractor and ceases to be in his employ. The superintendent shall represent the Contractor and all communications given to the superintendent shall be as binding as if given to the Contractor. Important communications will be confirmed in writing. Other communications will be so confirmed on written request in each case.

4.10 RESPONSIBILITY FOR THOSE PERFORMING THE WORK

4.10.1 The Contractor shall be responsible to the Owner for the acts and omissions of all his employees and all Subcontractors, their agents and employees, and all other persons performing any of the Work under a contract with the Contractor.

4.11 PROGRESS SCHEDULE

4.11.1 The Contractor, immediately after being awarded the Contract, shall prepare and submit for the Architect's approval an estimated progress schedule for the Work. The progress schedule shall be related to the entire Project to the extent required by the Contract Documents. This schedule shall indicate the dates for the starting and completion of the various stages of construction and shall be revised as required by the conditions of the Work, subject to the Architect's approval.

4.12 DRAWINGS AND SPECIFICATIONS AT THE SITE

4.12.1 The Contractor shall maintain at the site for the Owner one copy of all Drawings, Specifications, Addenda, approved Shop Drawings, Change Orders and other Modifications, in good order and marked to record all changes made during construction. These shall be available to the Architect. The Drawings, marked to record all changes made during construction, shall be delivered to him for the Owner upon completion of the Work.

4.13 SHOP DRAWINGS AND SAMPLES

4.13.1 Shop Drawings are drawings, diagrams, illustrations, schedules, performance charts, brochures and other data which are prepared by the Contractor or any Subcontractor, manufacturer, supplier or distributor, and which illustrate some portion of the Work.

4.13.2 Samples are physical examples furnished by the Contractor to illustrate materials, equipment or workmanship, and to establish standards by which the Work will be judged.

4.13.3 The Contractor shall review, stamp with his approval and submit, with reasonable promptness and in orderly sequence so as to cause no delay in the Work or in the work of any other contractor, all Shop Drawings and Samples required by the Contract Documents or subsequently by the Architect as covered by Modifications. Shop Drawings and Samples shall be properly identified as specified, or as the Architect may require. At the time of submission the Contractor shall inform the Architect in writing of any deviation in the Shop Drawings or Samples from the requirements of the Contract Documents.

4.13.4 By approving and submitting Shop Drawings and Samples, the Contractor thereby represents that he has determined and verified all field measurements, field construction criteria, materials, catalog numbers and similar data, or will do so, and that he has checked and coordinated each Shop Drawing and Sample with the requirements of the Work and of the Contract Documents.

4.13.5 The Architect will review and approve Shop Drawings and Samples with reasonable promptness so as to cause no delay, but only for conformance with the design concept of the Project and with the information given in the Contract Documents. The Architect's approval of a separate item shall not indicate approval of an assembly in which the item functions.

4.13.6 The Contractor shall make any corrections required by the Architect and shall resubmit the required number of corrected copies of Shop Drawings or new Samples until approved. The Contractor shall direct spe-

---

AIA DOCUMENT A201 • GENERAL CONDITIONS OF THE CONTRACT FOR CONSTRUCTION • TWELFTH EDITION • APRIL 1970 ED. AIA® • © 1970 • THE AMERICAN INSTITUTE OF ARCHITECTS, 1735 NEW YORK AVENUE, N.W., WASHINGTON, D.C. 20006

cific attention in writing or on resubmitted Shop Drawings to revisions other than the corrections requested by the Architect on previous submissions.

4.13.7 The Architect's approval of Shop Drawings or Samples shall not relieve the Contractor of responsibility for any deviation from the requirements of the Contract Documents unless the Contractor has informed the Architect in writing of such deviation at the time of submission and the Architect has given written approval to the specific deviation, nor shall the Architect's approval relieve the Contractor from responsibility for errors or omissions in the Shop Drawings or Samples.

4.13.8 No portion of the Work requiring a Shop Drawing or Sample submission shall be commenced until the submission has been approved by the Architect. All such portions of the Work shall be in accordance with approved Shop Drawings and Samples.

4.14 USE OF SITE

4.14.1 The Contractor shall confine operations at the site to areas permitted by law, ordinances, permits and the Contract Documents and shall not unreasonably encumber the site with any materials or equipment.

4.15 CUTTING AND PATCHING OF WORK

4.15.1 The Contractor shall do all cutting, fitting or patching of his Work that may be required to make its several parts fit together properly, and shall not endanger any Work by cutting, excavating or otherwise altering the Work or any part of it.

4.16 CLEANING UP

4.16.1 The Contractor at all times shall keep the premises free from accumulation of waste materials or rubbish caused by his operations. At the completion of the Work he shall remove all his waste materials and rubbish from and about the Project as well as all his tools, construction equipment, machinery and surplus materials, and shall clean all glass surfaces and leave the Work "broom-clean" or its equivalent, except as otherwise specified.

4.16.2 If the Contractor fails to clean up, the Owner may do so and the cost thereof shall be charged to the Contractor as provided in Paragraph 3.4.

4.17 COMMUNICATIONS

4.17.1 The Contractor shall forward all communications to the Owner through the Architect.

4.18 INDEMNIFICATION

4.18.1 The Contractor shall indemnify and hold harmless the Owner and the Architect and their agents and employees from and against all claims, damages, losses and expenses including attorneys' fees arising out of or resulting from the performance of the Work, provided that any such claim, damage, loss or expense (1) is attributable to bodily injury, sickness, disease or death, or to injury to or destruction of tangible property (other than the Work itself) including the loss of use resulting therefrom, and (2) is caused in whole or in part by any negligent act or omission of the Contractor, any Subcontractor, anyone directly or indirectly employed by any of them or anyone for whose acts any of them may be liable,

regardless of whether or not it is caused in part by a party indemnified hereunder.

4.18.2 In any and all claims against the Owner or the Architect or any of their agents or employees by any employee of the Contractor, any Subcontractor, anyone directly or indirectly employed by any of them or anyone for whose acts any of them may be liable, the indemnification obligation under this Paragraph 4.18 shall not be limited in any way by any limitation on the amount or type of damages, compensation or benefits payable by or for the Contractor or any Subcontractor under workmen's compensation acts, disability benefit acts or other employee benefit acts.

4.18.3 The obligations of the Contractor under this Paragraph 4.18 shall not extend to the liability of the Architect, his agents or employees arising out of (1) the preparation or approval of maps, drawings, opinions, reports, surveys, Change Orders, designs or specifications, or (2) the giving of or the failure to give directions or instructions by the Architect, his agents or employees provided such giving or failure to give is the primary cause of the injury or damage.

ARTICLE 5

SUBCONTRACTORS

5.1 DEFINITION

5.1.1 A Subcontractor is a person or organization who has a direct contract with the Contractor to perform any of the Work at the site. The term Subcontractor is referred to throughout the Contract Documents as if singular in number and masculine in gender and means a Subcontractor or his authorized representative.

5.1.2 A Sub-subcontractor is a person or organization who has a direct or indirect contract with a Subcontractor to perform any of the Work at the site. The term Sub-subcontractor is referred to throughout the Contract Documents as if singular in number and masculine in gender and means a Sub-subcontractor or an authorized representative thereof.

5.1.3 Nothing contained in the Contract Documents shall create any contractual relation between the Owner or the Architect and any Subcontractor or Sub-subcontractor.

5.2 AWARD OF SUBCONTRACTS AND OTHER CONTRACTS FOR PORTIONS OF THE WORK

5.2.1 Unless otherwise specified in the Contract Documents or in the Instructions to Bidders, the Contractor, as soon as practicable after the award of the Contract, shall furnish to the Architect in writing for acceptance by the Owner and the Architect a list of the names of the Subcontractors proposed for the principal portions of the Work. The Architect shall promptly notify the Contractor in writing if either the Owner or the Architect, after due investigation, has reasonable objection to any Subcontractor on such list and does not accept him. Failure of the Owner or Architect to make objection promptly to any Subcontractor on the list shall constitute acceptance of such Subcontractor.

AIA DOCUMENT A201 • GENERAL CONDITIONS OF THE CONTRACT FOR CONSTRUCTION • TWELFTH EDITION • APRIL 1970 ED.
AIA® • © 1970 • THE AMERICAN INSTITUTE OF ARCHITECTS, 1735 NEW YORK AVENUE, N.W., WASHINGTON, D.C. 20006

5.2.2 The Contractor shall not contract with any Subcontractor or any person or organization (including those who are to furnish materials or equipment fabricated to a special design) proposed for portions of the Work designated in the Contract Documents or in the Instructions to Bidders or, if none is so designated, with any Subcontractor proposed for the principal portions of the Work who has been rejected by the Owner and the Architect. The Contractor will not be required to contract with any Subcontractor or person or organization against whom he has a reasonable objection.

5.2.3 If the Owner or Architect refuses to accept any Subcontractor or person or organization on a list submitted by the Contractor in response to the requirements of the Contract Documents or the Instructions to Bidders, the Contractor shall submit an acceptable substitute and the Contract Sum shall be increased or decreased by the difference in cost occasioned by such substitution and an appropriate Change Order shall be issued; however, no increase in the Contract Sum shall be allowed for any such substitution unless the Contractor has acted promptly and responsively in submitting for acceptance any list or lists of names as required by the Contract Documents or the Instructions to Bidders.

5.2.4 If the Owner or the Architect requires a change of any proposed Subcontractor or person or organization previously accepted by them, the Contract Sum shall be increased or decreased by the difference in cost occasioned by such change and an appropriate Change Order shall be issued.

5.2.5 The Contractor shall not make any substitution for any Subcontractor or person or organization who has been accepted by the Owner and the Architect, unless the substitution is acceptable to the Owner and the Architect.

5.3   SUBCONTRACTUAL RELATIONS

5.3.1 All work performed for the Contractor by a Subcontractor shall be pursuant to an appropriate agreement between the Contractor and the Subcontractor (and where appropriate between Subcontractors and Subsubcontractors) which shall contain provisions that:

.1 preserve and protect the rights of the Owner and the Architect under the Contract with respect to the Work to be performed under the subcontract so that the subcontracting thereof will not prejudice such rights;

.2 require that such Work be performed in accordance with the requirements of the Contract Documents;

.3 require submission to the Contractor of applications for payment under each subcontract to which the Contractor is a party, in reasonable time to enable the Contractor to apply for payment in accordance with Article 9;

.4 require that all claims for additional costs, extensions of time, damages for delays or otherwise with respect to subcontracted portions of the Work shall be submitted to the Contractor (via any Subcontractor or Sub-subcontractor where appropriate) in sufficient time so that the Con-

tractor may comply in the manner provided in the Contract Documents for like claims by the Contractor upon the Owner;

.5 waive all rights the contracting parties may have against one another for damages caused by fire or other perils covered by the property insurance described in Paragraph 11.3, except such rights as they may have to the proceeds of such insurance held by the Owner as trustee under Paragraph 11.3; and

.6 obligate each Subcontractor specifically to consent to the provisions of this Paragraph 5.3.

5.4   PAYMENTS TO SUBCONTRACTORS

5.4.1 The Contractor shall pay each Subcontractor, upon receipt of payment from the Owner, an amount equal to the percentage of completion allowed to the Contractor on account of such Subcontractor's Work, less the percentage retained from payments to the Contractor. The Contractor shall also require each Subcontractor to make similar payments to his subcontractors.

5.4.2 If the Architect fails to issue a Certificate for Payment for any cause which is the fault of the Contractor and not the fault of a particular Subcontractor, the Contractor shall pay that Subcontractor on demand, made at any time after the Certificate for Payment should otherwise have been issued, for his Work to the extent completed, less the retained percentage.

5.4.3 The Contractor shall pay each Subcontractor a just share of any insurance moneys received by the Contractor under Article 11, and he shall require each Subcontractor to make similar payments to his subcontractors.

5.4.4 The Architect may, on request and at his discretion, furnish to any Subcontractor, if practicable, information regarding percentages of completion certified to the Contractor on account of Work done by such Subcontractors.

5.4.5 Neither the Owner nor the Architect shall have any obligation to pay or to see to the payment of any moneys to any Subcontractor except as may otherwise be required by law.

ARTICLE 6

SEPARATE CONTRACTS

6.1   OWNER'S RIGHT TO AWARD SEPARATE CONTRACTS

6.1.1 The Owner reserves the right to award other contracts in connection with other portions of the Project under these or similar Conditions of the Contract.

6.1.2 When separate contracts are awarded for different portions of the Project, "the Contractor" in the contract documents in each case shall be the contractor who signs each separate contract.

6.2   MUTUAL RESPONSIBILITY OF CONTRACTORS

6.2.1 The Contractor shall afford other contractors reasonable opportunity for the introduction and storage of their materials and equipment and the execution of their

AIA DOCUMENT A201 • GENERAL CONDITIONS OF THE CONTRACT FOR CONSTRUCTION • TWELFTH EDITION • APRIL 1970 ED.
AIA® • © 1970 • THE AMERICAN INSTITUTE OF ARCHITECTS, 1735 NEW YORK AVENUE, N.W., WASHINGTON, D.C. 20006

work, and shall properly connect and coordinate his Work with theirs.

6.2.2 If any part of the Contractor's Work depends for proper execution or results upon the work of any other separate contractor, the Contractor shall inspect and promptly report to the Architect any apparent discrepancies or defects in such work that render it unsuitable for such proper execution and results. Failure of the Contractor so to inspect and report shall constitute an acceptance of the other contractor's work as fit and proper to receive his Work, except as to defects which may develop in the other separate contractor's work after the execution of the Contractor's Work.

6.2.3 Should the Contractor cause damage to the work or property of any separate contractor on the Project, the Contractor shall, upon due notice, settle with such other contractor by agreement or arbitration, if he will so settle. If such separate contractor sues the Owner or initiates an arbitration proceeding on account of any damage alleged to have been so sustained, the Owner shall notify the Contractor who shall defend such proceedings at the Owner's expense, and if any judgment or award against the Owner arises therefrom the Contractor shall pay or satisfy it and shall reimburse the Owner for all attorneys' fees and court or arbitration costs which the Owner has incurred.

6.3   CUTTING AND PATCHING
UNDER SEPARATE CONTRACTS

6.3.1 The Contractor shall be responsible for any cutting, fitting and patching that may be required to complete his Work except as otherwise specifically provided in the Contract Documents. The Contractor shall not endanger any work of any other contractors by cutting, excavating or otherwise altering any work and shall not cut or alter the work of any other contractor except with the written consent of the Architect.

6.3.2 Any costs caused by defective or ill-timed work shall be borne by the party responsible therefor.

6.4   OWNER'S RIGHT TO CLEAN UP

6.4.1 If a dispute arises between the separate contractors as to their responsibility for cleaning up as required by Paragraph 4.16, the Owner may clean up and charge the cost thereof to the several contractors as the Architect shall determine to be just.

ARTICLE 7

MISCELLANEOUS PROVISIONS

7.1   GOVERNING LAW

7.1.1 The Contract shall be governed by the law of the place where the Project is located.

7.2   SUCCESSORS AND ASSIGNS

7.2.1 The Owner and the Contractor each binds himself, his partners, successors, assigns and legal representatives to the other party hereto and to the partners, successors, assigns and legal representatives of such other party in respect to all covenants, agreements and obligations contained in the Contract Documents. Neither party to the Contract shall assign the Contract or sublet it as a whole without the written consent of the other, nor shall the Contractor assign any moneys due or to become due to him hereunder, without the previous written consent of the Owner.

7.3   WRITTEN NOTICE

7.3.1 Written notice shall be deemed to have been duly served if delivered in person to the individual or member of the firm or to an officer of the corporation for whom it was intended, or if delivered at or sent by registered or certified mail to the last business address known to him who gives the notice.

7.4   CLAIMS FOR DAMAGES

7.4.1 Should either party to the Contract suffer injury or damage to person or property because of any act or omission of the other party or of any of his employees, agents or others for whose acts he is legally liable, claim shall be made in writing to such other party within a reasonable time after the first observance of such injury or damage.

7.5   PERFORMANCE BOND AND
LABOR AND MATERIAL PAYMENT BOND

7.5.1 The Owner shall have the right to require the Contractor to furnish bonds covering the faithful performance of the Contract and the payment of all obligations arising thereunder if and as required in the Instructions to Bidders or elsewhere in the Contract Documents.

7.6   RIGHTS AND REMEDIES

7.6.1 The duties and obligations imposed by the Contract Documents and the rights and remedies available thereunder shall be in addition to and not a limitation of any duties, obligations, rights and remedies otherwise imposed or available by law.

7.7   ROYALTIES AND PATENTS

7.7.1 The Contractor shall pay all royalties and license fees. He shall defend all suits or claims for infringement of any patent rights and shall save the Owner harmless from loss on account thereof, except that the Owner shall be responsible for all such loss when a particular design, process or the product of a particular manufacturer or manufacturers is specified, but if the Contractor has reason to believe that the design, process or product specified is an infringement of a patent, he shall be responsible for such loss unless he promptly gives such information to the Architect.

7.8   TESTS

7.8.1 If the Contract Documents, laws, ordinances, rules, regulations or orders of any public authority having jurisdiction require any Work to be inspected, tested or approved, the Contractor shall give the Architect timely notice of its readiness and of the date arranged so the Architect may observe such inspection, testing or approval. The Contractor shall bear all costs of such inspections, tests and approvals unless otherwise provided.

7.8.2 If after the commencement of the Work the Architect determines that any Work requires special inspection, testing, or approval which Subparagraph 7.8.1

AIA DOCUMENT A201 • GENERAL CONDITIONS OF THE CONTRACT FOR CONSTRUCTION • TWELFTH EDITION • APRIL 1970 ED.
AIA® • © 1970 • THE AMERICAN INSTITUTE OF ARCHITECTS, 1735 NEW YORK AVENUE, N.W., WASHINGTON, D.C. 20006

does not include, he will, upon written authorization from the Owner, instruct the Contractor to order such special inspection, testing or approval, and the Contractor shall give notice as in Subparagraph 7.8.1. If such special inspection or testing reveals a failure of the Work to comply (1) with the requirements of the Contract Documents or (2), with respect to the performance of the Work, with laws, ordinances, rules, regulations or orders of any public authority having jurisdiction, the Contractor shall bear all costs thereof, including the Architect's additional services made necessary by such failure; otherwise the Owner shall bear such costs, and an appropriate Change Order shall be issued.

7.8.3 Required certificates of inspection, testing or approval shall be secured by the Contractor and promptly delivered by him to the Architect.

7.8.4 If the Architect wishes to observe the inspections, tests or approvals required by this Paragraph 7.8, he will do so promptly and, where practicable, at the source of supply.

7.8.5 Neither the observations of the Architect in his Administration of the Construction Contract, nor inspections, tests or approvals by persons other than the Contractor shall relieve the Contractor from his obligations to perform the Work in accordance with the Contract Documents.

7.9   INTEREST

7.9.1 Any moneys not paid when due to either party under this Contract shall bear interest at the legal rate in force at the place of the Project.

7.10   ARBITRATION

7.10.1 All claims, disputes and other matters in question arising out of, or relating to, this Contract or the breach thereof, except as set forth in Subparagraph 2.2.9 with respect to the Architect's decisions on matters relating to artistic effect, and except for claims which have been waived by the making or acceptance of final payment as provided by Subparagraphs 9.7.5 and 9.7.6, shall be decided by arbitration in accordance with the Construction Industry Arbitration Rules of the American Arbitration Association then obtaining unless the parties mutually agree otherwise. This agreement to arbitrate shall be specifically enforceable under the prevailing arbitration law. The award rendered by the arbitrators shall be final, and judgment may be entered upon it in accordance with applicable law in any court having jurisdiction thereof.

7.10.2 Notice of the demand for arbitration shall be filed in writing with the other party to the Contract and with the American Arbitration Association, and a copy shall be filed with the Architect. The demand for arbitration shall be made within the time limits specified in Subparagraphs 2.2.10 and 2.2.11 where applicable, and in all other cases within a reasonable time after the claim, dispute or other matter in question has arisen, and in no event shall it be made after the date when institution of legal or equitable proceedings based on such claim, dispute or other matter in question would be barred by the applicable statute of limitations.

7.10.3 The Contractor shall carry on the Work and maintain the progress schedule during any arbitration proceedings, unless otherwise agreed by him and the Owner in writing.

ARTICLE 8

TIME

8.1   DEFINITIONS

8.1.1 The Contract Time is the period of time alloted in the Contract Documents for completion of the Work.

8.1.2 The date of commencement of the Work is the date established in a notice to proceed. If there is no notice to proceed, it shall be the date of the Agreement or such other date as may be established therein.

8.1.3 The Date of Substantial Completion of the Work or designated portion thereof is the Date certified by the Architect when construction is sufficiently complete, in accordance with the Contract Documents, so the Owner may occupy the Work or designated portion thereof for the use for which it is intended.

8.1.4 The term day as used in the Contract Documents shall mean calendar day.

8.2   PROGRESS AND COMPLETION

8.2.1 All time limits stated in the Contract Documents are of the essence of the Contract.

8.2.2 The Contractor shall begin the Work on the date of commencement as defined in Subparagraph 8.1.2. He shall carry the Work forward expeditiously with adequate forces and shall complete it within the Contract Time.

8.2.3 If a date or time of completion is included in the Contract, it shall be the Date of Substantial Completion as defined in Subparagraph 8.1.3, including authorized extensions thereto, unless otherwise provided.

8.3   DELAYS AND EXTENSIONS OF TIME

8.3.1 If the Contractor is delayed at any time in the progress of the Work by any act or neglect of the Owner or the Architect, or by any employee of either, or by any separate contractor employed by the Owner, or by changes ordered in the Work, or by labor disputes, fire, unusual delay in transportation, unavoidable casualties or any causes beyond the Contractor's control, or by delay authorized by the Owner pending arbitration, or by any cause which the Architect determines may justify the delay, then the Contract Time shall be extended by Change Order for such reasonable time as the Architect may determine.

8.3.2 All claims for extension of time shall be made in writing to the Architect no more than twenty days after the occurrence of the delay; otherwise they shall be waived. In the case of a continuing cause of delay only one claim is necessary.

8.3.3 If no schedule or agreement is made stating the dates upon which written interpretations as set forth in Subparagraph 1.2.5 shall be furnished, then no claim for delay shall be allowed on account of failure to furnish

AIA DOCUMENT A201 • GENERAL CONDITIONS OF THE CONTRACT FOR CONSTRUCTION • TWELFTH EDITION • APRIL 1970 ED.
AIA® • © 1970 • THE AMERICAN INSTITUTE OF ARCHITECTS, 1735 NEW YORK AVENUE, N.W., WASHINGTON, D.C. 20006

such interpretations until fifteen days after demand is made for them, and not then unless such claim is reasonable.

8.3.4 This Paragraph 8.3 does not exclude the recovery of damages for delay by either party under other provisions of the Contract Documents.

ARTICLE 9

PAYMENTS AND COMPLETION

9.1 CONTRACT SUM

9.1.1 The Contract Sum is stated in the Agreement and is the total amount payable by the Owner to the Contractor for the performance of the Work under the Contract Documents.

9.2 SCHEDULE OF VALUES

9.2.1 Before the first Application for Payment, the Contractor shall submit to the Architect a schedule of values of the various portions of the Work, including quantities if required by the Architect, aggregating the total Contract Sum, divided so as to facilitate payments to Subcontractors in accordance with Paragraph 5.4, prepared in such form as specified or as the Architect and the Contractor may agree upon, and supported by such data to substantiate its correctness as the Architect may require. Each item in the schedule of values shall include its proper share of overhead and profit. This schedule, when approved by the Architect, shall be used only as a basis for the Contractor's Applications for Payment.

9.3 PROGRESS PAYMENTS

9.3.1 At least ten days before each progress payment falls due, the Contractor shall submit to the Architect an itemized Application for Payment, supported by such data substantiating the Contractor's right to payment as the Owner or the Architect may require.

9.3.2 If payments are to be made on account of materials or equipment not incorporated in the Work but delivered and suitably stored at the site, or at some other location agreed upon in writing, such payments shall be conditioned upon submission by the Contractor of bills of sale or such other procedures satisfactory to the Owner to establish the Owner's title to such materials or equipment or otherwise protect the Owner's interest including applicable insurance and transportation to the site.

9.3.3 The Contractor warrants and guarantees that title to all Work, materials and equipment covered by an Application for Payment, whether incorporated in the Project or not, will pass to the Owner upon the receipt of such payment by the Contractor, free and clear of all liens, claims, security interests or encumbrances, hereinafter referred to in this Article 9 as "liens"; and that no Work, materials or equipment covered by an Application for Payment will have been acquired by the Contractor, or by any other person performing the Work at the site or furnishing materials and equipment for the Project, subject to an agreement under which an interest therein or an encumbrance thereon is retained by the seller or otherwise imposed by the Contractor or such other person.

9.4 CERTIFICATES FOR PAYMENT

9.4.1 If the Contractor has made Application for Payment as above, the Architect will, with reasonable promptness but not more than seven days after the receipt of the Application, issue a Certificate for Payment to the Owner, with a copy to the Contractor, for such amount as he determines to be properly due, or state in writing his reasons for withholding a Certificate as provided in Subparagraph 9.5.1.

9.4.2 The issuance of a Certificate for Payment will constitute a representation by the Architect to the Owner, based on his observations at the site as provided in Subparagraph 2.2.4 and the data comprising the Application for Payment, that the Work has progressed to the point indicated; that, to the best of his knowledge, information and belief, the quality of the Work is in accordance with the Contract Documents (subject to an evaluation of the Work for conformance with the Contract Documents upon Substantial Completion, to the results of any subsequent tests required by the Contract Documents, to minor deviations from the Contract Documents correctable prior to completion, and to any specific qualifications stated in his Certificate); and that the Contractor is entitled to payment in the amount certified. In addition, the Architect's final Certificate for Payment will constitute a further representation that the conditions precedent to the Contractor's being entitled to final payment as set forth in Subparagraph 9.7.2 have been fulfilled. However, by issuing a Certificate for Payment, the Architect shall not thereby be deemed to represent that he has made exhaustive or continuous on-site inspections to check the quality or quantity of the Work or that he has reviewed the construction means, methods, techniques, sequences or procedures, or that he has made any examination to ascertain how or for what purpose the Contractor has used the moneys previously paid on account of the Contract Sum.

9.4.3 After the Architect has issued a Certificate for Payment, the Owner shall make payment in the manner provided in the Agreement.

9.4.4 No certificate for a progress payment, nor any progress payment, nor any partial or entire use or occupancy of the Project by the Owner, shall constitute an acceptance of any Work not in accordance with the Contract Documents.

9.5 PAYMENTS WITHHELD

9.5.1 The Architect may decline to approve an Application for Payment and may withhold his Certificate in whole or in part, to the extent necessary reasonably to protect the Owner, if in his opinion he is unable to make representations to the Owner as provided in Subparagraph 9.4.2. The Architect may also decline to approve any Applications for Payment or, because of subsequently discovered evidence or subsequent inspections, he may nullify the whole or any part of any Certificate for Payment previously issued, to such extent as may be necessary in his opinion to protect the Owner from loss because of:

    .1 defective work not remedied,
    .2 third party claims filed or reasonable evidence indicating probable filing of such claims,

AIA DOCUMENT A201 • GENERAL CONDITIONS OF THE CONTRACT FOR CONSTRUCTION • TWELFTH EDITION • APRIL 1970 ED.
AIA® • © 1970 • THE AMERICAN INSTITUTE OF ARCHITECTS, 1735 NEW YORK AVENUE, N.W., WASHINGTON, D.C. 20006

.3 failure of the Contractor to make payments properly to Subcontractors or for labor, materials or equipment,

.4 reasonable doubt that the Work can be completed for the unpaid balance of the Contract Sum,

.5 damage to another contractor,

.6 reasonable indication that the Work will not be completed within the Contract Time, or

.7 unsatisfactory prosecution of the Work by the Contractor.

9.5.2 When the above grounds in Subparagraph 9.5.1 are removed, payment shall be made for amounts withheld because of them.

9.6   FAILURE OF PAYMENT

9.6.1 If the Architect should fail to issue any Certificate for Payment, through no fault of the Contractor, within seven days after receipt of the Contractor's Application for Payment, or if the Owner should fail to pay the Contractor within seven days after the date of payment established in the Agreement any amount certified by the Architect or awarded by arbitration, then the Contractor may, upon seven additional days' written notice to the Owner and the Architect, stop the Work until payment of the amount owing has been received.

9.7   SUBSTANTIAL COMPLETION AND FINAL PAYMENT

9.7.1 When the Contractor determines that the Work or a designated portion thereof acceptable to the Owner is substantially complete, the Contractor shall prepare for submission to the Architect a list of items to be completed or corrected. The failure to include any items on such list does not alter the responsibility of the Contractor to complete all Work in accordance with the Contract Documents. When the Architect on the basis of an inspection determines that the Work is substantially complete, he will then prepare a Certificate of Substantial Completion which shall establish the Date of Substantial Completion, shall state the responsibilities of the Owner and the Contractor for maintenance, heat, utilities, and insurance, and shall fix the time within which the Contractor shall complete the items listed therein. The Certificate of Substantial Completion shall be submitted to the Owner and the Contractor for their written acceptance of the responsibilities assigned to them in such Certificate.

9.7.2 Upon receipt of written notice that the Work is ready for final inspection and acceptance and upon receipt of a final Application for Payment, the Architect will promptly make such inspection and, when he finds the Work acceptable under the Contract Documents and the Contract fully performed, he will promptly issue a final Certificate for Payment stating that to the best of his knowledge, information and belief, and on the basis of his observations and inspections, the Work has been completed in accordance with the terms and conditions of the Contract Documents and that the entire balance found to be due the Contractor, and noted in said final Certificate, is due and payable.

9.7.3 Neither the final payment nor the remaining retained percentage shall become due until the Contractor submits to the Architect (1) an Affidavit that all payrolls, bills for materials and equipment, and other indebtedness connected with the Work for which the Owner or his property might in any way be responsible, have been paid or otherwise satisfied, (2) consent of surety, if any, to final payment and (3), if required by the Owner, other data establishing payment or satisfaction of all such obligations, such as receipts, releases and waivers of liens arising out of the Contract, to the extent and in such form as may be designated by the Owner. If any Subcontractor refuses to furnish a release or waiver required by the Owner, the Contractor may furnish a bond satisfactory to the Owner to indemnify him against any such lien. If any such lien remains unsatisfied after all payments are made, the Contractor shall refund to the Owner all moneys that the latter may be compelled to pay in discharging such lien, including all costs and reasonable attorneys' fees.

9.7.4 If after Substantial Completion of the Work final completion thereof is materially delayed through no fault of the Contractor, and the Architect so confirms, the Owner shall, upon certification by the Architect, and without terminating the Contract, make payment of the balance due for that portion of the Work fully completed and accepted. If the remaining balance for Work not fully completed or corrected is less than the retainage stipulated in the Agreement, and if bonds have been furnished as required in Subparagraph 7.5.1, the written consent of the surety to the payment of the balance due for that portion of the Work fully completed and accepted shall be submitted by the Contractor to the Architect prior to certification of such payment. Such payment shall be made under the terms and conditions governing final payment, except that it shall not constitute a waiver of claims.

9.7.5 The making of final payment shall constitute a waiver of all claims by the Owner except those arising from:

.1 unsettled liens,

.2 faulty or defective Work appearing after Substantial Completion,

.3 failure of the Work to comply with the requirements of the Contract Documents, or

.4 terms of any special guarantees required by the Contract Documents.

9.7.6 The acceptance of final payment shall constitute a waiver of all claims by the Contractor except those previously made in writing and still unsettled.

ARTICLE 10

PROTECTION OF PERSONS AND PROPERTY

10.1   SAFETY PRECAUTIONS AND PROGRAMS

10.1.1 The Contractor shall be responsible for initiating, maintaining and supervising all safety precautions and programs in connection with the Work.

10.2   SAFETY OF PERSONS AND PROPERTY

10.2.1 The Contractor shall take all reasonable precautions for the safety of, and shall provide all reasonable protection to prevent damage, injury or loss to:

AIA DOCUMENT A201 • GENERAL CONDITIONS OF THE CONTRACT FOR CONSTRUCTION • TWELFTH EDITION • APRIL 1970 ED.
AIA® • © 1970 • THE AMERICAN INSTITUTE OF ARCHITECTS, 1735 NEW YORK AVENUE, N.W., WASHINGTON, D.C. 20006

.1 all employees on the Work and all other persons who may be affected thereby;

.2 all the Work and all materials and equipment to be incorporated therein, whether in storage on or off the site, under the care, custody or control of the Contractor or any of his Subcontractors or Sub-subcontractors; and

.3 other property at the site or adjacent thereto, including trees, shrubs, lawns, walks, pavements, roadways, structures and utilities not designated for removal, relocation or replacement in the course of construction.

10.2.2 The Contractor shall comply with all applicable laws, ordinances, rules, regulations and lawful orders of any public authority having jurisdiction for the safety of persons or property or to protect them from damage, injury or loss. He shall erect and maintain, as required by existing conditions and progress of the Work, all reasonable safeguards for safety and protection, including posting danger signs and other warnings against hazards, promulgating safety regulations and notifying owners and users of adjacent utilities.

10.2.3 When the use or storage of explosives or other hazardous materials or equipment is necessary for the execution of the Work, the Contractor shall exercise the utmost care and shall carry on such activities under the supervision of properly qualified personnel.

10.2.4 All damage or loss to any property referred to in Clauses 10.2.1.2 and 10.2.1.3 caused in whole or in part by the Contractor, any Subcontractor, any Sub-subcontractor, or anyone directly or indirectly employed by any of them, or by anyone for whose acts any of them may be liable, shall be remedied by the Contractor, except damage or loss attributable to faulty Drawings or Specifications or to the acts or omissions of the Owner or Architect or anyone employed by either of them or for whose acts either of them may be liable, and not attributable to the fault or negligence of the Contractor.

10.2.5 The Contractor shall designate a responsible member of his organization at the site whose duty shall be the prevention of accidents. This person shall be the Contractor's superintendent unless otherwise designated in writing by the Contractor to the Owner and the Architect.

10.2.6 The Contractor shall not load or permit any part of the Work to be loaded so as to endanger its safety.

10.3 EMERGENCIES

10.3.1 In any emergency affecting the safety of persons or property, the Contractor shall act, at his discretion, to prevent threatened damage, injury or loss. Any additional compensation or extension of time claimed by the Contractor on account of emergency work shall be determined as provided in Article 12 for Changes in the Work.

ARTICLE 11

INSURANCE

11.1 CONTRACTOR'S LIABILITY INSURANCE

11.1.1 The Contractor shall purchase and maintain such insurance as will protect him from claims set forth below which may arise out of or result from the Contractor's operations under the Contract, whether such operations be by himself or by any Subcontractor or by anyone directly or indirectly employed by any of them, or by anyone for whose acts any of them may be liable:

.1 claims under workmen's compensation, disability benefit and other similar employee benefit acts;

.2 claims for damages because of bodily injury, occupational sickness or disease, or death of his employees;

.3 claims for damages because of bodily injury, sickness or disease, or death of any person other than his employees;

.4 claims for damages insured by usual personal injury liability coverage which are sustained (1) by any person as a result of an offense directly or indirectly related to the employment of such person by the Contractor, or (2) by any other person; and

.5 claims for damages because of injury to or destruction of tangible property, including loss of use resulting therefrom.

11.1.2 The insurance required by Subparagraph 11.1.1 shall be written for not less than any limits of liability specified in the Contract Documents, or required by law, whichever is greater, and shall include contractual liability insurance as applicable to the Contractor's obligations under Paragraph 4.18.

11.1.3 Certificates of Insurance acceptable to the Owner shall be filed with the Owner prior to commencement of the Work. These Certificates shall contain a provision that coverages afforded under the policies will not be cancelled until at least fifteen days' prior written notice has been given to the Owner.

11.2 OWNER'S LIABILITY INSURANCE

11.2.1 The Owner shall be responsible for purchasing and maintaining his own liability insurance and, at his option, may purchase and maintain such insurance as will protect him against claims which may arise from operations under the Contract.

11.3 PROPERTY INSURANCE

11.3.1 Unless otherwise provided, the Owner shall purchase and maintain property insurance upon the entire Work at the site to the full insurable value thereof. This insurance shall include the interests of the Owner, the Contractor, Subcontractors and Sub-subcontractors in the Work and shall insure against the perils of Fire, Extended Coverage, Vandalism and Malicious Mischief.

11.3.2 The Owner shall purchase and maintain such steam boiler and machinery insurance as may be required by the Contract Documents or by law. This insurance shall include the interests of the Owner, the Contractor, Subcontractors and Sub-subcontractors in the Work.

11.3.3 Any insured loss is to be adjusted with the Owner and made payable to the Owner as trustee for the insureds, as their interests may appear, subject to the requirements of any applicable mortgagee clause and of Subparagraph 11.3.8.

AIA DOCUMENT A201 • GENERAL CONDITIONS OF THE CONTRACT FOR CONSTRUCTION • TWELFTH EDITION • APRIL 1970 ED.
AIA® • © 1970 • THE AMERICAN INSTITUTE OF ARCHITECTS, 1735 NEW YORK AVENUE, N.W., WASHINGTON, D.C. 20006

11.3.4 The Owner shall file a copy of all policies with the Contractor before an exposure to loss may occur. If the Owner does not intend to purchase such insurance, he shall inform the Contractor in writing prior to commencement of the Work. The Contractor may then effect insurance which will protect the interests of himself, his Subcontractors and the Sub-subcontractors in the Work, and by appropriate Change Order the cost thereof shall be charged to the Owner. If the Contractor is damaged by failure of the Owner to purchase or maintain such insurance and so to notify the Contractor, then the Owner shall bear all reasonable costs properly attributable thereto.

11.3.5 If the Contractor requests in writing that insurance for special hazards be included in the property insurance policy, the Owner shall, if possible, include such insurance, and the cost thereof shall be charged to the Contractor by appropriate Change Order.

11.3.6 The Owner and Contractor waive all rights against each other for damages caused by fire or other perils to the extent covered by insurance provided under this Paragraph 11.3, except such rights as they may have to the proceeds of such insurance held by the Owner as trustee. The Contractor shall require similar waivers by Subcontractors and Sub-subcontractors in accordance with Clause 5.3.1.5.

11.3.7 If required in writing by any party in interest, the Owner as trustee shall, upon the occurrence of an insured loss, give bond for the proper performance of his duties. He shall deposit in a separate account any money so received, and he shall distribute it in accordance with such agreement as the parties in interest may reach, or in accordance with an award by arbitration in which case the procedure shall be as provided in Paragraph 7.10. If after such loss no other special agreement is made, replacement of damaged work shall be covered by an appropriate Change Order.

11.3.8 The Owner as trustee shall have power to adjust and settle any loss with the insurers unless one of the parties in interest shall object in writing within five days after the occurrence of loss to the Owner's exercise of this power, and if such objection be made, arbitrators shall be chosen as provided in Paragraph 7.10. The Owner as trustee shall, in that case, make settlement with the insurers in accordance with the directions of such arbitrators. If distribution of the insurance proceeds by arbitration is required, the arbitrators will direct such distribution.

11.4 LOSS OF USE INSURANCE

11.4.1 The Owner, at his option, may purchase and maintain such insurance as will insure him against loss of use of his property due to fire or other hazards, however caused.

ARTICLE 12

CHANGES IN THE WORK

12.1 CHANGE ORDERS

12.1.1 The Owner, without invalidating the Contract, may order Changes in the Work within the general scope of the Contract consisting of additions, deletions or other revisions, the Contract Sum and the Contract Time being adjusted accordingly. All such Changes in the Work shall be authorized by Change Order, and shall be executed under the applicable conditions of the Contract Documents.

12.1.2 A Change Order is a written order to the Contractor signed by the Owner and the Architect, issued after the execution of the Contract, authorizing a Change in the Work or an adjustment in the Contract Sum or the Contract Time. Alternatively, the Change Order may be signed by the Architect alone, provided he has written authority from the Owner for such procedure and that a copy of such written authority is furnished to the Contractor upon request. A Change Order may also be signed by the Contractor if he agrees to the adjustment in the Contract Sum or the Contract Time. The Contract Sum and the Contract Time may be changed only by Change Order.

12.1.3 The cost or credit to the Owner resulting from a Change in the Work shall be determined in one or more of the following ways:

.1 by mutual acceptance of a lump sum properly itemized;

.2 by unit prices stated in the Contract Documents or subsequently agreed upon; or

.3 by cost and a mutually acceptable fixed or percentage fee.

12.1.4 If none of the methods set forth in Subparagraph 12.1.3 is agreed upon, the Contractor, provided he receives a Change Order, shall promptly proceed with the Work involved. The cost of such Work shall then be determined by the Architect on the basis of the Contractor's reasonable expenditures and savings, including, in the case of an increase in the Contract Sum, a reasonable allowance for overhead and profit. In such case, and also under Clause 12.1.3.3 above, the Contractor shall keep and present, in such form as the Architect may prescribe, an itemized accounting together with appropriate supporting data. Pending final determination of cost to the Owner, payments on account shall be made on the Architect's Certificate for Payment. The amount of credit to be allowed by the Contractor to the Owner for any deletion or change which results in a net decrease in cost will be the amount of the actual net decrease as confirmed by the Architect. When both additions and credits are involved in any one change, the allowance for overhead and profit shall be figured on the basis of net increase, if any.

12.1.5 If unit prices are stated in the Contract Documents or subsequently agreed upon, and if the quantities originally contemplated are so changed in a proposed Change Order that application of the agreed unit prices to the quantities of Work proposed will create a hardship on the Owner or the Contractor, the applicable unit prices shall be equitably adjusted to prevent such hardship.

12.1.6 Should concealed conditions encountered in the performance of the Work below the surface of the ground be at variance with the conditions indicated by the Contract Documents or should unknown physical conditions below the surface of the ground of an unusual nature,

---

AIA DOCUMENT A201 • GENERAL CONDITIONS OF THE CONTRACT FOR CONSTRUCTION • TWELFTH EDITION • APRIL 1970 ED.
AIA® • © 1970 • THE AMERICAN INSTITUTE OF ARCHITECTS, 1735 NEW YORK AVENUE, N.W., WASHINGTON, D.C. 20006

differing materially from those ordinarily encountered and generally recognized as inherent in work of the character provided for in this Contract, be encountered, the Contract Sum shall be equitably adjusted by Change Order upon claim by either party made within twenty days after the first observance of the conditions.

12.1.7 If the Contractor claims that additional cost is involved because of (1) any written interpretation issued pursuant to Subparagraph 1.2.5, (2) any order by the Owner to stop the Work pursuant to Paragraph 3.3 where the Contractor was not at fault, or (3) any written order for a minor change in the Work issued pursuant to Paragraph 12.3, the Contractor shall make such claim as provided in Paragraph 12.2.

12.2 CLAIMS FOR ADDITIONAL COST

12.2.1 If the Contractor wishes to make a claim for an increase in the Contract Sum, he shall give the Architect written notice thereof within twenty days after the occurrence of the event giving rise to such claim. This notice shall be given by the Contractor before proceeding to execute the Work, except in an emergency endangering life or property in which case the Contractor shall proceed in accordance with Subparagraph 10.3.1. No such claim shall be valid unless so made. If the Owner and the Contractor cannot agree on the amount of the adjustment in the Contract Sum, it shall be determined by the Architect. Any change in the Contract Sum resulting from such claim shall be authorized by Change Order.

12.3 MINOR CHANGES IN THE WORK

12.3.1 The Architect shall have authority to order minor changes in the Work not involving an adjustment in the Contract Sum or an extension of the Contract Time and not inconsistent with the intent of the Contract Documents. Such changes may be effected by Field Order or by other written order. Such changes shall be binding on the Owner and the Contractor.

12.4 FIELD ORDERS

12.4.1 The Architect may issue written Field Orders which interpret the Contract Documents in accordance with Subparagraph 1.2.5 or which order minor changes in the Work in accordance with Paragraph 12.3 without change in Contract Sum or Contract Time. The Contractor shall carry out such Field Orders promptly.

ARTICLE 13

UNCOVERING AND CORRECTION OF WORK

13.1 UNCOVERING OF WORK

13.1.1 If any Work should be covered contrary to the request of the Architect, it must, if required by the Architect, be uncovered for his observation and replaced, at the Contractor's expense.

13.1.2 If any other Work has been covered which the Architect has not specifically requested to observe prior to being covered, the Architect may request to see such Work and it shall be uncovered by the Contractor. If such Work be found in accordance with the Contract Documents, the cost of uncovering and replacement

shall, by appropriate Change Order, be charged to the Owner. If such Work be found not in accordance with the Contract Documents, the Contractor shall pay such costs unless it be found that this condition was caused by a separate contractor employed as provided in Article 6, and in that event the Owner shall be responsible for the payment of such costs.

13.2 CORRECTION OF WORK

13.2.1 The Contractor shall promptly correct all Work rejected by the Architect as defective or as failing to conform to the Contract Documents whether observed before or after Substantial Completion and whether or not fabricated, installed or completed. The Contractor shall bear all cost of correcting such rejected Work, including the cost of the Architect's additional services thereby made necessary.

13.2.2 If, within one year after the Date of Substantial Completion or within such longer period of time as may be prescribed by law or by the terms of any applicable special guarantee required by the Contract Documents, any of the Work is found to be defective or not in accordance with the Contract Documents, the Contractor shall correct it promptly after receipt of a written notice from the Owner to do so unless the Owner has previously given the Contractor a written acceptance of such condition. The Owner shall give such notice promptly after discovery of the condition.

13.2.3 All such defective or non-conforming Work under Subparagraphs 13.2.1 and 13.2.2 shall be removed from the site if necessary, and the Work shall be corrected to comply with the Contract Documents without cost to the Owner.

13.2.4 The Contractor shall bear the cost of making good all work of separate contractors destroyed or damaged by such removal or correction.

13.2.5 If the Contractor does not remove such defective or non-conforming Work within a reasonable time fixed by written notice from the Architect, the Owner may remove it and may store the materials or equipment at the expense of the Contractor. If the Contractor does not pay the cost of such removal and storage within ten days thereafter, the Owner may upon ten additional days' written notice sell such Work at auction or at private sale and shall account for the net proceeds thereof, after deducting all the costs that should have been borne by the Contractor including compensation for additional architectural services. If such proceeds of sale do not cover all costs which the Contractor should have borne, the difference shall be charged to the Contractor and an appropriate Change Order shall be issued. If the payments then or thereafter due the Contractor are not sufficient to cover such amount, the Contractor shall pay the difference to the Owner.

13.2.6 If the Contractor fails to correct such defective or non-conforming Work, the Owner may correct it in accordance with Paragraph 3.4.

**13.3 ACCEPTANCE OF DEFECTIVE
OR NON-CONFORMING WORK**

13.3.1 If the Owner prefers to accept defective or non-conforming Work, he may do so instead of requiring its

AIA DOCUMENT A201 • GENERAL CONDITIONS OF THE CONTRACT FOR CONSTRUCTION|• TWELFTH EDITION • APRIL 1970 ED.
AIA® • © 1970 • THE AMERICAN INSTITUTE OF ARCHITECTS, 1735 NEW YORK AVENUE, N.W., WASHINGTON, D.C. 20006

removal and correction, in which case a Change Order will be issued to reflect an appropriate reduction in the Contract Sum, or, if the amount is determined after final payment, it shall be paid by the Contractor.

ARTICLE 14

TERMINATION OF THE CONTRACT

14.1 TERMINATION BY THE CONTRACTOR

14.1.1 If the Work is stopped for a period of thirty days under an order of any court or other public authority having jurisdiction, or as a result of an act of government, such as a declaration of a national emergency making materials unavailable, through no act or fault of the Contractor or a Subcontractor or their agents or employees or any other persons performing any of the Work under a contract with the Contractor, or if the Work should be stopped for a period of thirty days by the Contractor for the Architect's failure to issue a Certificate for Payment as provided in Paragraph 9.6 or for the Owner's failure to make payment thereon as provided in Paragraph 9.6, then the Contractor may, upon seven days' written notice to the Owner and the Architect, terminate the Contract and recover from the Owner payment for all Work executed and for any proven loss sustained upon any materials, equipment, tools, construction equipment and machinery, including reasonable profit and damages.

14.2 TERMINATION BY THE OWNER

14.2.1 If the Contractor is adjudged a bankrupt, or if he makes a general assignment for the benefit of his creditors, or if a receiver is appointed on account of his insolvency, or if he persistently or repeatedly refuses or fails, except in cases for which extension of time is provided, to supply enough properly skilled workmen or proper materials, or if he fails to make prompt payment to Subcontractors or for materials or labor, or persistently disregards laws, ordinances, rules, regulations or orders of any public authority having jurisdiction, or otherwise is guilty of a substantial violation of a provision of the Contract Documents, then the Owner, upon certification by the Architect that sufficient cause exists to justify such action, may, without prejudice to any right or remedy and after giving the Contractor and his surety, if any, seven days' written notice, terminate the employment of the Contractor and take possession of the site and of all materials, equipment, tools, construction equipment and machinery thereon owned by the Contractor and may finish the Work by whatever method he may deem expedient. In such case the Contractor shall not be entitled to receive any further payment until the Work is finished.

14.2.2 If the unpaid balance of the Contract Sum exceeds the costs of finishing the Work, including compensation for the Architect's additional services, such excess shall be paid to the Contractor. If such costs exceed such unpaid balance, the Contractor shall pay the difference to the Owner. The costs incurred by the Owner as herein provided shall be certified by the Architect.

AIA DOCUMENT A201 • GENERAL CONDITIONS OF THE CONTRACT FOR CONSTRUCTION • TWELFTH EDITION • APRIL 1970 ED.
AIA® • © 1970 • THE AMERICAN INSTITUTE OF ARCHITECTS, 1735 NEW YORK AVENUE, N.W., WASHINGTON, D.C. 20006

NSPE Standard General Conditions of the Construction Contract

STANDARD
GENERAL CONDITIONS
OF THE
CONSTRUCTION CONTRACT

PROFESSIONAL ENGINEERS IN PRIVATE PRACTICE

a practice division of the

NATIONAL SOCIETY OF PROFESSIONAL ENGINEERS

These General Conditions have been prepared for use with the NSPE Owner-Contractor Agreement (Document 1910-8-A-1 or 1910-8-A-2, 1974 edition) and with the NSPE Instructions to Bidders (Document 1910-12, 1974 edition). Their provisions are interrelated and a change in one may necessitate a change in the others.

NSPE 1910-8 (1974 Edition)

TABLE OF CONTENTS OF GENERAL CONDITIONS

3

INDEX TO GENERAL CONDITIONS

4

5

6

7

GENERAL CONDITIONS

ARTICLE 1—DEFINITIONS

Wherever used in these General Conditions or in the other Contract Documents, the following terms have the meanings indicated which are applicable to both the singular and plural thereof:

Agreement—The written agreement between OWNER and CONTRACTOR covering the Work to be performed; other Contract Documents are attached to the Agreement.

Application for Payment—The form furnished by ENGINEER which is to be used by CONTRACTOR in requesting progress payments and which is to include the schedule of values required by paragraph 14.1 and an affidavit of CONTRACTOR that progress payments theretofore received on account of the Work have been applied by CONTRACTOR to discharge in full all of CONTRACTOR's obligations reflected in prior Applications for Payment.

Bid—The offer or proposal of the Bidder submitted on the prescribed form setting forth the prices for the Work to be performed.

Bidder—Any person, firm or corporation submitting a Bid for the Work.

Bonds—Bid, performance and payment bonds and other instruments of security, furnished by CONTRACTOR and his surety in accordance with the Contract Documents.

Change Order—A written order to CONTRACTOR signed by OWNER authorizing an addition, deletion or revision in the Work, or an adjustment in the Contract Price or the Contract Time issued after execution of the Agreement.

Contract Documents—The Agreement, Addenda (whether issued prior to the opening of Bids or the execution of the Agreement), Instructions to Bidders, CONTRACTOR's Bid, the Bonds, the Notice of Award, these General Conditions, the Supplementary Conditions, the Specifications, Drawings and Modifications.

Contract Price—The total moneys payable to CONTRACTOR under the Contract Documents.

Contract Time—The number of days stated in the Agreement for the completion of the Work, computed as provided in paragraph 17.2.

CONTRACTOR—The person, firm or corporation with whom OWNER has executed the Agreement.

Day—A calendar day of twenty-four hours measured from midnight to the next midnight.

Drawings—The drawings which show the character and scope of the Work to be performed and which have been prepared or approved by ENGINEER and are referred to in the Contract Documents.

ENGINEER—The person, firm or corporation named as such in the Agreement.

Field Order—A written order issued by ENGINEER which clarifies or interprets the Contract Documents in accordance with paragraph 9.3 or orders minor changes in the Work in accordance with paragraph 10.2.

Modification—(a) A written amendment of the Contract Documents signed by both parties, (b) a Change Order, (c) a written clarification or interpretation issued by ENGINEER in accordance with paragraph 9.3 or (d) a written order for a minor change or alteration in the Work issued by ENGINEER pursuant to paragraph 10.2. A Modification may only be issued after execution of the Agreement.

Notice of Award—The written notice by OWNER to the apparent successful Bidder stating that upon compliance with the conditions precedent to be fulfilled by him within the time specified, OWNER will execute and deliver the Agreement to him.

Notice to Proceed—A written notice given by OWNER to CONTRACTOR (with a copy to ENGINEER) fixing the date on which the Contract Time will commence to run and on which CONTRACTOR shall start to perform his obligations under the Contract Documents.

OWNER—A public body or authority, corporation, association, partnership, or individual for whom the Work is to be performed.

Project—The entire construction to be performed as provided in the Contract Documents.

Resident Project Representative—The authorized representative of ENGINEER who is assigned to the Project site or any part thereof.

Shop Drawings—All drawings, diagrams, illustrations, brochures, schedules and other data which are prepared by CONTRACTOR, a Subcontractor, manufacturer, supplier or distributor and which illustrate the equipment, material or some portion of the Work.

Specifications—Those portions of the Contract Documents consisting of written technical descriptions of materials, equipment, construction systems, standards and workmanship as applied to the Work. The specifications are customarily organized in 16 divisions in accordance with the Uniform System for Construction Specifications endorsed by the Construction Specifications Institute. [*Note: the term "Technical Provisions" formerly described what is now referred to as the Specifications. For uniformity with the usage of other professional societies the term "Project Manual" is used to describe the volume formerly referred to as "The Specifications." The Project Manual contains documents concerning bidding requirements which in general govern relationships prior to the execution of the Agreement (such as the Invitation to Bid, Instructions to Bidders, Bid Bonds and Notice of Award) and the other portions of the Contract Documents.*]

Subcontractor—An individual, firm or corporation having a direct contract with CONTRACTOR or with any other Subcontractor for the performance of a part of the Work at the site.

8

Substantial Completion—The date as certified by ENGI-NEER when the construction of the Project or a specified part thereof is sufficiently completed, in accordance with the Contract Documents, so that the Project or specified part can be utilized for the purposes for which it was intended; or if there be no such certification, the date when final payment is due in accordance with paragraph 14.13.

Work—Any and all obligations, duties and responsibilities necessary to the successful completion of the Project assigned to or undertaken by CONTRACTOR under the Contract Documents, including all labor, materials, equipment and other incidentals, and the furnishing thereof.

ARTICLE 2—PRELIMINARY MATTERS

Execution of Agreement:

2.1. At least three counterparts of the Agreement and such other Contract Documents as practicable will be executed and delivered by CONTRACTOR to OWNER within fifteen days of the Notice of Award; and OWNER will execute and deliver one counterpart to CONTRAC-TOR within ten days of receipt of the executed Agreement from CONTRACTOR. ENGINEER will identify those portions of the Contract Documents not so signed and such identification will be binding on all parties. OWNER, CONTRACTOR and ENGINEER shall each receive an executed counterpart of the Contract Documents and additional conformed copies as required.

Delivery of Bonds:

2.2. When he delivers the executed Agreements to OWNER, CONTRACTOR shall also deliver to OWNER such Bonds as he may be required to furnish in accordance with paragraph 5.1.

Copies of Documents:

2.3. OWNER shall furnish to CONTRACTOR up to ten copies (unless otherwise provided in the Supplementary Conditions) of the Contract Documents as are reasonably necessary for the execution of the Work. Additional copies will be furnished, upon request, at the cost of reproduction.

Contractor's Pre-Start Representations:

2.4. CONTRACTOR represents that he has familiarized himself with, and assumes full responsibility for having familiarized himself with, the nature and extent of the Contract Documents, Work, locality, and with all local conditions and federal, state and local laws, ordinances, rules and regulations that may in any manner affect performance of the Work, and represents that he has correlated his study and observations with the requirements of the Contract Documents. CONTRACTOR also represents that he has studied all surveys and investigation reports of subsurface and latent physical conditions referred to in the General Requirements (Division 1) of the Specifications and made such additional surveys and investigations as he deems necessary for the performance of the Work at the Contract Price in accordance with the requirements of the Contract Documents and that he has correlated the results of all such data with the requirements of the Contract Documents.

Commencement of Contract Time; Notice to Proceed:

2.5. The Contract Time will commence to run on the thirtieth day after the day on which the executed Agreement is delivered by OWNER to CONTRACTOR; or, if a Notice to Proceed is given, on the day indicated in the Notice to Proceed; but in no event shall the Contract Time commence to run later than the ninetieth day after the day of Bid opening or the thirtieth day after the day on which OWNER delivers the executed Agreement to CONTRACTOR. A Notice to Proceed may be given at any time within thirty days after the day on which OWNER delivers the executed Agreement to CONTRAC-TOR.

Starting the Project:

2.6. CONTRACTOR shall start to perform his obligations under the Contract Documents on the date when the Contract Time commences to run. No Work shall be done at the site prior to the date on which the Contract Time commences to run.

Before Starting Construction:

2.7. Before undertaking each part of the Work, CON-TRACTOR shall carefully study and compare the Contract Documents and check and verify pertinent figures shown thereon and all applicable field measurements. He shall at once report in writing to ENGINEER any conflict, error or discrepancy which he may discover; however, he shall not be liable to OWNER or ENGINEER for his failure to discover any conflict, error or discrepancy in the Drawings or Specifications.

2.8. Within ten days after delivery of the executed Agreement by OWNER to CONTRACTOR, CONTRAC-TOR shall submit to ENGINEER for approval, an estimated progress schedule indicating the starting and completion dates of the various stages of the Work, and a preliminary schedule of Shop Drawing submissions.

2.9. Before starting the Work at the site, CONTRAC-TOR shall furnish OWNER and ENGINEER certificates of insurance as required by Article 5. Within twenty days after delivery of the executed Agreement by OWNER to CONTRACTOR, but before starting the Work at the site, a conference will be held to review the above schedules, to establish procedures for handling Shop Drawings and other submissions and for processing Applications for Payment, and to establish a working understanding between the parties as to the Project. Present at the conference will be OWNER or his representative, ENGINEER, Resident Project Representatives, CONTRACTOR and his Superintendent.

9

ARTICLE 3—CORRELATION, INTERPRETATION AND INTENT OF CONTRACT DOCUMENTS

3.1. It is the intent of the Specifications and Drawings to describe a complete Project to be constructed in accordance with the Contract Documents. The Contract Documents comprise the entire Agreement between OWNER and CONTRACTOR. They may be altered only by a Modification.

3.2. The Contract Documents are complementary; what is called for by one is as binding as if called for by all. If CONTRACTOR finds a conflict, error or discrepancy in the Contract Documents, he shall call it to ENGINEER's attention in writing at once and before proceeding with the Work affected thereby; however, he shall not be liable to OWNER or ENGINEER for his failure to discover any conflict, error or discrepancy in the Specifications or Drawings. In resolving such conflicts, errors and discrepancies, the documents shall be given precedence in the following order: Agreement, Modifications, Addenda, Supplementary Conditions, Instructions to Bidders, General Conditions, Specifications and Drawings. Figure dimensions on Drawings shall govern over scale dimensions, and detailed Drawings shall govern over general Drawings. Any Work that may reasonably be inferred from the Specifications or Drawings as being required to produce the intended result shall be supplied whether or not it is specifically called for. Work, materials or equipment described in words which so applied have a well-known technical or trade meaning shall be deemed to refer to such recognized standards.

ARTICLE 4—AVAILABILITY OF LANDS; PHYSICAL CONDITIONS; REFERENCE POINTS

Availability of Lands:

4.1. OWNER shall furnish, as indicated in the Contract Documents and not later than the date when needed by CONTRACTOR, the lands upon which the Work is to be done, rights-of-way for access thereto, and such other lands which are designated for the use of CONTRACTOR. Easements for permanent structures or permanent changes in existing facilities will be obtained and paid for by OWNER, unless otherwise specified in the Contract Documents. If CONTRACTOR believes that any delay in OWNER's furnishing these lands or easements entitles him to an extension of the Contract Time, he may make a claim therefor as provided in Article 12. CONTRACTOR shall provide for all additional lands and access thereto that may be required for temporary construction facilities or storage of materials and equipment.

Physical Conditions—Surveys and Reports:

4.2. Reference is made to the General Requirements (Division 1) of the Specifications for identification of those surveys and investigation reports of subsurface and latent physical conditions at the Project site or otherwise affecting performance of the Work which have been relied upon by ENGINEER in preparation of the Drawings and Specifications.

Unforeseen Physical Conditions:

4.3. CONTRACTOR shall promptly notify OWNER and ENGINEER in writing of any subsurface or latent physical conditions at the site differing materially from those indicated in the Contract Documents. ENGINEER will promptly investigate those conditions and advise OWNER in writing if further surveys or subsurface tests are necessary. Promptly thereafter, OWNER shall obtain the necessary additional surveys and tests and furnish copies to ENGINEER and CONTRACTOR. If ENGINEER finds that the results of such surveys or tests indicate that there are subsurface or latent physical conditions which differ materially from those intended in the Contract Documents, and which could not reasonably have been anticipated by CONTRACTOR, a Change Order shall be issued incorporating the necessary revisions.

Reference Points:

4.4. OWNER shall provide engineering surveys for construction to establish reference points which in his judgment are necessary to enable CONTRACTOR to proceed with the Work. CONTRACTOR shall be responsible for surveying and laying out the Work (unless otherwise provided in the Supplementary Conditions), and shall protect and preserve the established reference points and shall make no changes or relocations without the prior written approval of OWNER. He shall report to ENGINEER whenever any reference point is lost or destroyed or requires relocation because of necessary changes in grades or locations. CONTRACTOR shall replace and accurately relocate all reference points so lost, destroyed or moved.

ARTICLE 5—BONDS AND INSURANCE

Performance, Payment and Other Bonds:

5.1. CONTRACTOR shall furnish performance and payment Bonds as security for the faithful performance and payment of all his obligations under the Contract Documents. These Bonds shall be in amounts at least equal to the Contract Price, and (except as otherwise provided in the Supplementary Conditions) in such form and with such sureties as are licensed to conduct business in the state where the Project is located and are named in the current list of "Surety Companies Acceptable on Federal Bonds" as published in the Federal Register by the Audit Staff Bureau of Accounts, U.S. Treasury Department.

5.2. If the surety on any Bond furnished by CONTRACTOR is declared a bankrupt or becomes insolvent or its right to do business is terminated in any state where any part of the Project is located is revoked. CONTRACTOR shall within five days thereafter substitute another Bond and surety, both of which shall be acceptable to OWNER.

10

Contractor's Liability Insurance:

5.3.   CONTRACTOR shall purchase and maintain such insurance as will protect him from claims under workmen's compensation laws, disability benefit laws or other similar employee benefit laws; from claims for damages because of bodily injury, occupational sickness or disease, or death of his employees, and claims insured by usual personal injury liability coverage; from claims for damages because of bodily injury, sickness or disease, or death of any person other than his employees including claims insured by usual personal injury liability coverage; and from claims for injury to or destruction of tangible property, including loss of use resulting therefrom—any or all of which may arise out of or result from CONTRACTOR's operations under the Contract Documents, whether such operations be by himself or by any Subcontractor or anyone directly or indirectly employed by any of them or for whose acts any of them may be legally liable. This insurance shall include the specific coverages and be written for not less than any limits of liability and maximum deductibles specified in the Supplementary Conditions or General Requirements (Division 1) or required by law, whichever is greater, shall include contractual liability insurance and shall include OWNER and ENGINEER as additional insured parties. Before starting the Work, CONTRACTOR shall file with OWNER and ENGINEER certificates of such insurance, acceptable to OWNER; these certificates shall contain a provision that the coverage afforded under the policies will not be cancelled or materially changed until at least fifteen days' prior written notice has been given to OWNER and ENGINEER.

Owner's Liability Insurance:

5.4.   OWNER shall be responsible for purchasing and maintaining his own liability insurance and, at his option, may purchase and maintain such insurance as will protect him against claims which may arise from operations under the Contract Documents.

Property Insurance:

5.5.   Unless otherwise provided, OWNER shall purchase and maintain property insurance upon the Project to the full insurable value hereof. This insurance shall include the interests of OWNER, CONTRACTOR and Subcontractors in the Work, shall insure against the perils of Fire, Extended Coverage, Vandalism and Malicious Mischief and such other perils as may be specified in the Supplementary Conditions or General Requirements (Division 1), and shall include damages, losses and expenses arising out of or resulting from any insured loss or incurred in the repair or replacement of any insured property (including fees and charges of engineers, architects, attorneys and other professionals).

5.6.   OWNER shall purchase and maintain such steam boiler and machinery insurance as may be required by the Supplementary Conditions or by law. This insurance shall include the interests of OWNER, CONTRACTOR and Subcontractors in the Work.

5.7.   Any insured loss under the policies of insurance required by paragraphs 5.5 and 5.6 is to be adjusted with OWNER and made payable to OWNER as trustee for the insureds, as their interests may appear, subject to the requirements of any applicable mortgage clause and of paragraph 5.11.

5.8.   OWNER shall file a copy of all policies with CONTRACTOR before an exposure to loss may occur. If OWNER does not intend to purchase such insurance, he shall inform CONTRACTOR in writing prior to commencement of the Work. CONTRACTOR may then effect insurance which will protect the interests of himself and his Subcontractors in the Work, and by appropriate Change Order the cost thereof shall be charged to OWNER. If CONTRACTOR is damaged by failure of OWNER to purchase or maintain such insurance and so to notify CONTRACTOR, then OWNER shall bear reasonable costs properly attributable thereto.

5.9.   If CONTRACTOR requests in writing that other special insurance be included in the property insurance policy, OWNER shall, if possible, include such insurance, and the cost thereof shall be charged to CONTRACTOR by appropriate Change Order.

5.10.   OWNER and CONTRACTOR waive all rights against each other for damages caused by fire or other perils to the extent covered by insurance provided under paragraphs 5.5 through 5.11, inclusive, except such rights as they may have to the proceeds of such insurance held by OWNER as trustee. CONTRACTOR shall require similar waivers by Subcontractors in accordance with paragraph 6.12.

5.11.   OWNER as trustee shall have power to adjust and settle any loss with the insurers unless one of the parties in interest shall object in writing within five days after the occurrence of loss to OWNER's exercise of this power, and if such objection be made, arbitrators shall be chosen as provided in Article 16. OWNER as trustee shall, in that case, make settlement with the insurers in accordance with the directions of such arbitrators. If distribution of the insurance proceeds by arbitration is required, the arbitrators will direct such distribution.

Additional Bonds and Insurance:

5.12.   Prior to delivery of the executed Agreement by OWNER to CONTRACTOR, OWNER may require CONTRACTOR to furnish such other Bonds and such additional insurance, in such form and with such sureties as OWNER may require. If such other Bonds or such other insurance are specified by written instructions given prior to opening of Bids, the premiums shall be paid by CONTRACTOR; if subsequent thereto, they shall be paid by OWNER (except as otherwise provided in paragraph 6.7).

11

ARTICLE 6—CONTRACTOR'S RESPONSIBILITIES

Supervision and Superintendence:

6.1. CONTRACTOR shall supervise and direct the Work efficiently and with his best skill and attention. He shall be solely responsible for the means, methods, techniques, sequences and procedures of construction, but he shall not be solely responsible for the negligence of others in the design or selection of a specific means, method, technique, sequence or procedure of construction which is indicated in and required by the Contract Documents. CONTRACTOR shall be responsible to see that the finished Work complies accurately with the Contract Documents.

6.2. CONTRACTOR shall keep on the Work at all times during its progress a competent resident superintendent, who shall not be replaced without written notice to OWNER and ENGINEER except under extraordinary circumstances. The superintendent will be CONTRACTOR's representative at the site and shall have authority to act on behalf of CONTRACTOR. All communications given to the superintendent shall be as binding as if given to CONTRACTOR.

Labor, Materials and Equipment:

6.3. CONTRACTOR shall provide competent, suitably qualified personnel to survey and lay out the Work and perform construction as required by the Contract Documents. He shall at all times maintain good discipline and order at the site.

6.4. CONTRACTOR shall furnish all materials, equipment, labor, transportation, construction equipment and machinery, tools, appliances, fuel, power, light, heat, telephone, water and sanitary facilities and all other facilities and incidentals necessary for the execution, testing, initial operation and completion of the Work.

6.5. All materials and equipment shall be new, except as otherwise provided in the Contract Documents. If required by ENGINEER, CONTRACTOR shall furnish satisfactory evidence as to the kind and quality of materials and equipment.

6.6. All materials and equipment shall be applied, installed, connected, erected, used, cleaned and conditioned in accordance with the instructions of the applicable manufacturer, fabricator or processors, except as otherwise provided in the Contract Documents.

Substitute Materials or Equipment:

6.7. If the General Requirements (Division 1 of the Specifications), law, ordinance or applicable rules or regulations permit CONTRACTOR to furnish or use a substitute that is equal to any material or equipment specified, and if CONTRACTOR wishes to furnish or use a proposed substitute, he shall, prior to the conference called for by paragraph 2.9 (unless another time is provided in the General Requirements), make written application to ENGINEER for approval of such a substitute certifying in writ-

ing that the proposed substitute will perform adequately the functions called for by the general design, be similar and of equal substance to that specified and be suited to the same use and capable of performing the same function as that specified; stating whether or not its incorporation in or use in connection with the Project is subject to the payment of any license fee or royalty; and identifying all variations of the proposed substitute from that specified and indicating available maintenance service. No substitute shall be ordered or installed without the written approval of ENGINEER who will be the judge of equality and may require CONTRACTOR to furnish such other data about the proposed substitute as he considers pertinent. No substitute shall be ordered or installed without such performance guarantee and bonds as OWNER may require which shall be furnished at CONTRACTOR's expense.

Concerning Subcontractors:

6.8. CONTRACTOR shall not employ any Subcontractor or other person or organization (including those who are to furnish the principal items of materials or equipment), whether initially or as a substitute, against whom OWNER or ENGINEER may have reasonable objection. A Subcontractor or other person or organization identified in writing to OWNER and ENGINEER by CONTRACTOR prior to the Notice of Award and not objected to in writing by OWNER or ENGINEER prior to the Notice of Award will be deemed acceptable to OWNER and ENGINEER. Acceptance of any Subcontractor, other person or organization by OWNER or ENGINEER shall not constitute a waiver of any right of OWNER or ENGINEER to reject defective Work or Work not in conformance with the Contract Documents. If OWNER or ENGINEER after due investigation has reasonable objection to any Subcontractor, other person or organization proposed by CONTRACTOR after the Notice of Award, CONTRACTOR shall submit an acceptable substitute and the Contract Price shall be increased or decreased by the difference in cost occasioned by such substitution, and an appropriate Change Order shall be issued. CONTRACTOR shall not be required to employ any Subcontractor, other person or organization against whom he has reasonable objection. CONTRACTOR shall not without the consent of OWNER and ENGINEER make any substitution for any Contractor, other person or organization who has been accepted by OWNER and ENGINEER unless ENGINEER determines that there is good cause for doing so.

6.9. CONTRACTOR shall be fully responsible for all acts and omissions of his Subcontractors and of persons and organizations directly or indirectly employed by them and of persons and organizations for whose acts any of them may be liable to the same extent that he is responsible for the acts and omissions of persons directly employed by him. Nothing in the Contract Documents shall create any contractual relationship between OWNER or ENGINEER and any Subcontractor or other person or organization having a direct contract with CONTRACTOR, nor shall it create any obligation on the part of

12

OWNER or ENGINEER to pay or to see to the payment of any moneys due any Subcontractor or other person or organization, except as may otherwise be required by law. OWNER or ENGINEER may furnish to any Subcontractor or other person or organization, to the extent practicable, evidence of amounts paid to CONTRACTOR on account of specific Work done in accordance with the schedule of values.

6.10. The divisions and sections of the Specifications and the identifications of any Drawings shall not control CONTRACTOR in dividing the Work among Subcontractors or delineating the Work to be performed by any specific trade.

6.11. CONTRACTOR agrees to bind specifically every Subcontractor to the applicable terms and conditions of the Contract Documents for the benefit of OWNER.

6.12. All Work performed for CONTRACTOR by a Subcontractor shall be pursuant to an appropriate agreement between CONTRACTOR and the Subcontractor which shall contain provisions that waive all rights the contracting parties may have against one another for damages caused by fire or other perils covered by insurance provided in accordance with paragraphs 5.5 through 5.11, inclusive, except such rights as they may have to the proceeds of such insurance held by OWNER as trustee under paragraph 5.9. CONTRACTOR shall pay each Subcontractor a just share of any insurance moneys received by CONTRACTOR under paragraphs 5.5 through 5.11, inclusive.

Patent Fees and Royalties:
6.13. CONTRACTOR shall pay all license fees and royalties and assume all costs incident to the use in the performance of the Work of any invention, design, process, product or device which is the subject of patent rights or copyrights held by others. If a particular invention, design, process, product or device is specified in the Contract Documents for use in the performance of the Work and if to the actual knowledge of OWNER or ENGINEER its use is subject to patent rights or copyrights calling for the payment of any license fee or royalty to others, the existence of such rights shall be disclosed by OWNER in the Contract Documents. CONTRACTOR shall indemnify and hold harmless OWNER and ENGINEER and anyone directly or indirectly employed by either of them from and against all claims, damages, losses and expenses (including attorneys' fees) arising out of any infringement of patent rights or copyrights incident to the use in the performance of the Work or resulting from the incorporation in the Work of any invention, design, process, product or device not specified in the Contract Documents, and shall defend all such claims in connection with any alleged infringement of such rights.

Permits:
6.14. CONTRACTOR shall obtain and pay for all construction permits and licenses and shall pay all govern-

mental charges and inspection fees necessary for the prosecution of the Work, which are applicable at the time of his Bid. OWNER shall assist CONTRACTOR, when necessary, in obtaining such permits and licenses. CONTRACTOR shall also pay all public utility charges.

Laws and Regulations:
6.15. CONTRACTOR shall give all notices and comply with all laws, ordinances, rules and regulations applicable to the Work. If CONTRACTOR observes that the Specifications or Drawings are at variance therewith, he shall give ENGINEER prompt written notice thereof, and any necessary changes shall be adjusted by an appropriate Modification. If CONTRACTOR performs any Work knowing it to be contrary to such laws, ordinances, rules and regulations, and without such notice to ENGINEER, he shall bear all costs arising therefrom; however, it shall not be his primary responsibility to make certain that the Specifications and Drawings are in accordance with such laws, ordinances, rules and regulations.

Taxes:
6.16. CONTRACTOR shall pay all sales, consumer, use and other similar taxes required to be paid by him in accordance with the law of the place where the Work is to be performed.

Use of Premises:
6.17. CONTRACTOR shall confine his equipment, the storage of materials and equipment and the operations of his workmen to areas permitted by law, ordinances, permits, or the requirements of the Contract Documents, and shall not unreasonably encumber the premises with materials or equipment.

6.18. CONTRACTOR shall not load nor permit any part of any structure to be loaded with weights that will endanger the structure, nor shall he subject any part of the Work to stresses or pressures that will endanger it.

Record Drawings:
6.19. CONTRACTOR shall keep one record copy of all Specifications, Drawings, Addenda, Modifications, and Shop Drawings at the site in good order and annotated to show all changes made during the construction process. These shall be available to ENGINEER and shall be delivered to him for OWNER upon completion of the Project. [*Note: Further provisions in respect of such record drawings may be included in the General Requirements (Division 1).*]

Safety and Protection:
6.20. CONTRACTOR shall be responsible for initiating, maintaining and supervising all safety precautions and programs in connection with the Work. He shall take all necessary precautions for the safety of, and shall provide the necessary protection to prevent damage, injury or loss to:

    6.20.1. all employees on the Work and other persons who may be affected thereby,

13

6.20.2. all the Work and all materials or equipment to be incorporated therein, whether in storage on or off the site, and

6.20.3. other property at the site or adjacent thereto, including trees, shrubs, lawns, walks, pavements, roadways, structures and utilities not designated for removal, relocation or replacement in the course of construction.

CONTRACTOR shall comply with all applicable laws, ordinances, rules, regulations and orders of any public body having jurisdiction for the safety of persons or property or to protect them from damage, injury or loss. He shall erect and maintain, as required by the conditions and progress of the Work, all necessary safeguards for its safety and protection. He shall notify owners of adjacent utilities when prosecution of the Work may affect them. All damage, injury or loss to any property referred to in paragraph 6.20.2 or 6.20.3 caused, directly or indirectly, in whole or in part, by CONTRACTOR, any Subcontractor or anyone directly or indirectly employed by any of them or anyone for whose acts any of them may be liable, shall be remedied by CONTRACTOR: except damage or loss attributable to the fault of Drawings or Specifications or to the acts or omissions of OWNER or ENGINEER or anyone employed by either of them or anyone for whose acts either of them may be liable, and not attributable, directly or indirectly, in whole or in part, to the fault or negligence of CONTRACTOR. CONTRACTOR's duties and responsibilities for the safety and protection of the Work shall continue until such time as all the Work is completed and ENGINEER has issued a notice to OWNER and CONTRACTOR in accordance with paragraph 14.13 that Work is acceptable.

6.21. CONTRACTOR shall designate a responsible member of his organization at the site whose duty shall be the prevention of accidents. This person shall be CONTRACTOR's superintendent unless otherwise designated in writing by CONTRACTOR to OWNER.

Emergencies:

6.22. In emergencies affecting the safety of persons or the Work or property at the site or adjacent thereto, CONTRACTOR, without special instruction or authorization from ENGINEER or OWNER, is obligated to act, at his discretion, to prevent threatened damage, injury or loss. He shall give ENGINEER prompt written notice of any significant changes in the Work or deviations from the Contract Documents caused thereby, and a Change Order shall thereupon be issued covering the changes and deviations involved. If CONTRACTOR believes that additional work done by him in an emergency which arose from causes beyond his control entitles him to an increase in the Contract Price or an extension of the Contract Time, he may make a claim therefor as provided in Articles 11 and 12.

Shop Drawings and Samples:

6.23. After checking and verifying all field measurements, CONTRACTOR shall submit to ENGINEER for approval, in accordance with the accepted schedule of Shop Drawing submissions (see paragraph 2.8) five copies (or at ENGINEER's option, one reproducible copy) of all Shop Drawings, which shall have been checked by and stamped with the approval of CONTRACTOR and identified as ENGINEER may require. The data shown on the Shop Drawings will be complete with respect to dimensions, design criteria, materials of construction and the like to enable ENGINEER to review the information as required.

6.24. CONTRACTOR shall also submit to ENGINEER for approval with such promptness as to cause no delay in Work, all samples required by the Contract Documents. All samples will have been checked by and stamped with the approval of CONTRACTOR, identified clearly as to material, manufacturer, any pertinent catalog numbers and the use for which intended.

6.25. At the time of each submission, CONTRACTOR shall in writing call ENGINEER's attention to any deviations that the Shop Drawing or sample may have from the requirements of the Contract Documents.

6.26. ENGINEER will review and approve with reasonable promptness Shop Drawings and samples, but his review and approval shall be only for conformance with the design concept of the Project and for compliance with the information given in the Contract Documents. The approval of a separate item as such will not indicate approval of the assembly in which the item functions. CONTRACTOR shall make any corrections required by ENGINEER and shall return the required number of corrected copies of Shop Drawings and resubmit new samples until approved. CONTRACTOR shall direct specific attention in writing or on resubmitted Shop Drawings to revisions other than the corrections called for by ENGINEER on previous submissions. CONTRACTOR's stamp of approval on any Shop Drawing or sample shall constitute a representation to OWNER and ENGINEER that CONTRACTOR has either determined and verified all quantities, dimensions, field construction criteria, materials, catalog numbers, and similar data or he assumes full responsibility for doing so, and that he has reviewed or coordinated each Shop Drawing or sample with the requirements of the Work and the Contract Documents.

6.27. Where a Shop Drawing or sample submission is required by the Specifications, no related Work shall be commenced until the submission has been approved by ENGINEER. A copy of each approved Shop Drawing and each approved sample shall be kept in good order by CONTRACTOR at the site and shall be available to ENGINEER.

6.28. ENGINEER's approval of Shop Drawings or samples shall not relieve CONTRACTOR from his responsibility for any deviations from the requirements of the Contract Documents unless CONTRACTOR has in writing called ENGINEER's attention to such deviation at the time of submission and ENGINEER has given written

14

approval to the specific deviation, nor shall any approval by ENGINEER relieve CONTRACTOR from responsibility for errors or omissions in the Shop Drawings.

[Note: Further provisions in respect to Shop Drawings and samples may be included in the General Requirements (Division 1).]

Cleaning:

6.29. CONTRACTOR shall keep the premises free from accumulations of waste materials, rubbish and other debris resulting from the Work, and at the completion of the Work he shall remove all waste materials, rubbish and debris from and about the premises as well as all tools, construction equipment and machinery, and surplus materials, and shall leave the site clean and ready for occupancy by OWNER. CONTRACTOR shall restore to their original condition those portions of the site not designated for alteration by the Contract Documents. *[Note: Further provisions in respect of cleaning may be included in the General Requirements (Division 1).]*

Indemnification:

6.30. CONTRACTOR shall indemnify and hold harmless OWNER and ENGINEER and their agents and employees from and against all claims, damages, losses and expenses including attorneys' fees arising out of or resulting from the performance of the Work, provided that any such claim, damage, loss or expense (a) is attributable to bodily injury, sickness, disease or death, or to injury to or destruction of tangible property (other than the Work itself) including the loss of use resulting therefrom and (b) is caused in whole or in part by any negligent act or omission of CONTRACTOR, any Subcontractor, anyone directly or indirectly employed by any of them or anyone for whose acts any of them may be liable, regardless of whether or not it is caused in part by a party indemnified hereunder.

6.31. In any and all claims against OWNER or ENGINEER or any of their agents or employees by any employee of CONTRACTOR, any Subcontractor, anyone directly or indirectly employed by any of them or anyone for whose acts any of them may be liable, the indemnification obligation under paragraph 6.30 shall not be limited in any way by any limitation on the amount or type of damages, compensation or benefits payable by or for CONTRACTOR or any Subcontractor under workmen's compensation acts, disability benefit acts or other employee benefit acts.

6.32. The obligations of CONTRACTOR under paragraph 6.30 shall not extend to the liability of ENGINEER, his agents or employees arising out of (a) the preparation or approval of maps, drawings, opinions, reports, surveys, Change Orders, designs or specifications or (b) the giving of or the failure to give directions or instructions by ENGINEER, his agents or employees provided such giving or failure to give is the primary cause of injury or damage.

ARTICLE 7—WORK BY OTHERS

7.1. OWNER may perform additional work related to the Project by himself, or he may let other direct contracts therefor which shall contain General Conditions similar to these. CONTRACTOR shall afford the other contractors who are parties to such direct contracts (or OWNER, if he is performing the additional work himself), reasonable opportunity for the introduction and storage of materials and equipment and the execution of work, and shall properly connect and coordinate his Work with theirs.

7.2. If any part of CONTRACTOR's Work depends for proper execution or results upon the work of any such other contractor (or OWNER), CONTRACTOR shall inspect and promptly report to ENGINEER in writing any defects or deficiencies in such work that render it unsuitable for such proper execution and results. His failure so to report shall constitute an acceptance of the other work as fit and proper for the relationship of his Work except as to defects and deficiencies which may appear in the other work after the execution of his Work.

7.3. CONTRACTOR shall do all cutting, fitting and patching of his Work that may be required to make its several parts come together properly and fit it to receive or be received by such other work. CONTRACTOR shall not endanger any work of others by cutting, excavating or otherwise altering their work and will only cut or alter their work with the written consent of ENGINEER and of the other contractors whose work will be affected.

7.4. If the performance of additional work by other contractors or OWNER is not noted in the Contract Documents prior to the execution of the contract, written notice thereof shall be given to CONTRACTOR prior to starting any such additional work. If CONTRACTOR believes that the performance of such additional work by OWNER or others involves him in additional expense or entitles him to an extension of the Contract Time, he may make a claim therefor as provided in Articles 11 and 12.

ARTICLE 8—OWNER'S RESPONSIBILITIES

8.1. OWNER shall issue all communications to CONTRACTOR through ENGINEER.

8.2. In case of termination of the employment of ENGINEER, OWNER shall appoint an engineer against whom CONTRACTOR makes no unreasonable objection, whose status under the Contract Documents shall be that of the former ENGINEER. Any dispute in connection with such appointment shall be subject to arbitration.

8.3. OWNER shall furnish the data required of him under the Contract Documents promptly and shall make payments to CONTRACTOR promptly after they are due as provided in paragraphs 14.4 and 14.13.

8.4. OWNER's duties in respect of providing lands and easements and providing engineering surveys to establish

15

reference points are set forth in paragraphs 4.1 and 4.4. Paragraph 4.2 refers to OWNER's identifying and making available to CONTRACTOR copies of surveys and investigation reports of subsurface and latent physical conditions at the site or otherwise affecting performance of the Work which have been relied upon by ENGINEER in preparing the Drawings and Specifications.

8.5. OWNER's responsibilities in respect of liability and property insurance are set forth in paragraph 5.4 and 5.5.

8.6. In addition to his rights to request changes in the Work in accordance with Article 10, OWNER (especially in certain instances as provided in paragraph 10.4) shall be obligated to execute Change Orders.

8.7. OWNER's responsibility in respect of certain inspections, tests and approvals is set forth in paragraph 13.2.

8.8. In connection with OWNER's right to stop Work or suspend Work, see paragraphs 13.8 and 15.1. Paragraph 15.2 deals with OWNER's right to terminate services of CONTRACTOR under certain circumstances.

ARTICLE 9—ENGINEER'S STATUS DURING CONSTRUCTION

Owner's Representative:

9.1. ENGINEER will be OWNER's representative during the construction period. The duties and responsibilities and the limitations of authority of ENGINEER as OWNER's representative during construction are set forth in Articles 1 through 17 of these General Conditions and shall not be extended without written consent of OWNER and ENGINEER.

Visits to Site:

9.2. ENGINEER will make periodic visits to the site to observe the progress and quality of the executed Work and to determine, in general, if the Work is proceeding in accordance with the Contract Documents. He will not be required to make exhaustive or continuous on-site inspections to check the quality or quantity of the Work. His efforts will be directed toward providing assurance for OWNER that the completed Project will conform to the requirements of the Contract Documents. On the basis of his on-site observations as an experienced and qualified design professional, he will keep OWNER informed of the progress of the Work and will endeavor to guard OWNER against defects and deficiencies in the Work of contractors.

Clarifications and Interpretations:

9.3. ENGINEER will issue with reasonable promptness such written clarifications or interpretations of the Contract Documents (in the form of Drawings or otherwise) as he may determine necessary, which shall be consistent with or reasonably inferable from the overall intent of the Contract Documents. If CONTRACTOR believes that a written clarification and interpretation entitles him to an increase in the Contract Price, he may make a claim therefor as provided in Article 11.

Rejecting Defective Work:

9.4. ENGINEER will have authority to disapprove or reject Work which is "defective" (which term is hereinafter used to describe Work that is unsatisfactory, faulty or defective, or does not conform to the requirements of the Contract Documents or does not meet the requirements of any inspection, test or approval referred to in paragraph 13.2 or has been damaged prior to approval of final payment). He will also have authority to require special inspection or testing of the Work as provided in paragraph 13.7, whether or not the Work is fabricated, installed or completed.

Shop Drawings, Change Orders and Payments:

9.5. In connection with ENGINEER's responsibility for Shop Drawings and samples, see paragraphs 6.23 through 6.28 inclusive.

9.6. In connection with ENGINEER's responsibility for Change Orders, see Articles 10, 11 and 12.

9.7. In connection with ENGINEER's responsibilities in respect of Applications for Payment, etc., see Article 14.

Resident Project Representatives:

9.8. If OWNER and ENGINEER agree, ENGINEER will furnish a Resident Project Representative and assistants to assist ENGINEER in carrying out his responsibilities at the site. The duties, responsibilities and limitations of authority of any such Resident Project Representative and assistants shall be as set forth in an exhibit to be incorporated in the Contract Documents.

Decisions on Disagreements:

9.9. ENGINEER will be the interpreter of the requirements of the Contract Documents and the judge of the performance thereunder. In his capacity as interpreter and judge he will exercise his best efforts to insure faithful performance by both OWNER and CONTRACTOR. He will not show partiality to either and will not be liable for the result of any interpretation or decision rendered in good faith. Claims, disputes and other matters relating to the execution and progress of the Work or the interpretation of or performance under the Contract Documents shall be referred to ENGINEER for decision; which he will render in writing within a reasonable time.

9.10. Either OWNER or CONTRACTOR may demand arbitration with respect to any such claim, dispute or other matter that has been referred to ENGINEER, except any which have been waived by the making or acceptance of final payment as provided in paragraph 14.16, such arbitration to be in accordance with Article 16. However, no demand for arbitration of any such claim, dispute or other matter shall be made until the earlier of (a) the date on which ENGINEER has rendered his decision or (b) the tenth day after the parties have pre-

16

sented their evidence to ENGINEER if he has not rendered his written decision before that date. No demand for arbitration shall be made later than thirty days after the date on which ENGINEER rendered his written decision in respect of the claim, dispute or other matter as to which arbitration is sought; and the failure to demand arbitration within said thirty days' period shall result in ENGINEER's decision being final and binding upon OWNER and CONTRACTOR. If ENGINEER renders a decision after arbitration proceedings have been initiated, such decision may be entered as evidence but shall not supersede the arbitration proceedings, except where the decision is acceptable to the parties concerned.

Limitations on ENGINEER's Responsibilities:

9.11. Neither ENGINEER's authority to act under this Article 9 or elsewhere in the Contract Documents nor any decision made by him in good faith either to exercise or not exercise such authority shall give rise to any duty or responsibility of ENGINEER to CONTRACTOR, any Subcontractor, any materialman, fabricator, supplier or any of their agents or employees or any other person performing any of the Work.

9.12. ENGINEER will not be responsible for CONTRACTOR's means, methods, techniques, sequences or procedures of construction, or the safety precautions and programs incident thereto, and he will not be responsible for CONTRACTOR's failure to perform the Work in accordance with the Contract Documents.

9.13. ENGINEER will not be responsible for the acts or omissions of CONTRACTOR, or any Subcontractors, or any of his or their agents or employees, or any other persons at the site or otherwise performing any of the Work.

ARTICLE 10—CHANGES IN THE WORK

10.1. Without invalidating the Agreement, OWNER may, at any time or from time to time, order additions, deletions or revisions in the Work; these will be authorized by Change Orders. Upon receipt of a Change Order, CONTRACTOR shall proceed with the Work involved. All such Work shall be executed under the applicable conditions of the Contract Documents. If any Change Order causes an increase or decrease in the Contract Price or an extension or shortening of the Contract Time, an equitable adjustment will be made as provided in Article 11 or Article 12 on the basis of a claim made by either party.

10.2. ENGINEER may. authorize minor changes or alterations in the Work not involving extra cost and not inconsistent with the overall intent of the Contract Documents. These may be accomplished by a Field Order. If CONTRACTOR believes that any minor change or alteration authorized by ENGINEER entitles him to an increase in the Contract Price, he may make a claim therefor as provided in Article 11.

10.3. Additional Work performed by CONTRACTOR without authorization of a Change Order will not entitle him to an increase in the Contract Price or an extension of the Contract Time, except in the case of an emergency as provided in paragraph 6.22 and except as provided in paragraphs 10.2 and 13.7.

10.4. OWNER shall execute appropriate Change Orders prepared by ENGINEER covering changes in the Work to be performed as provided in paragraph 4.3, and Work performed in an emergency as provided in paragraph 6.22 and any other claim of CONTRACTOR for a change in the Contract Time or the Contract Price which is approved by ENGINEER.

10.5. It is CONTRACTOR's responsibility to notify his Surety of any changes affecting the general scope of the Work or change in the Contract Price and the amount of the applicable Bonds shall be adjusted accordingly. CONTRACTOR shall furnish proof of such adjustment to OWNER.

ARTICLE 11—CHANGE OF CONTRACT PRICE

11.1. The Contract Price constitutes the total compensation payable to CONTRACTOR for performing the Work. All duties, responsibilities and obligations assigned to or undertaken by CONTRACTOR shall be at his expense without change in the Contract Price.

11.2. The Contract Price may only be changed by a Change Order. Any claim for an increase in the Contract Price shall be based on written notice delivered to OWNER and ENGINEER within fifteen days of the occurrence of the event giving rise to the claim. Notice of the amount of the claim with supporting data shall be delivered within forty-five days of such occurrence unless ENGINEER allows an additional period of time to ascertain accurate cost data. All claims for adjustments in the Contract Price shall be determined by ENGINEER if OWNER and CONTRACTOR cannot otherwise agree on the amount involved. Any change in the Contract Price resulting from any such claim shall be incorporated in a Change Order.

11.3. The value of any Work covered by a Change Order or of any claim for an increase or decrease in the Contract Price shall be determined in one of the following ways:

11.3.1. Where the Work involved is covered by unit prices contained in the Contract Documents, by application of unit prices to the quantities of the items involved.

11.3.2. By mutual acceptance of a lump sum.

11.3.3. On the basis of the Cost of the Work (determined as provided in paragraphs 11.4 and 11.5) plus a Contractor's Fee for overhead and profit (determined as provided in paragraph 11.6).

17

Cost of the Work:

11.4. The term Cost of the Work means the sum of all costs necessarily incurred and paid by the CONTRACTOR in the proper performance of the Work. Except as otherwise may be agreed to in writing by OWNER, such costs shall be in amounts no higher than those prevailing in the locality of the Project, shall include only the following items and shall not include any of the costs itemized in paragraph 11.5:

11.4.1. Payroll costs for employees in the direct employ of CONTRACTOR in the performance of the Work under schedules of job classifications agreed upon by OWNER and CONTRACTOR. Payroll costs for employees not employed full time on the Work shall be apportioned on the basis of their time spent on the Work. Payroll costs shall include, but not be limited to, salaries and wages plus the cost of fringe benefits which shall include social security contributions, unemployment, excise and payroll taxes, workmen's compensation, health and retirement benefits, bonuses, sick leave, vacation and holiday pay applicable thereto. Such employees shall include superintendents and foremen at the site. The expenses of performing work after regular working hours, on Sunday or legal holidays shall be included in the above to the extent authorized by OWNER.

11.4.2. Cost of all materials and equipment furnished and incorporated in the Work, including costs of transportation and storage thereof, and manufacturers' field services required in connection therewith. All cash discounts shall accrue to CONTRACTOR unless OWNER deposits funds with CONTRACTOR with which to make payments, in which case the cash discounts shall accrue to OWNER. All trade discounts, rebates and refunds, and all returns from sale of surplus materials and equipment shall accrue to OWNER. and CONTRACTOR shall make provisions so that they may be obtained.

11.4.3. Payments made by CONTRACTOR to the Subcontractors for Work performed by Subcontractors. If required by OWNER, CONTRACTOR shall obtain competitive bids from Subcontractors acceptable to him and shall deliver such bids to OWNER who will then determine with the advice of ENGINEER, which bids will be accepted. If a subcontract provides that the Subcontractor is to be paid on the basis of Cost of the Work Plus a Fee, the Cost of the Work shall be determined in accordance with paragraphs 11.4 and 11.5. All subcontracts shall be subject to the other provisions of the Contract Documents insofar as applicable.

11.4.4. Costs of special consultants (including, but not limited to, engineers, architects, testing laboratories, surveyors, lawyers and accountants) employed for services specifically related to the Work.

11.4.5. Supplemental costs including the following:

11.4.5.1. The proportion of necessary transportation, traveling and subsistence expenses of CONTRACTOR's employees incurred in discharge of duties connected with the Work.

11.4.5.2. Cost, including transportation and maintenance, of all materials, supplies, equipment, machinery, appliances, office and temporary facilities at the site and hand tools not owned by the workmen, which are consumed in the performance of the Work, and cost less market value of such items used but not consumed which remain the property of CONTRACTOR.

11.4.5.3. Rentals of all construction equipment and machinery and the parts thereof whether rented from CONTRACTOR or others in accordance with rental agreements approved by OWNER with the advice of ENGINEER, and the costs of transportation, loading, unloading, installation, dismantling and removal thereof—all in accordance with terms of said rental agreements. The rental of any such equipment, machinery or parts shall cease when the use thereof is no longer necessary for the Work.

11.4.5.4. Sales, use or similar taxes related to the Work, and for which CONTRACTOR is liable, imposed by any governmental authority.

11.4.5.5. Deposits lost for causes other than CONTRACTOR's negligence, royalty payments and fees for permits and licenses.

11.4.5.6. Losses, damages and expenses, not compensated by insurance or otherwise, sustained by CONTRACTOR in connection with the execution of, and to, the Work, provided they have resulted from causes other than the negligence of CONTRACTOR, any Subcontractor, or anyone directly or indirectly employed by any of them or for whose acts any of them may be liable. Such losses shall include settlements made with the written consent and approval of OWNER. No such losses, damages and expenses shall be included in the Cost of the Work for the purpose of determining Contractor's Fee. If, however, any such loss or damage requires reconstruction and CONTRACTOR is placed in charge thereof, he shall be paid for his services a fee proportionate to that stated in paragraph 11.6.2.

11.4.5.7. The cost of utilities, fuel and sanitary facilities at the site.

11.4.5.8. Minor expenses such as telegrams, long distance telephone calls, telephone service at the site, expressage and similar petty cash items in connection with the Work.

11.4.5.9. Cost of premiums for bonds and insurance which OWNER is required to pay in accordance with paragraph 5.12.

18

11.5. The term Cost of the Work shall not include any of the following:

11.5.1. Payroll costs and other compensation of CONTRACTOR's officers, executives, principals (of partnership and sole proprietorships), general managers, engineers, architects, estimators, lawyers, auditors, accountants, purchasing and contracting agents, expeditors, timekeepers, clerks and other personnel employed by CONTRACTOR whether at the site or in his principal or a branch office for general administration of the Work and not specifically included in the schedule referred to in subparagraph 11.4.1—all of which are to be considered administrative costs covered by the Contractor's Fee.

11.5.2. Expenses of CONTRACTOR's principal and branch offices other than his office at the site.

11.5.3. Any part of CONTRACTOR's capital expenses, including interest on CONTRACTOR's capital employed for the Work and charges against CONTRACTOR for delinquent payments.

11.5.4. Cost of premiums for all bonds and for all insurance policies whether or not CONTRACTOR is required by the Contract Documents to purchase and maintain the same (except as otherwise provided in subparagraph 11.4.5.9).

11.5.5. Costs due to the negligence of CONTRACTOR, any Subcontractor, or anyone directly or indirectly employed by any of them or for whose acts any of them may be liable, including but not limited to, the correction of defective work, disposal of materials or equipment wrongly supplied and making good any damage to property.

11.5.6. Other overhead or general expense costs of any kind and the costs of any item not specifically and expressly included in paragraph 11.4.

Contractor's Fee:

11.6. The Contractor's Fee which shall be allowed to CONTRACTOR for his overhead and profit shall be determined as follows:

11.6.1. a mutually acceptable fixed fee; or if none can be agreed upon,

11.6.2. a fee based on the following percentages of the various portions of the Cost of the Work:

11.6.2.1. for costs incurred under paragraphs 11.4.1 and 11.4.2, the Contractor's Fee shall be ten percent,

11.6.2.2. for costs incurred under paragraph 11.4.3, the Contractor's Fee shall be five percent; and if a subcontract is on the basis of Cost of the Work Plus a Fee, the maximum allowable to the Subcontractor as a fee for overhead and profit shall be ten percent, and

11.6.2.3. no fee shall be payable on the basis of costs itemized under paragraphs 11.4.4, 11.4.5 and 11.5.

11.7. The amount of credit to be allowed by CONTRACTOR to OWNER for any such change which results in a net decrease in cost, will be the amount of the actual net decrease. When both additions and credits are involved in any one change, the combined overhead and profit shall be figured on the basis of the net increase, if any.

11.8. Whenever the cost of any Work is to be determined pursuant to paragraphs 11.4. and 11.5, CONTRACTOR will submit in form prescribed by ENGINEER an itemized cost breakdown together with supporting data.

Cash Allowances:

11.9. It is understood that CONTRACTOR has included in the Contract Price all allowances so named in the Contract Documents and shall cause the Work so covered to be done by such materialmen, suppliers or Subcontractors and for such sums within the limit of the allowances as ENGINEER may approve. Upon final payment, the Contract Price shall be adjusted as required and an appropriate Change Order issued. CONTRACTOR agrees that the original Contract Price includes such sums as he deems proper for costs and profit on account of cash allowances. No demand for additional cost or profit in connection therewith will be allowed.

ARTICLE 12—CHANGE OF THE CONTRACT TIME

12.1. The Contract Time may only be changed by a Change Order. Any claim for an extension in the Contract Time shall be based on written notice delivered to OWNER and ENGINEER within fifteen days of the occurrence of the event giving rise to the claim. Notice of the extent of the claim with supporting data shall be delivered within forty-five days of such occurrence unless ENGINEER allows an additional period of time to ascertain more accurate data. All claims for adjustment in the Contract Time shall be determined by ENGINEER if OWNER and CONTRACTOR cannot otherwise agree. Any change in the Contract Time resulting from any such claim shall be incorporated in a Change Order.

12.2. The Contract Time will be extended in an amount equal to time lost due to delays beyond the control of CONTRACTOR if he makes a claim therefor as provided in paragraph 12.1. Such delays shall include, but not be restricted to, acts or neglect by any separate contractor employed by OWNER, fires, floods, labor disputes, epidemics, abnormal weather conditions, or acts of God.

12.3. All time limits stated in the Contract Documents are of the essence of the Agreement. The provisions of this Article 12 shall not exclude recovery for damages (including compensation for additional professional services) for delay by either party.

19 —

ARTICLE 13—WARRANTY AND GUARANTEE; TESTS AND INSPECTIONS; CORRECTION, REMOVAL OR ACCEPTANCE OF DEFECTIVE WORK

Warranty and Guarantee:

13.1. CONTRACTOR warrants and guarantees to OWNER and ENGINEER that all materials and equipment will be new unless otherwise specified and that all Work will be of good quality and free from faults or defects and in accordance with the requirements of the Contract Documents and of any inspections, tests or approvals referred to in paragraph 13.2. All unsatisfactory Work, all faulty or defective Work, and all Work not conforming to the requirements of the Contract Documents at the time of acceptance thereof or of such inspections, tests or approvals, shall be considered defective. Prompt notice of all defects shall be given to CONTRACTOR. All defective Work, whether or not in place, may be rejected, corrected or accepted as provided in this Article 13.

Tests and Inspections:

13.2. If the Contract Documents, laws, ordinances, rules, regulations or orders of any public authority having jurisdiction require any Work to specifically be inspected, tested, or approved by some public body, CONTRACTOR shall assume full responsibility therefor, pay all costs in connection therewith and furnish ENGINEER the required certificates of inspection, testing or approval. All other inspections, tests and approvals required by the Contract Documents shall be performed by organizations acceptable to OWNER and CONTRACTOR and the costs thereof shall be borne by OWNER unless otherwise specified.

13.3. CONTRACTOR shall give ENGINEER timely notice of readiness of the Work for all inspections, tests or approvals. If any such Work required so to be inspected, tested or approved is covered without written approval of ENGINEER, it must, if requested by ENGINEER, be uncovered for observation, and such uncovering shall be at CONTRACTOR's expense unless CONTRACTOR has given ENGINEER timely notice of his intention to cover such Work and ENGINEER has not acted with reasonable promptness in response to such notice.

13.4. Neither observations by ENGINEER nor inspections, tests or approvals by persons other than CONTRACTOR shall relieve CONTRACTOR from his obligations to perform the Work in accordance with the requirements of the Contract Documents.

Access to Work:

13.5. ENGINEER and his representatives and other representatives of OWNER will at reasonable times have access to the Work. CONTRACTOR shall provide proper and safe facilities for such access and observation of the Work and also for any inspection or testing thereof by others.

Uncovering Work:

13.6. If any Work is covered contrary to the written request of ENGINEER, it must, if requested by ENGINEER, be uncovered for his observation and replaced at CONTRACTOR's expense.

13.7. If any Work has been covered which ENGINEER has not specifically requested to observe prior to its being covered, or if ENGINEER considers it necessary or advisable that covered Work be inspected or tested by others, CONTRACTOR, at ENGINEER's request, shall uncover, expose or otherwise make available for observation, inspection or testing as ENGINEER may require, that portion of the Work in question, furnishing all necessary labor, material and equipment. If it is found that such Work is defective, CONTRACTOR shall bear all the expenses of such uncovering, exposure, observation, inspection and testing and of satisfactory reconstruction, including compensation for additional professional services, and an appropriate deductive Change Order shall be issued. If, however, such Work is not found to be defective, CONTRACTOR shall be allowed an increase in the Contract Price or an extension of the Contract Time, or both, directly attributable to such uncovering, exposure, observation, inspection, testing and reconstruction if he makes a claim therefor as provided in Articles 11 and 12.

Owner May Stop the Work:

13.8. If the Work is defective, or CONTRACTOR fails to supply sufficient skilled workmen or suitable materials or equipment, or if CONTRACTOR fails to make prompt payments to Subcontractors or for labor, materials or equipment, OWNER may order CONTRACTOR to stop the Work, or any portion thereof, until the cause for such order has been eliminated; however, this right of OWNER to stop the Work shall not give rise to any duty on the part of OWNER to exercise this right for the benefit of CONTRACTOR or any other party.

Correction or Removal of Defective Work:

13.9. If required by ENGINEER prior to approval of final payment, CONTRACTOR shall promptly, without cost to OWNER and as specified by ENGINEER, either correct any defective Work, whether or not fabricated, installed or completed, or, if the Work has been rejected by ENGINEER, remove it from the site and replace it with nondefective Work. If CONTRACTOR does not correct such defective Work or remove and replace such rejected Work within a reasonable time, all as specified in a written notice from ENGINEER, OWNER may have the deficiency corrected or the rejected Work removed and replaced. All direct or indirect costs of such correction or removal and replacement, including compensation for additional professional services, shall be paid by CONTRACTOR, and an appropriate deductive Change Order shall be issued. CONTRACTOR shall also bear the expenses of making good all Work of others destroyed or damaged by his correction, removal or replacement of his defective Work.

20

13.10. If, after the approval of final payment and prior to the expiration of one year after the date of Substantial Completion or such longer period of time as may be prescribed by law or by the terms of any applicable special guarantee required by the Contract Documents, any Work is found to be defective, CONTRACTOR shall promptly, without cost to OWNER and in accordance with OWNER's written instructions, either correct such defective Work, or, if it has been rejected by OWNER, remove it from the site and replace it with nondefective Work. If CONTRACTOR does not promptly comply with the terms of such instructions, OWNER may have the defective Work corrected or the rejected Work removed and replaced, and all direct and indirect costs of such removal and replacement, including compensation for additional professional services, shall be paid by CONTRACTOR.

Acceptance of Defective Work:

13.11. If, instead of requiring correction or removal and replacement of defective Work, OWNER (and, prior to approval of final payment, also ENGINEER) prefers to accept it, he may do so. In such case, if acceptance occurs prior to approval of final payment, a Change Order shall be issued incorporating the necessary revisions in the Contract Documents, including appropriate reduction in the Contract Price; or, if the acceptance occurs after approval of final payment, an appropriate amount shall be paid by CONTRACTOR to OWNER.

Neglected Work by Contractor:

13.12. If CONTRACTOR should fail to prosecute the Work in accordance with the Contract Documents, including any requirements of the progress schedule, OWNER, after seven days' written notice to CONTRACTOR may, without prejudice to any other remedy he may have, make good such deficiencies and the cost thereof (including compensation for additional professional services) shall be charged against CONTRACTOR if ENGINEER approves such action, in which case a Change Order shall be issued incorporating the necessary revisions in the Contract Documents including an appropriate reduction in the Contract Price. If the payments then or thereafter due CONTRACTOR are not sufficient to cover such amount, CONTRACTOR shall pay the difference to OWNER.

ARTICLE 14—PAYMENTS AND COMPLETION

Schedules:

14.1. At least ten days prior to submitting the first Application for a progress payment, CONTRACTOR shall submit a progress schedule, a final schedule of Shop Drawing submission and a schedule of values of the Work. These schedules shall be satisfactory in form and substance to ENGINEER. The schedule of values shall include quantities and unit prices aggregating the Contract Price, and shall subdivide the Work into component parts in sufficient detail to serve as the basis for progress payments during construction. Upon approval of the schedules of values by ENGINEER, it shall be incorporated into the form of Application for Payment furnished by ENGINEER.

Application for Progress Payment:

14.2. At least ten days before each progress payment falls due (but not more often than once a month), CONTRACTOR shall submit to ENGINEER for review an Application for Payment filled out and signed by CONTRACTOR covering the Work completed as of the date of the Application and accompanied by such data and schedules as ENGINEER may reasonably require. If payment is requested on the basis of materials and equipment not incorporated in the Work but delivered and suitably stored at the site or at another location agreed to in writing, the Application for Payment shall also be accompanied by such data, satisfactory to OWNER, as will establish OWNER's title to the material and equipment and protect his interest therein, including applicable insurance. Each subsequent Application for Payment shall include an affidavit of CONTRACTOR stating that all previous progress payments received on account of the Work have been applied to discharge in full all of CONTRACTOR's obligations reflected in prior Applications for Payment.

Contractor's Warranty of Title:

14.3. CONTRACTOR warrants and guarantees that title to all Work, materials and equipment covered by any Application for Payment, whether incorporated in the Project or not, will pass to OWNER at the time of payment free and clear of all liens, claims, security interests and encumbrances (hereafter in these General Conditions referred to as "Liens").

Approval of Payments:

14.4. ENGINEER will, within ten days after receipt of each Application for Payment, either indicate in writing his approval of payment and present the Application to OWNER, or return the Application to CONTRACTOR indicating in writing his reasons for refusing to approve payment. In the latter case, CONTRACTOR may make the necessary corrections and resubmit the Application. OWNER shall, within ten days of presentation to him of an approved Application for Payment, pay CONTRACTOR the amount approved by ENGINEER.

14.5. ENGINEER's approval of any payment requested in an Application for Payment will constitute a representation by him to OWNER, based on ENGINEER's on-site observations of the Work in progress as an experienced and qualified design professional and on his review of the Application for Payment and the accompanying data and schedules that the Work has progressed to the point indicated; that, to the best of his knowledge, information and belief, the quality of the Work is in accordance with the Contract Documents (subject to an evaluation of the Work as a functioning Project upon Substantial Completion, to the results of any subsequent tests called for in the Contract Documents and any qualifications stated in his approval); and that CONTRACTOR is entitled to

21

payment of the amount approved. However, by approving any such payment ENGINEER will not thereby be deemed to have represented that he made exhaustive or continuous on-site inspections to check the quality or the quantity of the Work, or that he has reviewed the means, methods, techniques, sequences, and procedures of construction, or that he has made any examination to ascertain how or for what purpose CONTRACTOR has used the moneys paid or to be paid to him on account of the Contract Price, or that title to any Work, materials or equipment has passed to OWNER free and clear of any Liens.

14.6.   ENGINEER's approval of final payment will constitute an additional representation by him to OWNER that the conditions precedent to CONTRACTOR's being entitled to final payment as set forth in paragraph 14.13 have been fulfilled.

14.7.   ENGINEER may refuse to approve the whole or any part of any payment if, in his opinion, it would be incorrect to make such representations to OWNER. He may also refuse to approve any such payment, or, because of subsequently discovered evidence or the results of subsequent inspections or tests, nullify any such payment previously approved, to such extent as may be necessary in his opinion to protect OWNER from loss because:

14.7.1.   the Work is defective, or completed Work has been damaged requiring correction or replacement,

14.7.2.   claims or Liens have been filed or there is reasonable cause to believe such may be filed,

14.7.3.   the Contract Price has been reduced because of Modifications,

14.7.4.   OWNER has been required to correct defective Work or complete the Work in accordance with paragraph 13.11, or

14.7.5.   of unsatisfactory prosecution of the Work, including failure to furnish acceptable submittals or to clean up.

Substantial Completion:

14.8.   Prior to final payment, CONTRACTOR may, in writing to OWNER and ENGINEER, certify that the entire Project is substantially complete and request that ENGINEER issue a certificate of Substantial Completion. Within a reasonable time thereafter, OWNER, CONTRACTOR and ENGINEER shall make an inspection of the Project to determine the status of completion. If ENGINEER does not consider the Project substantially complete, he will notify CONTRACTOR in writing giving his reasons therefor. If ENGINEER considers the Project substantially complete, he will prepare and deliver to OWNER a tentative certificate of Substantial Completion which shall fix the date of Substantial Completion and the responsibilities between OWNER and CONTRACTOR for maintenance, heat and utilities. There shall be attached to the certificate a tentative list of items to be completed or corrected before final payment, and the certificate shall fix the

time within which such items shall be completed or corrected, said time to be within the Contract Time. OWNER shall have seven days after receipt of the tentative certificate during which he may make written objection to ENGINEER as to any provisions of the certificate or attached list. If, after considering such objections, ENGINEER concludes that the Project is not substantially complete, he will within fourteen days after submission of the tentative certificate to OWNER notify CONTRACTOR in writing, stating his reasons therefor. If, after consideration of OWNER's objections, ENGINEER considers the PROJECT substantially complete, he will within said fourteen days execute and deliver to OWNER and CONTRACTOR a definitive certificate of Substantial Completion (with a revised tentative list of items to be completed or corrected) reflecting such changes from the tentative certificate as he believes justified after consideration of any objections from OWNER.

14.9.   OWNER shall have the right to exclude CONTRACTOR from the Project after the date of Substantial Completion, but OWNER shall allow CONTRACTOR reasonable access to complete or correct items on the tentative list.

Partial Utilization:

14.10.   Prior to final payment, OWNER may request CONTRACTOR in writing to permit him to use a specified part of the Project which he believes he may use without significant interference with construction of the other parts of the Project. If CONTRACTOR agrees, he will certify to OWNER and ENGINEER that said part of the Project is substantially complete and request ENGINEER to issue a certificate of Substantial Completion for that part of the Project. Within a reasonable time thereafter OWNER, CONTRACTOR and ENGINEER shall make an inspection of that part of the Project to determine its status of completion. If ENGINEER does not consider that it is substantially complete, he will notify OWNER and CONTRACTOR in writing giving his reasons therefor. If ENGINEER considers that part of the Project to be substantially complete, he will execute and deliver to OWNER and CONTRACTOR a certificate to that effect, fixing the date of Substantial Completion as to that part of the Project, attaching thereto a tentative list of items to be completed or corrected before final payment and fixing the responsibility between OWNER and CONTRACTOR for maintenance, heat and utilities as to that part of the Project. OWNER shall have the right to exclude CONTRACTOR from any part of the Project which ENGINEER has so certified to be substantially complete, but OWNER shall allow CONTRACTOR reasonable access to complete or correct items on the tentative list.

Final Inspection:

14.11.   Upon written notice from CONTRACTOR that the Project is complete, ENGINEER will make a final inspection with OWNER and CONTRACTOR and will notify CONTRACTOR in writing of all particulars in

22

which this inspection reveals that the Work is incomplete or defective. CONTRACTOR shall immediately take such measures as are necessary to remedy such deficiences.

Final Application for Payment:

14.12. After CONTRACTOR has completed all such corrections to the satisfaction of ENGINEER and delivered all maintenance and operating instructions, schedules, guarantees, Bonds, certificates of inspection and other documents—all as required by the Contract Documents, he may make application for final payment following the procedure for progress payments. The final Application for Payment shall be accompanied by such data and schedules as ENGINEER may reasonably require, together with complete and legally effective releases or waivers (satisfactory to OWNER) of all Liens arising out of the Contract Documents and the labor and services performed and the material and equipment furnished thereunder. In lieu thereof and as approved by OWNER, CONTRACTOR may furnish receipts or releases in full; an affidavit of CONTRACTOR that the releases and receipts include all labor, services, material and equipment for which a Lien could be filed, and that all payrolls, material and equipment bills, and other indebtedness connected with the Work for which OWNER or his property might in any way be responsible, have been paid or otherwise satisfied; and consent of the Surety, if any, to final payment. If any Subcontractor materialman, fabricator or supplier fails to furnish a release or receipt in full, CONTRACTOR may furnish a Bond or other collateral satisfactory to OWNER to indemnify him against any Lien.

Approval of Final Payment:

14.13. If, on the basis of his observation and review of the Work during construction, his final inspection and his review of the final Application for Payment—all as required by the Contract Documents, ENGINEER is satisfied that the Work has been completed and CONTRACTOR has fulfilled all of his obligations under the Contract Documents, he will, within ten days after receipt of the final Application for Payment, indicate in writing his approval of payment and present the Application to OWNER for payment. Thereupon ENGINEER will give written notice to OWNER and CONTRACTOR that the Work is acceptable subject to the provisions of paragraph 14.16. Otherwise, he will return the Application to CONTRACTOR, indicating in writing his reasons for refusing to approve final payment, in which case CONTRACTOR shall make the necessary corrections and resubmit the Application. OWNER shall, within ten days of presentation to him of an approved final Application for Payment, pay CONTRACTOR the amount approved by ENGINEER.

14.14. If after Substantial Completion of the Work final completion thereof is materially delayed through no fault of CONTRACTOR, and ENGINEER so confirms, OWNER shall, upon certification by ENGINEER, and without terminating the Agreement, make payment of the balance due for that portion of the Work fully completed and accepted. If the remaining balance for Work not fully completed or corrected is less than the retainage stipulated in the Agreement, and if Bonds have been furnished as required in paragraph 5.1, the written consent of the Surety to the payment of the balance due for that portion of the Work fully completed and accepted shall be submitted by the CONTRACTOR to the ENGINEER prior to certification of such payment. Such payment shall be made under the terms and conditions governing final payment, except that it shall not constitute a waiver of claims.

Contractor's Continuing Obligation:

14.15. CONTRACTOR's obligation to perform the Work and complete the Project in accordance with the Contract Documents shall be absolute. Neither approval of any progress or final payment by ENGINEER, nor the issuance of a certificate of Substantial Completion, nor any payment by OWNER to CONTRACTOR under the Contract Documents, nor any use or occupancy of the Project or any part thereof by OWNER, nor any act of acceptance by OWNER nor any failure to do so, nor any correction of defective work by OWNER shall constitute an acceptance of Work not in accordance with the Contract Documents.

Waiver of Claims:

14.16. The making and acceptance of final payment shall constitute:

14.16.1. a waiver of all claims by OWNER against CONTRACTOR other than those arising from unsettled Liens, from defective work appearing after final inspection pursuant to paragraph 14.11 or from failure to comply with the requirements of the Contract Documents or the terms of any special guarantees specified therein, and

14.16.2. a waiver of all claims by CONTRACTOR against OWNER other than those previously made in writing and still unsettled.

ARTICLE 15—SUSPENSION OF WORK AND TERMINATION

Owner May Suspend Work:

15.1. OWNER may, at any time and without cause, suspend the Work or any portion thereof for a period of not more than ninety days by notice in writing to CONTRACTOR and ENGINEER which shall fix the date on which Work shall be resumed. CONTRACTOR shall resume the Work on the date so fixed. CONTRACTOR will be allowed an increase in the Contract Price or an extension of the Contract Time, or both, directly attributable to any suspension if he makes a claim therefor as provided in Articles 11 and 12.

Owner May Terminate:

15.2. If CONTRACTOR is adjudged a bankrupt or insolvent, or if he makes a general assignment for the

23

benefit of his creditors, or if a trustee or receiver is appointed for CONTRACTOR or for any of his property, or if he files a petition to take advantage of any debtor's act, or to reorganize under the bankruptcy or similar laws, or if he repeatedly fails to supply sufficient skilled workmen or suitable materials or equipment, or if he repeatedly fails to make prompt payments to Subcontractors or for labor, materials or equipment or if he disregards laws, ordinances, rules, regulations or orders of any public body having jurisdiction, or if he disregards the authority of ENGINEER, or if he otherwise violates any provision of the Contract Documents, then OWNER may, without prejudice to any other right or remedy and after giving CONTRACTOR and his Surety seven days' written notice, terminate the services of CONTRACTOR and take possession of the Project and of all materials, equipment, tools, construction equipment and machinery thereon owned by CONTRACTOR, and finish the Work by whatever method he may deem expedient. In such case CONTRACTOR shall not be entitled to receive any further payment until the Work is finished. If the unpaid balance of the Contract Price exceeds the direct and indirect costs of completing the Project, including compensation for additional professional services, such excess shall be paid to CONTRACTOR. If such costs exceed such unpaid balance, CONTRACTOR shall pay the difference to OWNER. Such costs incurred by OWNER shall be determined by ENGINEER and incorporated in a Change Order.

15.3. Where CONTRACTOR's services have been so terminated by OWNER, said terminations shall not affect any rights of OWNER against CONTRACTOR then existing or which may thereafter accrue. Any retention or payment of moneys by OWNER due CONTRACTOR will not release CONTRACTOR from liability.

15.4. Upon seven days' written notice to CONTRACTOR and ENGINEER, OWNER may, without cause and without prejudice to any other right or remedy, elect to abandon the Project and terminate the Agreement. In such case, CONTRACTOR shall be paid for all Work executed and any expense sustained plus a reasonable profit.

Contractor May Stop Work or Terminate:

15.5. If, through no act or fault of CONTRACTOR, the Work is suspended for a period of more than ninety days by OWNER or under an order of court or other public authority, or ENGINEER fails to act on any Application for Payment within thirty days after it is submitted, or OWNER fails to pay CONTRACTOR any sum approved by ENGINEER or awarded by arbitrators within thirty days of its approval and presentation, then CONTRACTOR may, upon seven days' written notice to OWNER and ENGINEER, terminate the Agreement and recover from OWNER payment for all Work executed and any expense sustained plus a reasonable profit. In addition and in lieu of terminating the Agreement, if ENGINEER has failed to act on an Application for Payment or OWNER has failed to make any payment as afore-

said, CONTRACTOR may upon seven days' notice to OWNER and ENGINEER stop the Work until he has been paid all amounts then due.

ARTICLE 16—ARBITRATION

16.1. All claims, disputes and other matters in question arising out of, or relating to, this Agreement or the breach thereof except for claims which have been waived by the making or acceptance of final payment as provided by paragraph 14.16, shall be decided by arbitration in accordance with the Construction Industry Arbitration Rules of the American Arbitration Association then obtaining. This agreement so to arbitrate shall be specifically enforceable under the prevailing arbitration law. The award rendered by the arbitrators shall be final, and judgment may be entered upon it in any court having jurisdiction thereof.

16.2. Notice of the demand for arbitration shall be filed in writing with the other party to the Agreement and with the American Arbitration Association, and a copy shall be filed with ENGINEER. The demand for arbitration shall be made within the thirty-day period specified in paragraph 9.10 where applicable, and in all other cases within a reasonable time after the claim, dispute or other matter in question has arisen, and in no event shall it be made after institution of legal or equitable proceedings based on such claim, dispute or other matter in question would be barred by the applicable statute of limitations.

16.3. CONTRACTOR will carry on the Work and maintain the progress schedule during any arbitration proceedings, unless otherwise agreed by him and OWNER in writing.

ARTICLE 17—MISCELLANEOUS

Giving Notice:

17.1. Whenever any provision of the Contract Documents requires the giving of written notice it shall be deemed to have been validly given if delivered in person to the individual or to a member of the firm or to an officer of the corporation for whom it is intended, or if delivered at or sent by registered or certified mail, postage prepaid, to the last business address known to him who gives the notice.

Computation of Time:

17.2. When any period of time is referred to in the Contract Documents by days, it shall be computed to exclude the first and include the last day of such period. If the last day of any such period falls on a Saturday or Sunday or on a day made a legal holiday by the law of the applicable jurisdiction, such day shall be omitted from the computation.

24

General:

17.3. All moneys not paid when due hereunder shall bear interest at the maximum rate allowed by law at the place of the Project.

17.4. All Specifications, Drawings and copies thereof furnished by ENGINEER shall remain his property. They shall not be used on another Project, and, with the exception of those sets which have been signed in connection with the execution of the Agreement, shall be returned to him on request upon completion of the Project.

17.5. The duties and obligations imposed by these General Conditions and the rights and remedies available hereunder, and, in particular but without limitation, the warranties, guarantees and obligations imposed upon CONTRACTOR by paragraphs 6.30, 13.1, 13.10 and 14.3 and the rights and remedies available to OWNER and ENGINEER thereunder, shall be in addition to, and shall not be construed in any way as a limitation of, any rights and remedies available to them which are otherwise imposed or available by law, by special guarantee or by other provisions of the Contract Documents.

17.6. Should OWNER or CONTRACTOR suffer injury or damage to his person or property because of any error, omission or act of the other or of any of his employees or agents or others for whose acts he is legally liable, claim shall be made in writing to the other party within a reasonable time of the first observance of such injury or damage.

17.7. The Contract Documents shall be governed by the law of the place of the Project.

25

Sample Instructions to Bidders and Proposal Form

INSTRUCTIONS TO BIDDERS

1.01 THE PROPOSAL

A. Sealed proposals will be received by the Architect until 2:00 P.M., Eastern Standard Time, on Tuesday, November 12, 1974, for the work included in the contract documents.

B. The proposal forms will be furnished by the Architect. The Bidder is requested to complete these forms in accordance with the instructions stated below. Five (5) copies of the proposal shall be sealed in an opaque envelope marked on the outside with "Proposal for Wire Major Supply Depot." This envelope shall be delivered to the Architects at 2000 Bankrupt Building, Feeling, Ill.

1.02 INSTRUCTIONS

A. <u>Name</u>

The bidder is requested to place his name and address at the top of the Bid Form.

B. <u>Base Bid</u>

The bidder is requested to state the lump sum price he will charge for performing all work called for in the contract documents. This amount shall appear in both words and figures.

C. <u>Building Breakdown</u>

The bidder is requested to break down his lump sum quotation for the various structures to assist the Owner in his accounting procedure. The total of the breakdown prices shall equal the lump sum quotation.

D. <u>Alternates</u>

The bidder is requested to submit prices for the Alternates described in Division 4 of the Specification. He

K-1

1.02 D. (Cont'd.)

is requested to insert the amount he will require for doing this work and indicate whether it should be added to or deducted from his contract price by crossing out the words that do not apply.

E. Fees for Assuming Contracts

1. In accordance with Division 11 of this Specification, the Bidder is requested to write in the space provided, the percentage of the contract price for the structural Steel he will charge in the event he is requested to assume the Structural Steel Contract.

2. In accordance with Division 51 of the Specifications, the Bidder is requested to write in the space provided, the percentage of the contract price for the Plumbing work he will charge in the event he is requested to assume this contract.

3. In accordance with Division 53 of the Specifications, the Bidder is requested to write in the space provided, the percentage of the contract price for the heating, ventilating and air conditioning work he will charge in the event he is requested to assume this contract.

F. Fees for Additional Work

1. With the Contractor's Forces

a. The Bidder is requested to write in the space provided the fee he will charge for doing extra work with his own forces.

b. This fee shall be a percentage of the actual cost of the job, and shall include all overhead and profit as described in detail in Subdivision 2.07, Section B.

2. With Subcontractor's Forces

a. The Bidder is requested to write in the space provided in the proposal form the fee that he

K-2

1.02 F. 2. a. (Cont'd.)

will charge for having work done by his
Subcontractor.

b. This fee shall be a percentage of the Subcontractor's charges for the job.

c. The fee shall include all of the Contractor's
charges for overhead, taxes and profit as
described in detail in Subdivision 2.07,
Section B.

3. With An Assigned Contractor's Forces

a. The bidder is requested to write in the space
provided in the proposal form the fee that he
will charge for having work done by an Assigned
Contractor.

b. This fee shall be a percentage of the Assigned
Contractor's charges for the job.

c. The fee shall include all of the Contractor's
charges for overhead, taxes, and profit.

G. Unit Prices

1. General

The bidder is requested to write in the space provided on the proposal, the unit prices he will charge
for various types of extra work.

2. Excavating in Rock

a. General

For the purpose of unit prices, rock excavation is
defined as the excavation, removal and disposal of
boulders one-half cubic yard or greater in volume
and of all solid or ledge rock, slate, shale, sand-
stone, or other hard material found in place which
in the opinion of the Clerk of the Work's

K-3

Superintendent cannot be removed without re-
sorting to continuous use of pneumatic tools or
by drilling and blasting. Payment for rock
excavations to which unit prices shall apply
shall be computed on the following basis and
shall apply to all rock excavation. The prices
appearing on the proposal are to be the difference between rock excavating and general excavating. When rock is encountered in areas
where excavating is required by the contract,
the amount paid will be that quoted in the
proposal. When extra excavating in rock is
required, the amount paid will be the amount
quoted for General Excavating plus that quoted
for rock excavating.

b. Footings and Pits

Payment shall be made on basis of a rectangular
cross section one foot greater in width than
the width between the outside edges of the footing or pit and for a depth from the recorded
profile of the rock elevation to six inches (6")
below bottom of footing or pit. The width of
the footing or pit shall be the width of the
narrowest section and where offsets are indicated, the additional width of offset shall be
added.

c. Other Rock Excavating

The top of rock shall be cross sectioned and payment shall be made on the basis of the recorded
profile from top of rock to the minimum depth
necessary to permit the construction shown. All
rock which has been calculated in footing or pit
excavations occurring within the areas of general
excavation shall be deducted from the total. In
his computations for this unit price, the Contractor shall make proper allowance, from his
practice and experience, for any variation in
the width of trench, slope of bank, overbreakage
and slides, which might require removal of

K-4

materials in quantities different from that
established by the above prescribed formula.

3. Felling Trees

In addition to the vegetation specified to be removed, the Owner may designate additional trees to
be cut down. The contractor is requested to quote
a price for removing various size trees. This
price shall include felling the trees, stripping,
sawing, removal of the stumps, backfilling, and the
disposal of the debris. The timber will become the
property of the Subcontractor doing the work, and
the salvage value of the lumber shall be deducted
from the unit price.

H. Time

Time is the essence of the contract. The bidder is requested to state the number of consecutive calendar days
after the notice of award before he will be able to
start work and the number of consecutive calendar days
he will require to complete the contract.

I. Substitutions

1. The Contractor will be required to use the materials
or methods specified unless exceptions are noted at
the time of bidding.

2. Where one product is specified by name, only that
product shall be used.

3. Where two or more products are specified by name,
the Contractor may use any product named at his option.

4. Where the term "or an approved equal" or similar
wording is used after naming a product or products,
the Architect-Engineer will be the one to determine
if any product other than the ones named is acceptable.

K-5

5. If the Contractor's proposal is figured on using any product or method other than that specified, he is requested to write in the space provided what he proposes to substitute and any difference in contract price occasioned by such a change. Acceptance or rejection of all substitutions will be made before the contract is signed.

6. Substitutions will not be approved after the contract is signed unless specifically approved in writing by the Architect-Engineer.

J. Addenda

During the bidding period, addenda may be issued revising the work called for on the drawings and specifications. The Bidder is requested to list in the proper location the number and the date of each addendum that he receives. The work called for in the addenda shall be included in the proposal price.

K. Subcontractors

In accordance with the specifications, the Contractor is required to employ a Professional Engineer or a Land Surveyor, and Subcontractors to install the concrete floor finishing and the insulation roofing and sheet metal. The Contractor is requested to state in the space provided on the Proposal Form the name of the Subcontractor he intends to employ for each of the above trades. He is also requested to state the name of the Roofing Manufacturer that the Roofing Subcontractor represents.

L. Legal Status

The bidder is requested to check the legal status of his business in the space provided on the Proposal Form.

M. Signature

The proposal shall be signed personally by the bidder, by a partner or by a duly authorized officer of a corporation

K-6

1.03 RESERVATION

The Owner reserves the right to reject any or all bids,
and to award the Contract to other than the low Bidder.
The Owner further reserves the right to waive any informali-
ties in bids.

K-7

1.04 PROPOSAL

    A. <u>Name and Address of Bidder</u>

        _____

        _____

        _____

    B. <u>Base Bid</u>

We, the undersigned, agree to furnish all materials, tools, equipment, apparatus, appliances, transportation, labor, and supervision required for the construction and completion of the Architectural trades for the Wier Major Supply Depot for the Contamination Division of the Gulp Oil Company in accordance with the plans and specifications prepared by Walker, Home, and Lever, Architects and Engineers, 2000 Bankrupt Building, Feeling, Ill., for the lump sum of:

_____

_____ Dollars ($)

    C. <u>Building Breakdown</u>

Our proposed lump sum price is subdivided as follows:

1. The Office Building $_____.

2. Warehouse $_____.

3. Sewage Pumping Station $_____.

4. Guard House $_____.

5. Elevated Water Tank Foundation $_____.

6. Site Work $_____.

K-8

1.04 (Cont'd.)

    D. <u>Alternates</u>

        1. <u>Alternate No. 1</u>

            If Alternate No. 1, as described in Division 4 of
            this Specification is accepted, _____

            _____Dollars ($_____)
            shall be added to
                   deducted from our proposed prive.

        2. <u>Alternate No. 2</u>

            If alternate No. 2 as described in Division 4 is
            accepted, _____

            _____Dollars ($_____)
            shall be added to
                   deducted from our proposed prive.

        3. <u>Alternate No. 3</u>

            If alternate No. 3, as described in Division 4 of
            the Specifications, is accepted, _____

            _____Dollars ($_____)
            shall be added to
                   deducted from our proposed prive.

    E. <u>Fees for Assuming Contracts</u>

        1. The structural steel for this project is to be
            awarded under separate contract. If requested, we,
            the undersigned, agree to assume the contract for
            all the work according to the specifications for the
            structural steel for this project. We will charge
            the amount charged us by the Structural Steel Con-
            tractor, plus a fee of _____per cent (_____%)
            which will include all of our charges, the overhead,
            and the profit.

K-9

1.04   E.   (Cont'd.)

   2.   The plumbing work for this project is to be awarded
        under a separate contract. If requested, we, the
        undersigned, agree to assume this contract according
        to the specifications for the structural steel for
        this project. We will charge the amount charged us
        by the Plumbing Contractor, plus a fee of _____
        per cent (_____%) which will include all our
        charges, the overhead, and the profit.

   3.   The Heating, Ventilating, and Air Conditioning work
        for this project is to be awarded under a separate
        contract. If requested, we, the undersigned, agree
        to assume this contract according to the specifica-
        tions for the heating, ventilating and air condi-
        tioning work on this project. We will charge the
        amount charged us by the Contractor, plus a fee of
        _____per cent (_____%) which will include
        all our charges, the overhead, and the profit.

   4.   The electrical work for this project is to be
        awarded under a separate contract. If requested,
        we, the undersigned, agree to assume this contract
        according to the specifications for the electrical
        work for this project. We will charge the amount
        charged us by the Electrical Contractor, plus a fee
        of _____per cent (_____%) which will
        include all of our charges for overhead and profit.

   F.   Fees for Additional Work

   1.   With_Our_Own_Forces

        If requested in writing by the Architects, we will
        perform extra work and charge the Owner the actual
        cost of the work as defined in the Instructions to
        Bidders plus a fee of

        _____per cent (_____%) of
        our actual cost.

K-10

1.04 F. (Cont'd.)

2. With the Subcontractor's Forces

If requested in writing by the Architects, we will
have our Subcontractors perform additional work and
charge the Owner the Subcontractor's price plus a
fee of

_____percent (_____%) which
shall include our charge for overhead and profit.

3. With an Assigned Contractor's Forces

If requested in writing by the Architect, we will have
our Assigned Contractors perform additional work and
charge the Owner the Assigned Contractor's price plus
a fee of

_____percent (_____%) which
shall include our charge for overhead and profit.

G. Unit Prices

1. General

In the event we are required to do extra work covered
by unit prices, we, the undersigned, will charge the
Owner the following prices:

2. Rock Excavation

a. General Excavating in rock as defined
in the Instructions to Bidders. This
includes the disposal of the excavated
material per cubic yard. $_____.___

b. Excavating in rock, as defined in
the Instructions to Bidders, for
footings and pits, including the
disposal of the excavated rock,
per cubic yard. $_____.___

K-11

1.04   G.   (Cont'd.)

    3.   Removing_and_Disposing_of Trees _and Stumps_

        a.   Trees six inches (6") to twelve
            inches (12") in diameter, each $_____.

        b.   Trees twelve inches (12") to
            eighteen inches (18") in
            diameter, each $_____.

        c.   Trees eighteen (18) to twenty-four
            (24") inches in diameter, each $_____.

        d.   Trees over eighteen inches (18")
            in diameter, each $_____.

H.   Time

We, the undersigned, agree to start work in the field
within _____(_____) con-
secutive calendar days following the award of the contract.
We agree to have all work complete as called for in the
Contract Documents within

_____(_____) consecutive calendar
days after starting work.

I.   Substitutions

_____

_____

_____

_____

_____

K-12

1.04 (Cont'd.)

J. Addenda

We, the undersigned, confirm the receipt and consideration
of the following addenda prior to the submittal of our
proposal. We have included the work called for in these
addenda in our proposed price.

1. ADDENDUM NO._____DATED_____

2. ADDENDUM NO._____DATED_____

3. ADDENDUM NO._____DATED_____

4. ADDENDUM NO._____DATED_____

5. ADDENDUM NO._____DATED_____

K. Subcontractors

1. In the event we are awarded the Contract for this
work, we will employ:

_____
who is registered in the State of

_____
as a Professional Engineer or a Land Surveyor.

2. In the event we are awarded the Contract for this
work, we will employ:

_____
as our Concrete Floor Finishing Subcontractor.

3. In the event we are awarded the Contract for this
work, we will employ:

_____
as our Subcontractor for the Insulation, Roofing and
Sheet Metal Work. This Subcontractor has a franchise
from the

_____
to install bonded roofs.   (Company)

K-13

1.04   (Cont'd.)

L.   Legal Status

We, the undersigned, hereby declare that we have the
legal status checked below

1.   /_/ Individual

2.   /_/ Partnership, having the following partners.

a. _____

b. _____

c. _____

3.   /_/ Corporation, Incorporated under the state laws of

_____

M.   Executing the Contract

1.   The prices stated in this proposal will be held for a
period of _____days from the date hereof,
and if authorized to proceed within that period, we
agree to complete the work covered by this proposal
at the prices stated herein.

2.   This proposal is submitted in the name of

_____

By_____
                    (Signature)

Title_____

Signed and sealed this_____day of_____, 19

K-14

Index

Index